AN ESSAY CONCERNING HUMAN UNDERSTANDING

COLLIER CLASSICS IN THE HISTORY OF THOUGHT

•

General Editors: Crane Brinton and Paul Edwards

(TITLES PUBLISHED)

BERKELEY: *Berkeley's Philosophical Writings.* Ed. by D. M. Armstrong

GIBBON: *Christianity and the Decline of Rome* (Vol. I of *The Decline and Fall of the Roman Empire*). Abridged and edited by Jacob Sloan, with an Introduction by C. D. Gordon

GIBBON: *Barbarism and the Fall of Rome* (Vol. II of *The Decline and Fall of the Roman Empire*). Abridged and edited by Jacob Sloan, with an Introduction by C. D. Gordon

HOBBES: *Body, Man, and Citizen.* Ed. by Richard S. Peters

HOBBES: *Leviathan.* Ed. by Richard S. Peters

HUME: *Hume's Ethical Writings.* Ed. by Alasdair MacIntyre

HUME: *On Human Nature and Understanding.* Ed. by Anthony Flew

JAMES: *Psychology: Briefer Course.* Foreword by Gardner Murphy

JAMES: *The Varieties of Religious Experience.* Introduction by Reinhold Niebuhr

LOCKE: *Locke's Essay Concerning Human Understanding.* Ed. by Maurice Cranston

LOCKE: *Locke on Politics, Religion, and Education.* Ed. by Maurice Cranston

MILL: *Mill's Essays on Literature and Society.* Ed. by J. B. Schneewind

MILL: *Mill's Ethical Writings.* Ed. by J. B. Schneewind

PRIESTLEY: *Priestley's Writings on Philosophy, Science, and Politics.* Ed. by John Passmore

American Thought before 1900: A Sourcebook from Puritanism to Darwinism. Ed. by Paul Kurtz

American Philosophy in the Twentieth Century: A Sourcebook from Pragmatism to Philosophical Analysis. Ed. by Paul Kurtz

Paradox 1/27/94 J. Parker

JOHN LOCKE

An Essay Concerning Human Understanding

ABRIDGED, EDITED AND INTRODUCED BY *MAURICE CRANSTON*

A Collier Books Original

COLLIER BOOKS, NEW YORK

COLLIER-MACMILLAN LTD., LONDON

J. Parker

Library of Congress Catalog Card Number: 65-17825

A Collier Books Original

First Edition 1965

The Macmillan Company, New York
Collier-Macmillan Canada Ltd., Toronto, Ontario
Printed in the United States of America

Contents

Book Three: OF WORDS

Book Four: OF KNOWLEDGE AND OPINION

Editor's Introduction

BY MAURICE CRANSTON

JOHN LOCKE was a handsome man; the portraits by Greenhill, Kneller and Verelst all depict a sensitive, fastidious, patrician face—the lineaments, one would think, of a poet. And there one would think wrongly. For Locke was many other things—economist, diplomat, theologian, traveler, scientist, physician, pedagogue as well as philosopher; but he was never a man of artistic and literary taste. David Hume was once said to have looked like "a turtle-eating alderman instead of a refined philosopher." Locke, who had the looks Hume lacked, wrote like a water-drinking local councilor—his style ungainly, his idioms commercial, his imagination puritanical, his humor labored, his interests wholly practical. "What is the *use*," he asked, "of poetry?"

He was a great materialist, in a sense, and an important sense. Our modern Western world has been made by scientists, merchants, statesmen, industrialists; Locke was the first philosopher to expound their view of life, to articulate their aspirations and justify their deeds. No philosopher has exercised a greater influence. Yet it could be said—and has been said—that Locke was not a philosopher at all; but to say this is only to say that Locke was not a metaphysician. He was certainly not one in the sense that Leibniz or Spinoza, his contemporaries, were metaphysicians. Locke offered no all-embracing system to explain the nature of the universe. On the contrary, he tried to show that the human understanding is so limited that such comprehensive knowledge is beyond men's powers to reach. Where philosophy is concerned Locke did not give the answers; he achieved greatness rather in his formulation of the problems. He set forth, as no one had done before, the questions philosophy should deal with, and also the ways of dealing with them; he gave epistemology, the theory of knowledge, its method.

Two powerful streams in seventeenth-century thought, the semi-skeptical rational theorizing of Descartes, and the *ad hoc* scientific experimenting of Bacon and the Royal Society came together in Locke. Their union was not perfect, because the streams were so different, but his mind was the meeting point, a point which marked a new beginning, not only in philosophy, but in the way in which men thought about the world. Locke, one might almost say, had the first modern mind. Descartes, though more original than Locke, was still in many ways a medieval thinker; his philosophy was still attached to theology. Even Gassendi, who anticipated much of Locke, did not quite leap free. Locke made the break; he separated philosophy from theology and set the proper study of philosophy within the boundaries of man's experience: "Our portion," he wrote, "lies only here in this little spot of earth, where we and all our concernments are shut up."

Yet Locke was not a skeptic, and in his capacity as theologian he had thoughts of his own about God to expound. He quarreled with bishops and the orthodox of most denominations. He maintained that a Christian need believe no more than the single proposition "that Christ is the Messiah"; but to that minimal creed he clung with the firmest assurance. He had a quiet and steady faith in the immortality of the soul, and in the prospect of happiness in the life to come. He had no belief in miracles, and no patience with people who had mystical experiences or visions of God. He detested religious enthusiasm, but in his own unemotional way he was, like Newton, a deeply religious man.

John Locke was born on August 29, 1632, at Wrington, Somerset in the West of England. His grandfather, Nicholas Locke, was a successful clothier of that county. His father, John Locke, was a less prosperous lawyer and clerk to the local magistrates. The future philosopher was baptized by Samuel Crook, one of the leading Calvinist intellectuals of the West of England, and brought up in an atmosphere of austerity and discipline. The Civil War broke out when Locke was ten years old, and his father was mounted as a captain of Parliamentary Horse by Alexander Popham, a rich local magistrate turned Colonel. Apart from demolishing some popish images in Wells's cathedral, the two officers saw little action, but a grateful Alexander Popham became the patron of his captain's eldest son, and when a few years later Westminster School was taken over by the Parliament, the colonel found a place for his protégé in what was then the best boarding school in the country.

At Westminster Locke came under the influence of the Royalist headmaster Richard Busby, whom the Parliamentary governors had imprudently allowed to remain in charge of the school; but when Locke left in 1652 to become an undergraduate at Christ Church, Oxford, he came once more under Puritan influence. He did not wholly enjoy the university, but he was appointed to a teaching place in his college after he had taken his M.A. degree, and gave lectures on such subjects as Natural Law, although medicine interested him more.

In the summer of 1666, Locke met and made friends with Anthony Ashley Cooper, then Lord Ashley, later first Earl of Shaftesbury. Shaftesbury was not yet the leader of a party, but he was already the outstanding politician of liberalism and the most forceful champion of religious toleration. A year later, at the age of thirty-four, Locke went to live at Shaftesbury's house in London. His Oxford career had not been a particularly distinguished one. He had been a temporary lecturer and a censor at Christ Church; he had made friends with Robert Boyle, one of the founders of the Royal Society, and helped him by collecting scientific data; and he had studied medicine. However, he had done no important laboratory work and he had failed to get a medical degree. Even so, it was as a domestic physician that Locke entered Shaftesbury's household, and he soon proved himself an able one. He saved his patron's life (as Shaftesbury believed) when it was threatened by a suppurating cyst of the liver. Afterward, Shaftesbury decided that Locke was far too great a genius to be spending his time on medicine alone, and work of other kinds was found for him.

It was under Shaftesbury's patronage that Locke discovered his own true gifts. First, he became a philosopher. At Oxford he had been as bored and dissatisfied as Hobbes had been with the medieval Aristotelian philosophy which was taught there. Reading Descartes first opened Locke's eyes to the "new philosophy," and discussions with Shaftesbury and other London friends led him to write, in his fourth year under Shaftesbury's roof, the earliest drafts of his masterpiece, the *Essay Concerning Human Understanding*. In London Locke also met Thomas Sydenham, the great physician, who introduced him to the new clinical method he had learned in Montpellier. Shaftesbury himself introduced Locke to the study of economics and gave him his earliest experience of political administration.

Locke stayed with Shaftesbury on and off until Shaftesbury's death in 1682. In those fifteen years Shaftesbury's Protestant zeal carried him to the point of organizing a rebellion. Charles II refused to deny his Catholic brother, James, his legitimate right to succeed him to the throne. Shaftesbury persuaded Parliament to pass a measure designed to make James's succession illegal. When Charles thwarted this maneuver, Shaftesbury replied by calling on his friends to rise and exclude James in favor of a Protestant successor by force of arms. But his supporters hesitated, the plot was nipped, and Shaftesbury withdrew to Holland, where, soon afterward, he died. Locke followed him to Holland, and remained there in exile until William of Orange invaded England in 1688 and reclaimed the country for Protestantism and liberty.

During his exile in Holland Locke wrote, from drafts he had made in 1671, his *Essay Concerning Human Understanding,* his first *Letter for Toleration,* and he may have done some work on his *Civil Government.* The *Letter for Toleration* was published in Locke's original Latin at Gouda in 1689, and an English translation made by the Socinian William Popple—made, Locke said afterward, "without my privity"—was published in London a few months later. The *Human Understanding* and the *Civil Government* were also brought out by different London booksellers in the winter of 1689–90. Only the *Human Understanding* bore Locke's name, but its success was so great that it made its author famous throughout Europe even in his lifetime.

In the Epistle to the Reader, printed at the beginning of his *Essay Concerning Human Understanding,* Locke says that in an age of such "master builders" as Boyle and Sydenham and Huygenius and "the incomparable Mr. Newton" it is, for him, "ambition enough to be employed as an under-laborer in clearing the ground a little and removing some of the rubbish that lies in the way of knowledge." Despite this modest explanation of his purpose Locke is generally, and rightly, believed to have done much more. He provides, among other things, the first modern philosophy of science. A recurrent word—perhaps the most important word—in the *Essay* is a Cartesian one, "idea." Locke's use of the word is curious. He does not merely say that we have ideas in our minds when we think; he says that we have ideas in our minds when we see, hear, smell, taste, or feel. The core of his epistemology is the notion that the objects of perception are not *things*, but ideas which are derived in part from things in the external world, but which also depend to some extent on our own minds for their existence. Locke defines an "idea" as the "object of the understanding" whether it is a notion, an entity, or an illusion, perception being for him a "species of understanding."

Locke opens his *Essay* with an attack on what was in his time the established opinion that certain ideas are innate. He claims that they have been thought to be innate only because people cannot remember when they first learned them. Locke's belief is that we are born in total ignorance, and that even our theoretical ideas of identity, quantity, and substance are derived from experience. He says that a child gets ideas of black and white, of sweet and bitter before and not after it gets an idea of abstract principles such as identity or impossibility. "The senses at first let in particular ideas, and furnish the yet empty cabinet. . . ." Afterward the mind abstracts these theoretical ideas, and so "comes to be furnished with ideas and language, the materials about which to exercise the discursive faculty." In the child's development, "the use of reason becomes daily more visible as these materials that give it employment increase."

Locke has thus to defend the belief that everything which he calls an idea is derived from sensation, though he admits that an idea may also be produced by reflection—"remembering, considering, reasoning, etc." He classifies ideas as simple or complex. Simple ideas are those which the mind receives passively. Complex ideas are produced by the exercise of the mind's own powers. It is in his chapters on "simple ideas" that Locke sets out the main lines of his theory of perception. Most people, if asked what it is that they see, smell, hear, taste, or touch would answer "things," though they might add "but sometimes illusions, chimeras, mirages, which are not real things." They would probably maintain that there are two elements in an act of perception: the observer and the object. Locke differs from this plain view in two respects: First, he claims that what we perceive is always an idea, as distinct from a thing; second, he claims that there are not two but three elements in perception, the observer, the idea, and the object which the idea represents.

The reasoning which leads Locke to this conclusion is not

difficult to appreciate. We look at a penny. We are asked to describe it. It is round, brown, and of modest dimensions. But do we really see just this? We think again and realize that what we see is elliptical, not circular; in some lights it is golden, in others black; close to the eye it is large; seen from afar it is tiny. The actual penny, we are certain, cannot be *both* circular and elliptical, *both* golden all over and black all over. So we may be led to agree that there must be something which is the one and something which is the other—something which changes, and something which does not change, the elliptical "penny" we see and the real circular penny—or, in Locke's own words, the "idea" in the mind of the observer and the material "body" itself.

Locke's theory of perception is both easily defended and easily attacked. It is easily defended in the twentieth century on the basis of what is said by many physicists about the structure of the universe and by many physiologists about the mechanism of perception. The penny we give a child is something that looks brown, feels warm, tastes sharp on the tongue. The penny we give to the scientist is described as a congeries of electrons and protons. He tells us that certain light-waves strike the retina of the observer's eye, while waves of other kinds strike nerve terminals of other sorts, and that these processes produce those modifications of the neurological system which we call "seeing," "feeling" or "tasting" a penny. Neither the electrons nor the protons, neither the waves outside nor the modifications inside are brown or warm or astringent. The scientist thus separates what Locke called the *secondary* qualities—color, taste, sound; and these are precisely those qualities which Locke said depended on the mind of the observer for their existence. At the same time, science seems to accept the objective existence of the qualities which Locke called *primary*, and which he thought of as belonging to material bodies themselves: namely impenetrability, extension, figure, mobility, and number. These are the qualities with which scientists are accustomed to deal. Nor is Locke's distinction between primary and secondary qualities acceptable only to scientists. Most people would probably be willing to agree that they could imagine an object divested one by one of its qualities of taste and smell and so forth, but they could not imagine a body divested of impenetrability, or shape or size or position in space: for a body without primary qualities would not exist at all.

While there is much to be said for Locke's epistemology, there is also much to be said against it. If we are aware in our perceptual experience only of ideas which represent objects, and never of objects themselves, there can be no means of knowing what, if anything, is represented by those ideas. The human predicament, according to Locke's account of it, is that of a man permanently imprisoned in a sort of diving bell, receiving some signals from without and some from within his apparatus, but having no means of knowing which, if any, of these signals come from outside and hence no means of testing the authenticity of any of the signals. Man cannot therefore have any definite knowledge whatever of the external world.

In the later chapters of the *Essay* the author puts an even heavier emphasis on human ignorance. Our knowledge, Locke says, "is not only limited to the paucity and imperfections of the ideas we have, and which we employ about it," it is something still more circumscribed. Our knowledge of identity and diversity in ideas extends only as far as our ideas themselves; our knowledge of their co-existence extends only a little way because knowledge of any necessary connection between primary and secondary qualities is unattainable. However, with the area of certainty thus diminished, Locke does not deny us the possibility of an assurance which falls short of perfect knowledge. We can have *probable* knowledge, even when we cannot have certain knowledge. Moreover, unlike most of his successors among empiricist philosophers, Locke admits the existence of substance. He says that substance is somehow present in all objects, even though we do not see or feel it. What we see and feel are the primary and secondary qualities. Substance is what stands under and props up those qualities. Beyond that Locke says the subject must necessarily remain a mystery: "It seems probable to me that the simple ideas we receive from sensation and reflection are the boundaries of our thoughts; beyond which the mind, whatever efforts it would make, is not able to advance one jot, nor can it make any discoveries, when it would pry into the nature and hidden causes of those ideas."

The *Essay Concerning Human Understanding* is a very English book both in its merits and its faults. Its tone is at once moral and pragmatic, its style is homely rather than elegant, its construction informal and even amateurish. The "pursuit of Truth" the author says, "is a duty we owe to God

. . . and a duty we owe also to ourselves"; utility is at one with piety. Truth, as Locke defines it, is the "proper riches and furniture of the mind"; and he does not claim to have added to that stock, but rather to have shown the conditions under which the mind could acquire its proper riches and furniture: "We have no reason to complain that we do not know the nature of the sun or the stars, that the consideration of light itself leaves us in the dark and a thousand other speculations in nature, since, if we knew them, they would be of no solid advantage, nor help to make our lives the happier, they being but the useless employment of idle or over-curious brains. . . ."

Locke's theory of knowledge has obvious implications for a theory of morals. The traditional view in Locke's time was that some sort of moral knowledge was innate in the human person. Locke thought otherwise. What God—or Nature—had given men was a faculty of reason and a sentiment of self-love. Reason in combination with self-love produced morality. Reason could discern the general principles of ethics, or Natural Law, and self-love should lead men to obey those principles.

For Locke, Christian ethics was Natural ethics. The teaching of the New Testament was a means to an end—happiness in this life and in the life to come. Loving one's neighbor and otherwise obeying the precepts of the Saviour was a way to that end. The reason for doing what Christ said was not simply that Christ had said it; there was the additional reason that by doing these things one promoted one's happiness. There was no need to ask why anyone should desire happiness, because all men were impelled by their natural self-love to desire it.

Wrong-doing was thus for Locke a sign of ignorance. People did not always realize that long-term happiness could usually only be bought at the cost of short-term pleasures. Folly drove them to destroy their own well-being. If people were enlightened, if they used their own powers of reason, they would be good; if they were prudent, reflective, calculating, instead of being moved by the transitory winds of impulse and emotion, they would have what they most desired. There is perhaps in this system of morals something rather naïve and commonplace; but then it must be said of Locke that he was in many ways a very ordinary thinker; but his was an inspired ordinariness, a prophetic common-sense.

The influence of his teaching has been so pervasive and far-reaching as to be strictly incalculable. The philosophers of the French Enlightenment all acknowledged Locke as their master, while the central British tradition of empiricism—the line of Berkeley, Hume, Mill, Russell, Ryle, Ayer—and the central American tradition of pragmatism are nothing if not Lockean. Rousseau and the makers of the American Republic claimed to be Locke's disciples in politics, as did both the champions, and several of the critics, of the French Revolution. Locke's influence in spheres other than philosophy and politics was not less marked. Even literature, for which he had himself so limited a taste, was shaped by his teaching. Defoe, Sterne, and Smollett are among those who invoke his name; not only Samuel Johnson and Henry Fielding, but equally Samuel Richardson and Jane Austen look at the world, and human conduct, in Lockean terms. Theirs is a world in which virtue is rewarded, in which cool self-love prevails, and where no one (who is not foolish) seeks to penetrate the mysteries of the universe which lie beyond appearances. Not for them the kind of truth that is "proved upon the pulses"; nor for them the attitude of those "to whom the miseries of the world are misery and will not let them rest." All that came with the Romantics; and if romanticism in England was a reaction against anything, it was a reaction—as William Blake was the first to realize—against the *Weltanschauung* that men had learned from Locke.

MAURICE CRANSTON
London School of Economics

Note on the Text

Locke's *Essay Concerning Human Understanding* is a work which lends itself to abridgement. It was written by fits and starts over a period of many years, and when it was finished the author felt it had grown too long, too prolix, and too repetitious; but he shrank from the labor of editing the text, which he handed to his publisher, Churchill, soon after his return, in 1689, from over five years' exile in Holland. Some three years after the appearance of the first edition, Locke wrote—in September, 1692—to his Irish friend William Molyneux asking "whether it would not be better now to pare off, in a second edition, a great part of that which cannot but appear superfluous to an intelligent and attentive reader." Molyneux, in his reply, implored Locke not to cut out one word. Locke was persuaded by Molyneux, and, though he added to the text of later editions, he cut nothing. But none of the editions which came out in his lifetime really satisfied Locke. His consciousness that he had been "too long upon some points" and "repetitious" continued to weigh on his mind.

Even before the *Essay* was published, Locke himself had prepared a very short abridgement of it which was translated into French and printed as early as 1687 in *La Bibliothèque Universelle* (Vol. VIII), a learned journal edited in Holland by Locke's friend, Jean le Clerc. But this *abrégé* was scarcely more than an epitome. A substantial abridgement—running to some 300 pages—was printed in London in 1696, some seven years after the publication of the first edition of the *Essay*. This was the work of an Oxford don, John Wynne, and it enjoyed a great success in the universities. Locke gave Wynne so much advice and help in preparing this abridgement that it can be regarded as an "authorized version." Wynne's text, together with the French translation of the *Essay* which was made by Pierre Coste under Locke's personal supervision (when Coste was living as Locke's secretary at Oates, in Essex), has been of the utmost utility to the editor of the present abridgement. It must, however, be added that the present editor, with twentieth-century standards of importance and interest, has restored many of the cuts that Locke allowed Wynne to make. The present text is more than twice as long as Wynne's.

The reader who compares this abridged text with the original will find that remarkably little of substance or importance has been sacrificed. The repetitions of which Locke spoke, the baroque ornaments of his writing, the classical allusions, the prolonged illustrations of particular points, the digressions into such fields as theology, psychology and history—such matter as this accounts for the bulk of the deletions made in the present edition. A linking commentary has been provided in those places where a mere cut would have entailed too abrupt a transition, or where the editor has considered a summary of Locke's thought at a certain stage in the argument a necessary compensation for what has been lost in the process of abridgement.

The last edition which incorporated changes made by Locke himself was the sixth, published by Churchill in London in 1705 in a single folio volume. This is the most reliable early edition, and the only later edition of any importance is that prepared by Alexander C. Fraser, and published in two volumes in 1894. The present edition is indebted to both those texts. No twentieth-century version of the *Essay* that has yet appeared is of any scholarly interest, but a critical edition is projected by the Oxford University Press as part of a definitive edition of all Locke's works, the general editor being Dr. Esmond de Beer, to whom the editor of this abridgement wishes to express his acknowledgements for many kindnesses and much good advice.

M. C.

AN ESSAY CONCERNING HUMAN UNDERSTANDING

The Epistle To The Reader

READER,

I have put into thy hands what has been the diversion of some of my idle and heavy hours. If it has the good luck to prove so of any of thine, and thou hast but half so much pleasure in reading as I had in writing it, thou wilt as little think thy money, as I do my pains, ill bestowed. Mistake not this for a commendation of my work; nor conclude, because I was pleased with the doing of it, that therefore I am fondly taken with it now it is done. He that hawks at larks and sparrows has no less sport, though a much less considerable quarry, than he that flies at nobler game: and he is little acquainted with the subject of this treatise—the UNDERSTANDING—who does not know that, as it is the most elevated faculty of the soul, so it is employed with a greater and more constant delight than any of the other. Its searches after truth are a sort of hawking and hunting, wherein the very pursuit makes a great part of the pleasure. Every step the mind takes in its progress towards Knowledge makes some discovery, which is not only new, but the best too, for the time at least.

It will possibly be censured as a great piece of vanity or insolence in me, to pretend to instruct this our knowing age; it amounting to little less, when I own, that I publish this *Essay* with hopes it may be useful to others. If I have not the good luck to please, yet nobody ought to be offended with me. I shall always have the satisfaction to have aimed sincerely at truth and usefulness, though in one of the meanest ways. The commonwealth of learning is not at this time without master-builders, whose mighty designs, in advancing the sciences, will leave lasting monuments to the admiration of posterity; but every one must not hope to be a Boyle[1] or a Sydenham;[2] and in an age that produces such masters as the great Huygenius[3] and the incomparable Mr. Newton,[4] with some others of that strain, it is ambition enough to be employed as an under-laborer in clearing the ground a little, and removing some of the rubbish that lies in the way to knowledge;—which cer-

[1] Robert Boyle (1626–91), Irish scientist
[2] Thomas Sydenham (1624–89), English physician
[3] Christian Huygens (1629–93), Dutch physicist
[4] Isaac Newton (1642–1727)

tainly had been very much more advanced in the world, if the endeavors of ingenious and industrious men had not been much cumbered with the learned but frivolous use of uncouth, affected, or unintelligible terms, introduced into the sciences, and there made an art of, to that degree that Philosophy, which is nothing but the true knowledge of things, was thought unfit or incapable to be brought into well-bred company and polite conversation. Vague and insignificant forms of speech, and abuse of language, have so long passed for mysteries of science; and hard and misapplied words, with little or no meaning, have, by prescription, such a right to be mistaken for deep learning and height of speculation, that it will not be easy to persuade either those who speak or those who hear them, that they are but the covers of ignorance, and hindrance of true knowledge. To break in upon the sanctuary of vanity and ignorance will be, I suppose, some service to human understanding.

Introduction

SINCE IT IS the *understanding* that sets man above the rest of sensible beings, and gives him all the advantage and dominion which he has over them; it is certainly a subject, even for its nobleness, worth our labor to inquire into. The understanding, like the eye, whilst it makes us see and perceive all other things, takes no notice of itself; and it requires art and pains to set it at a distance and make it its own object.

This, therefore, being my purpose—to inquire into the original, certainty, and extent of *human knowledge,* together with the grounds and degrees of *belief, opinion,* and *assent;*—I shall not at present meddle with the physical consideration of the mind; or trouble myself to examine wherein its essence consists; or by what motions of our spirits or alterations of our bodies we come to have any *sensation* by our organs, or any *ideas* in our understandings; and whether those ideas do in their formation, any or all of them, depend on matter or not. These are speculations which, however curious and entertaining, I shall decline, as lying out of my way in the design I am now upon. It shall suffice to my present purpose, to consider the discerning faculties of a man, as they are employed about the objects which they have to do with. And I shall imagine I have not wholly misemployed myself in the thoughts I shall have on this occasion, if, in this historical, plain method, I can give any account of the ways whereby our understandings come to attain those notions of things we have; and can set down any measures of the certainty of our knowledge; or the grounds of those persuasions which are to be found amongst men, so various, different, and wholly contradictory.

It is therefore worth while to search out the bounds between opinion and knowledge; and examine by what measures, in things whereof we have no certain knowledge, we ought to regulate our assent and moderate our persuasion. In order whereunto I shall pursue this following method:——

First, I shall inquire into the original of those *ideas,* notions, or whatever else you please to call them, which a man observes, and is conscious to himself he has in his mind; and the ways whereby the understanding comes to be furnished with them.

Secondly, I shall endeavor to show what *knowledge* the

understanding hath by those ideas; and the certainty, evidence, and extent of it.

Thirdly, I shall make some inquiry into the nature and grounds of *faith* or *opinion*: whereby I mean that assent which we give to any proposition as true, of whose truth yet we have no certain knowledge. And here we shall have occasion to examine the reasons and degrees of *assent*.

If by this inquiry into the nature of the understanding, I can discover the powers thereof; how far they reach; to what things they are in any degree proportionate; and where they fail us, I suppose it may be of use to prevail with the busy mind of man to be more cautious in meddling with things exceeding its comprehension; to stop when it is at the utmost extent of its tether; and to sit down in a quiet ignorance of those things which, upon examination, are found to be beyond the reach of our capacities. If we can find out how far the understanding can extend its view; how far it has faculties to attain certainty; and in what cases it can only judge and guess, we may learn to content ourselves with what is attainable by us in this state.

For though the comprehension of our understandings comes exceeding short of the vast extent of things, yet we shall have cause enough to magnify the bountiful Author of our being, for that proportion and degree of knowledge He has bestowed on us, so far above all the rest of the inhabitants of this our mansion. Men have reason to be well satisfied with what God hath thought fit for them, since He hath given them (as St. Peter says) whatsoever is necessary for the conveniences of life and information of virtue; and has put within the reach of their discovery, the comfortable provision for this life, and the way that leads to a better. We shall not have much reason to complain of the narrowness of our minds, if we will but employ them about what may be of use to us; for of that they are very capable. And it will be an unpardonable, as well as childish peevishness, if we undervalue the advantages of our knowledge, and neglect to improve it to the ends for which it was given us, because there are some things that are set out of the reach of it. If we will disbelieve everything, because we cannot certainly know all things, we shall do muchwhat as wisely as he who would not use his legs, but sit still and perish, because he had no wings to fly.

It is of great use to the sailor to know the length of his

line, though he cannot with it fathom all the depths of the ocean. It is well he knows that it is long enough to reach the bottom, at such places as are necessary to direct his voyage, and caution him against running upon shoals that may ruin him. Our business here is not to know all things, but those which concern our conduct.

This was that which gave the first rise to this *Essay* concerning the understanding. For I thought that the first step toward satisfying several inquiries the mind of man was very apt to run into, was, to take a survey of our own understandings, examine our own powers, and see to what things they were adapted.

But, before I proceed on to what I have thought on this subject, I must here in the entrance beg pardon of my reader for the frequent use of the word *idea,* which he will find in the following treatise. It being that term which, I think, serves best to stand for whatsoever is the *object* of the understanding when a man thinks, I have used it to express whatever is meant by *phantasm, notion, species,* or *whatever it is which the mind can be employed about in thinking;* and I could not avoid frequently using it.

I presume it will be easily granted me, that there are such *ideas* in men's minds; every one is conscious of them in himself; and men's words and actions will satisfy him that they are in others.

Our first inquiry then shall be,—how they come into the mind.

BOOK ONE

NEITHER PRINCIPLES NOR IDEAS ARE INNATE

I

No Innate Speculative Principles

IT IS AN ESTABLISHED OPINION amongst some men, that there are in the understanding certain *innate principles;* some primary notions, characters, as it were stamped upon the mind of man; which the soul receives in its very first being, and brings into the world with it. It would be sufficient to convince unprejudiced readers of the falseness of this supposition, if I should only show (as I hope I shall in the following parts of this Discourse) how men, barely by the use of their natural faculties, may attain to all the knowledge they have, without the help of any innate impressions; and may arrive at certainty, without any such original notions or principles.

There is nothing more commonly taken for granted than that there are certain *principles,* both *speculative* and *practical* (for they speak of both), universally agreed upon by all mankind: which therefore, they argue, must needs be the constant impressions which the souls of men receive in their first beings, and which they bring into the world with them, as necessarily and really as they do any of their inherent faculties.

This argument, drawn from universal consent, has this misfortune in it, that if it were true in matter of fact, that there were certain truths wherein all mankind agreed, it would not prove them innate, if there can be any other way shown how men may come to that universal agreement, in the things they do consent in, which I presume may be done.

But, which is worse, this argument of universal consent, which is made use of to prove innate principles, seems to me a demonstration that there are none such: because there are none to which all mankind gives a universal assent. I shall begin with the speculative, and instance in those magnified principles of demonstration, "Whatsoever is, is," and "It is impossible for the same thing to be and not to be"; which, of all others, I think have the most allowed title to innate. These have so settled a reputation of maxims universally received, that it will no doubt be thought strange if any one should seem to question it. But yet I take liberty to say, that these propositions are so far from having a universal assent, that there are a great part of mankind to whom they are not so much as known.

For, first, it is evident, that all children and idiots have not the least apprehension or thought of them. And the want of that is enough to destroy that universal assent which must needs be the necessary concomitant of all innate truths: it seeming to me near a contradiction to say, that there are truths imprinted on the soul, which it perceives or understands not: imprinting, if it signify anything, being nothing else but the making certain truths to be perceived. For to imprint anything on the mind without the mind's perceiving it, seems to me hardly intelligible. If therefore children and idiots have souls, have minds, with those impressions upon them, *they* must unavoidably perceive them, and necessarily know and assent to these truths; which since they do not, it is evident that there are no such impressions. For if they are not notions naturally imprinted, how can they be innate? and if they are notions imprinted, how can they be unknown? If therefore these two propositions, "Whatsoever is, is," and "It is impossible for the same thing to be and not to be," are by nature imprinted, children cannot be ignorant of them: infants, and all that have souls, must necessarily have them in their understandings, know the truth of them, and assent to it.

To avoid this, it is usually answered, that all men know and assent to them, *when they come to the use of reason;* and this is enough to prove them innate. I answer:

To apply this answer with any tolerable sense to our present purpose, it must signify one of these two things: either that as soon as men come to the use of reason these supposed native inscriptions come to be known and observed by them; or else, that the use and exercise of men's reason assists them in the discovery of these principles, and certainly makes them known to them.

If they mean, that by the use of reason men may discover these principles, and that this is sufficient to prove them innate; their way of arguing will stand thus, viz. that whatever truths reason can certainly discover to us, and make us firmly assent to, those are all naturally imprinted on the mind; since that universal assent, which is made the mark of them, amounts to no more but this,—that by the use of reason we are capable to come to a certain knowledge of and assent to them; and, by this means, there will be no difference between the maxims of the mathematicians, and theorems they deduce from them: all must be equally allowed innate; they being all discoveries made by the use of reason, and truths that a rational creature may certainly come to know, if he apply his thoughts rightly that way.

But how can these men think the use of reason necessary to discover principles that are supposed innate, when reason (if we may believe them) is nothing else but the faculty of deducing unknown truths from principles or propositions that are already known? That certainly can never be thought innate which we have need of reason to discover; unless, as I have said, we will have all the certain truths that reason ever teaches us, to be innate. So that to make reason discover those truths thus imprinted, is to say, that the use of reason discovers to a man what he knew before: and if men have those innate impressed truths originally, and before the use of reason, and yet are always ignorant of them till they come to the use of reason, it is in effect to say, that men know and know them not at the same time.

If by knowing and assenting to them "when we come to the use of reason," be meant, that this is the time when they come to be taken notice of by the mind; and that as soon as children come to the use of reason, they come also to know and assent to these maxims; this also is false and frivolous. First, it is false; because it is evident these maxims are not in the mind so early as the use of reason; and therefore the coming to the use of reason is falsely assigned as the time of their discovery. How many instances of the use of reason may we observe in children, a long time before they have any knowledge of this maxim, "That it is impossible for the same thing to be and not to be"? And a great part of illiterate people and savages pass many years, even of their rational age, without ever thinking on this and the like general propositions. I grant, men come not to the knowledge of these general and more abstract truths, which are thought innate, till they come to the use of reason; and I add, nor then neither. Which is so, because till after they come to the use of reason, those general abstract ideas are not framed in the mind, about which those general maxims are, which are mistaken for innate principles, but are indeed discoveries made and verities introduced and brought into the mind by the same way, and discovered by the same steps, as several other propositions, which nobody was ever so extravagant as to suppose innate. This I hope to make plain in the sequel of this Discourse. I allow therefore, a necessity that men should come to the use of reason before they get the knowledge of those general truths; but deny that men's coming to the use of reason is the time of their discovery.

In the meantime it is observable, that this saying, that men know and assent to these maxims "when they come to the use of reason," amounts in reality of fact to no more but this,—that they are never known nor taken notice of before the use of reason, but may possibly be assented to some time after, during a man's life; but when is uncertain. And so may all other knowable truths, as well as these; which therefore have no advantage nor distinction from others by this note of being known when we come to the use of reason; nor are thereby proved to be innate, but quite the contrary.

But, secondly, were it true that the precise time of their being known and assented to were when men come to the use of reason, neither would that prove them innate. This way of arguing is as frivolous as the supposition itself is false. For, by what kind of logic will it appear that any notion is originally by nature imprinted in the mind in its first constitution, because it comes first to be observed and assented to when a faculty of the mind, which has quite a distinct province, begins to exert itself? And therefore the coming to the use of speech, if it were supposed the time that these maxims are first assented to (which it may be with as much truth as the time when men come to the use of reason), would be as good a proof that they were innate, as to say they are innate because men assent to them when they come to the use of reason. I agree then with these men of innate principles, that there is no knowledge of these general and self-evident maxims in the mind, till it comes to the exercise of reason: but I deny that the coming to the use of reason is the precise time when they are first taken notice of; and if that were the precise time, I deny that it would prove them innate. All that can with any truth be meant by this proposition, that men "assent to them when they come to the use of reason," is no more but this,—that the making of general abstract ideas, and the understanding of general names, being a concomitant of the rational faculty, and growing up with it, children commonly get not those general ideas, nor learn the names that stand for them, till, having for a good while exercised their reason about familiar and more particular ideas, they are, by their ordinary discourse and actions with others, acknowledged to be capable of rational conversation. If assenting to these maxims, when men come to the use of reason, can be true in any other sense, I desire it may be shown; or at least, how in this, or any other sense, it proves them innate.

The senses at first let in *particular* ideas, and furnish the yet empty cabinet, and the mind by degrees growing familiar with some of them, they are lodged in the memory, and names got to them. Afterward, the mind proceeding further, abstracts them, and by degrees learns the use of general names. In this manner the mind comes to be furnished with ideas and language, the *materials* about which to exercise its discursive faculty. And the use of reason becomes daily more visible, as these materials that give it employment increase. But though the having of general ideas and the use of general words and reason usually grow together, yet I see not how this any way proves them innate. The knowledge of some truths, I confess, is very early in the mind; but in a way that shows them not to be innate. For, if we will observe, we shall find it still to be about ideas, not innate, but acquired; it being about those first which are imprinted by external things, with which infants have earliest to do, which make the most frequent impressions on their senses. In ideas thus got, the mind discovers that some agree and others differ, probably as soon as it has any use of memory; as soon as it is able to retain and perceive distinct ideas. But whether it be then or no, this is certain, it does so long before it has the use of words; or comes to that which we commonly call "the use of reason." For a child knows as certainly before it can speak the difference between the ideas of sweet and bitter (i.e. that sweet is not bitter), as it knows afterward (when it comes to speak) that wormwood and sugarplums are not the same thing.

A child knows not that three and four are equal to seven, till he comes to be able to count seven, and has got the name and idea of equality; and then, upon explaining those words, he presently assents to, or rather perceives the truth of that proposition. But neither does he then readily assent because it is an innate truth, nor was his assent wanting till then because he wanted the use of reason; but the truth of it appears to him as soon as he has settled in his mind the clear and distinct ideas that these names stand for. And then he knows the truth of that proposition upon the same grounds and by the same means, that he knew before that a rod and a cherry are not the same thing; and upon the same grounds also that he may come to know afterward "That it is impossible for the same thing to be and not to be," as shall be more fully shown hereafter. So that the later it is before anyone comes to have those general ideas about which those maxims are; or to know the signification of those general terms that stand for them; or to put together in his mind the ideas they stand for; the later also will it be before he comes to assent to those maxims;—whose terms, with the ideas they stand for, being no more innate than those of a cat or a weasel, he must stay till time and observation have acquainted him with them; and then he will be in a capacity to know the truth of these maxims, upon the first occasion that shall make him put together those ideas in his mind, and observe whether they agree or disagree, according as is expressed in those propositions.

This evasion therefore of general assent when men come to the use of reason, failing as it does, and leaving no difference between those supposed innate and other truths that are afterward acquired and learned, men have endeavored to secure a universal assent to those they call maxims, by saying, they are generally assented to as soon as proposed, and the terms they are proposed in understood; seeing all men, even children, as soon as they hear and understand the terms, assent to these propositions, they think it is sufficient to prove them innate. For, since men never fail after they have once understood the words, to acknowledge them for undoubted truths, they would infer, that certainly these propositions were first lodged in the understanding, which, without any teaching, the mind, at the very first proposal immediately closes with and assents to, and after that never doubts again.

In answer to this, I demand whether ready assent given to a proposition, upon first hearing and understanding the terms, be a certain mark of an innate principle? If it be not, such a general assent is in vain urged as a proof of them: if it be said that it is a mark of innate, they must then allow all such propositions to be innate which are generally assented to as soon as heard, whereby they will find themselves plentifully stored with innate principles. For upon the same ground, viz. of assent at first hearing and understanding the terms, that men would have those maxims pass for innate, they must also admit several propositions about numbers to be innate; and thus, that one and two are equal to three, that two and two are equal to four, and a multitude of other the like propositions in numbers, that everybody assents to at first hearing and understanding the terms, must have a place amongst these innate axioms. Nor is this the prerogative of numbers alone, and propositions made about several of them; but even natural philosophy, and all the other sciences, afford propositions which are sure to meet with assent as soon as they are understood. But, since no proposition can be innate unless the *ideas* about which it is be innate, this will be to suppose all our ideas of colors, sounds, tastes, figure, etc., innate, than which there cannot be anything more opposite to reason and experience. Universal and ready assent upon hearing and understanding the terms is, I grant, a mark of self-evidence; but self-evidence, depending not on innate impressions, but on something else (as we shall show hereafter), belongs to several propositions which nobody was yet so extravagant as to pretend to be innate.

Nor let it be said, that those more particular self-evident propositions, which are assented to at first hearing, as that "one and two are equal to three," that "green is not red," etc., are received as the consequences of those more universal propositions which are looked on as innate principles; since anyone, who will but take the pains to observe what passes in the understanding, will certainly find that these, and the like less general propositions, are certainly known, and firmly assented to by those who are utterly ignorant of those more general maxims; and so, being earlier in the mind than those (as they are called) first principles, cannot owe to them the assent wherewith they are received at first hearing.

[Locke next argues that if these maxims are not known until they are taught, then they cannot properly be said to be innate.]

If it be said, the understanding hath an *implicit* knowledge of these principles, but not an *explicit,* before this first hearing (as they must who will say "that they are in the understanding before they are known"), it will be hard to conceive what is meant by a principle imprinted on the understanding implicitly, unless it be this,—that the mind is capable of understanding and assenting firmly to such propositions. And thus all mathematical demonstrations, as well as first principles, must be received as native impressions on the mind; which I fear they will scarce allow them to be, who find it harder to demonstrate a proposition than assent to it when demonstrated. And few mathematicians will be forward to believe, that all the diagrams they have drawn were but copies of those innate characters which nature had engraven upon their minds.

There is, I fear, this further weakness in the foregoing argument, which would persuade us that therefore those maxims are to be thought innate, which men admit at first hearing; because they assent to propositions which they are not taught, nor do receive from the force of any argument or demonstration, but a bare explication or understanding of the terms. Under which there seems to me to lie this fallacy, that men are supposed not to be taught nor to learn anything *de novo;* when, in truth, they are taught, and do learn something they were ignorant of before. For, first, it is evident that they have learned the terms, and their signification; neither of which was born with them. But this is not all the acquired knowledge in the case: the ideas themselves, about which the proposition is, are not born with them, no more than their names, but got afterward. So that in all propositions that are assented to at first hearing, the terms of the proposition, their standing for such ideas, and the ideas themselves that they stand for, being neither of them innate, I would fain know what there is remaining in such propositions that is innate. For I would gladly have anyone name that proposition whose terms or ideas were either of them innate. We *by degrees* get ideas and names, and *learn* their appropriate connection one with another; and then to propositions made in such terms, whose signification we have learned, and wherein the agreement or disagreement we can perceive in our ideas when put together is expressed, we at first hearing assent; though to other propositions, in themselves as certain and evident, but which are concerning ideas not so soon or so easily got, we are at the same time no way capable of assenting. For, though a child quickly assents to this proposition, "That an apple is not fire," when by familiar acquaintance he has got the ideas of those two different things distinctly imprinted on his mind, and has learned that the names apple and fire stand for them;

yet it will be some years after, perhaps, before the same child will assent to this proposition, "That it is impossible for the same thing to be and not to be"; because that, though perhaps the words are as easy to be learned, yet the signification of them being more large, comprehensive, and abstract than of the names annexed to those sensible things the child hath to do with, it is longer before he learns their precise meaning, and it requires more time plainly to form in his mind those general ideas they stand for. Till that be done, you will in vain endeavor to make any child assent to a proposition made up of such general terms; but as soon as ever he has got those ideas, and learned their names, he forwardly closes with the one as well as the other of the forementioned propositions: and with both for the same reason; viz. because he finds the ideas he has in his mind to agree or disagree, according as the words standing for them are affirmed or denied one of another in the proposition. But if propositions be brought to him in words which stand for ideas he has not yet in his mind, to such propositions, however evidently true or false in themselves, he affords neither assent nor dissent, but is ignorant. For words being but empty sounds, any further than they are signs of our ideas, we cannot but assent to them as they correspond to those ideas we have, but no further than that. But the showing by what steps and ways knowledge comes into our minds; and the grounds of several degrees of assent, being the business of the following Discourse, it may suffice to have only touched on it here, as one reason that made me doubt of those innate principles.

To conclude this argument of universal consent, I agree with these defenders of innate principles—that if they are innate, they must needs have universal assent. For that a truth should be innate and yet not assented to, is to me as unintelligible as for a man to know a truth and be ignorant of it at the same time. But then, by these men's own confession, they cannot be innate; since they are not assented to by those who understand not the terms; nor by a great part of those who do understand them, but have yet never heard nor thought of those propositions; which, I think, is at least one half of mankind. But were the number far less, it would be enough to destroy universal assent, and thereby show these propositions not to be innate, if children alone were ignorant of them.

I know not how absurd this may seem to the masters of

demonstration. And probably it will hardly go down with anybody at first hearing. I must therefore beg a little truce with prejudice, and the forebearance of censure, till I have been heard out in the sequel of this Discourse, being very willing to submit to better judgments. And since I impartially search after truth, I shall not be sorry to be convinced, that I have been too fond of my own notions; which I confess we are all apt to be, when application and study have warmed our heads with them.

Upon the whole matter, I cannot see any ground to think these two speculative Maxims innate: since they are not universally assented to; and the assent they so generally find is no other than what several propositions, not allowed to be innate, equally partake in with them: and since the assent that is given them is produced another way, and comes not from natural inscription, as I doubt not but to make appear in the following Discourse. And if *these* "first principles" of knowledge and science are found not to be innate, no *other* speculative maxims can (I suppose), with better right pretend to be so.

II

No Innate Practical Principles

IF THOSE SPECULATIVE MAXIMS, whereof we discoursed in the foregoing chapter, have not an actual universal assent from all mankind, as we there proved, it is much more visible concerning *practical* Principles, that they come short of a universal reception: and I think it will be hard to instance any one moral rule which can pretend to so general and ready an assent as, "What is, is"; or to be so manifest a truth as this, that "It is impossible for the same thing to be and not to be." Whereby it is evident that they are further removed from a title to be innate; and the doubt of their being native impressions on the mind is stronger against those moral principles than the other. Not that it brings their truth at all in question. They are equally true, though not equally evident. Those speculative maxims carry their own evidence with them: but moral principles require reasoning and discourse, and some exercise of the mind, to discover the certainty of their truth. They lie not open as natural characters engraven on the mind; which, if any such were, they must needs be visible by themselves, and by their own light be certain and known to everybody. But this is no derogation to their truth and certainty; no more than it is to the truth or certainty of the three angles of a triangle being equal to two right ones: because it is not so evident as "the whole is bigger than a part," nor so apt to be assented to at first hearing. It may suffice that these moral rules are capable of demonstration: and therefore it is our own faults if we come not to a certain knowledge of them. But the ignorance wherein many men are of them, and the slowness of assent wherewith others receive them, are manifest proofs that they are not innate, and such as offer themselves to their view without searching.

Whether there be any such moral principles, wherein all men do agree, I appeal to any who have been but moderately conversant in the history of mankind, and looked abroad beyond the smoke of their own chimneys. Where is that practical truth that is universally received, without doubt or question, as it must be if innate? *Justice*, and keeping of contracts, is that which most men seem to agree in. This is a principle which is thought to extend itself to the dens of thieves, and the confederacies of the greatest villains; and they who have gone furthest toward the putting off of humanity itself, keep faith and rules of justice one with another. I grant that outlaws themselves do this one amongst another: but it is without receiving these as the innate laws of nature. They practice them as rules of convenience within their own communities: but it is impossible to conceive that he embraces justice as a practical principle, who acts fairly with his fellow-highwayman, and at the same time plunders or kills the next honest man he meets with. Justice and truth are the common ties of society; and therefore even outlaws and robbers, who break with all the world besides, must keep faith and rules of equity amongst themselves; or else they cannot hold together. But will anyone say, that those that live by fraud or rapine have innate principles of truth and justice which they allow and assent to?

Perhaps it will be urged, that the tacit assent of their minds agrees to what their practice contradicts. I answer, first, I have always thought the actions of men the best interpreters of their thoughts. But, since it is certain that most men's practices, and some men's open professions, have either questioned or denied these principles, it is impossible to establish a universal consent (though we should look for it only amongst grown men) without which it is impossible to conclude them innate. Secondly, it is very strange and unreasonable to suppose innate practical principles, that terminate only in contemplation. Practical principles, derived from nature, are there for operation, and must produce conformity of action, not barely speculative assent to their truth, or else they are in vain distinguished from speculative maxims. Nature, I confess, has put into man a desire of happiness and an aversion to misery: these indeed are innate practical principles which (as practical principles ought) *do* continue constantly to operate and influence all our actions without ceasing: these may be observed in all persons and all ages, steady and universal; but these are *inclinations of the appetite* to good, not impressions of truth on the understanding. I deny not that there are natural tendencies imprinted on the minds of men; and that from the very first instances of sense and perception, there are some things that are grateful and others unwelcome to them; some things that they incline to and others that they fly: but this makes nothing for innate characters on the mind, which are to be the principles of knowledge regulating our practice. Such natural impressions on the understanding are so far from being confirmed hereby, that this is an argument against them; since, if there were certain characters imprinted by nature on the understanding, as the principles of knowledge, we could not but perceive them constantly operate in us and influence our knowledge, as we do those others on the will and appetite; which never cease to be the constant springs and motives of all our actions, to which we perpetually feel them strongly impelling us.

Another reason that makes me doubt of any innate practical principles is, that I think *there cannot any one moral rule be proposed whereof a man may not justly demand a reason:* which would be perfectly ridiculous and absurd if they were innate; or so much as self-evident, which every innate principle must needs be, and not need any proof to ascertain its truth, nor want any reason to gain it approbation.

He would be thought void of common sense who asked on the one side, or on the other side went to give a reason *why* "it is impossible for the same thing to be and not to be." It carries its own light and evidence with it, and needs no other proof: he that understands the terms assents to it for its own sake or else nothing will ever be able to prevail with him to do it. But should that most unshaken rule of morality and foundation of all social virtue, "That one should do as he would be done unto," be proposed to one who never heard of it before, but yet is of capacity to understand its meaning; might he not without any absurdity ask a reason why? And were not he that proposed it bound to make out the truth and reasonableness of it to him? Which plainly shows it not to be innate; for if it were it could neither want nor receive any proof; but must needs (at least as soon as heard and understood) be received and assented to as any unqestionable truth, which a man can by no means doubt of. So that the truth of all these moral rules plainly depends upon some other antecedent to them, and from which they must be *deduced;* which could not be if either they were innate or so much as self-evident.

That men should keep their compacts is certainly a great and undeniable rule in morality. But yet, if a Christian, who has the view of happiness and misery in another life, be asked why a man must keep his word, he will give this as a reason: —Because God, who has the power of eternal life and death, requires it of us. But if a Hobbist be asked why? he will answer:—Because the public requires it, and the Leviathan will punish you if you do not. And if one of the old philosophers had been asked, he would have answered:—Because it was dishonest, below the dignity of a man, and opposite to virtue, the highest perfection of human nature, to do otherwise.

Hence naturally flows the great variety of opinions concerning moral rules which are to be found among men, according to the different sorts of happiness they have a prospect of, or propose to themselves; which could not be if practical principles were innate, and imprinted in our minds immediately by the hand of God. I grant the existence of God is so many ways manifest, and the obedience we owe him so congruous to the light of reason, that a great part of mankind give testimony to the law of nature: but yet I think it must be allowed that several moral rules may receive from mankind a very general approbation, without either knowing or admitting the true ground of morality; which can only be the will and law of a God, who sees men in the dark, has in his hand rewards and punishments, and power enough to call to account the proudest offender. For, God having, by an inseparable connection, joined virtue and public happiness together, and made the practice thereof necessary to the preservation of society, and visibly beneficial to all with whom the virtuous man has to do; it is no wonder that everyone should not only allow, but recommend and magnify those rules to others, from whose observance of them he is sure to reap advantage to himself. The great principle of morality, "To do as one would be done to," is more commended than practiced. But the breach of this rule cannot be a greater vice, than to teach others, that it is no moral rule, nor obligatory, would be thought madness, and contrary to that interest men sacrifice to, when they break it themselves. Perhaps *conscience* will be urged as checking us for such breaches, and so the internal obligation and establishment of the rule be preserved.

To which I answer, that I doubt not but, without being written on their hearts, many men may, by the same way that they come to the knowledge of other things, come to assent to several moral rules, and be convinced of their obligation.

Others also may come to be of the same mind, from their education, company, and customs of their country; which persuasion, however got, will serve to set conscience on work; which is nothing else but our own opinion or judgment of the moral rectitude or pravity of our own actions; and if conscience be a proof of innate principles, contraries may be innate principles; since some men with the same bent of conscience prosecute what others avoid.

But I cannot see how any men should ever transgress those moral rules, with confidence and serenity, were they innate, and stamped upon their minds. View but an army at the sacking of a town, and see what observation or sense of moral principles, or what touch of conscience for all the outrages they do. Robberies, murders, rapes, are the sports of men set at liberty from punishment and censure. Have there not been whole nations, and those of the most civilized people, amongst whom the exposing their children, and leaving them in the fields to perish by want or wild beasts has been the practice; as little condemned or scrupled as the begetting them? Do they not still, in some countries, put them into the same graves with their mothers, if they die in childbirth; or dispatch them, if a pretended astrologer declares them to have unhappy stars? And are there not places where, at a certain age, they kill or expose their parents, without any remorse at all? In a part of Asia, the sick, when their case comes to be thought desperate, are carried out and laid on the earth before they are dead; and left there, exposed to wind and weather, to perish without assistance or pity. It is familiar among the Mingrelians, a people professing Christianity, to bury their children alive without scruple. There are places where they eat their own children.

Where then are those innate principles of justice, piety, gratitude, equity, chastity? Or where is that universal consent that assures us there are such inbred rules? Murders in duels, when fashion has made them honorable, are committed without remorse of conscience: nay, in many places innocence in this case is the greatest ignominy. And if we look abroad to take a view of men as they are, we shall find that they have remorse, in one place, for doing or omitting that which others, in another place, think they merit by.

He that will carefully peruse the history of mankind, and look abroad into several tribes of men, and with indifferency survey their actions, will be able to satisfy himself, that there is scarce that principle of morality to be named, or rule of virtue to be thought on (those only excepted that are absolutely necessary to hold society together, which commonly too are neglected betwixt distinct societies), which is not, somewhere or other, slighted and condemned by the general fashion of whole societies of men, governed by practical opinions and rules of living quite opposite to others.

The breaking of a rule, say you, is no argument that it is unknown. I grant it: but the *generally allowed* breach of it anywhere, I say, is a proof that it is not innate. For example: let us take any of these rules, which, being the most obvious deductions of human reason, and conformable to the natural inclination of the greatest part of men, fewest people have had the impudence to deny or inconsideration to doubt of. If any can be thought to be naturally imprinted, none, I think, can have a fairer pretense to be innate than this: "Parents, preserve and cherish your children." When, therefore, you say that this is an innate rule, what do you mean? Either that it is an innate principle which upon all occasions excites and directs the actions of all men; or else, that it is a truth which all men have imprinted on their minds, and which therefore they know and assent to. But in neither of these senses is it innate. *First,* that it is not a principle which influences all men's actions, is what I have proved by the examples before cited. *Secondly,* that it is an innate truth, known to all men, is also false. For, "Parents, preserve your children," is so far from an innate truth, that it is no truth at all: it being a command, and not a proposition, and so not capable of truth or falsehood. To make it capable of being assented to as true, it must be reduced to some such proposition as this: "It is the duty of parents to preserve their children." But what duty is, cannot be understood without a law; nor a law be known or supposed without a lawmaker, or without reward and punishment; so that it is impossible that this, or any other, practical principle should be innate, i.e. be imprinted on the mind as a duty, without supposing the ideas of God, of law, of obligation, of punishment, of a life after this, innate: for that punishment follows not in this life the breach of this rule, and consequently that it has not the force of a law in countries where the generally allowed practice runs counter to it, is in itself evident. But these ideas (which must be all of them innate, if anything as a duty be so) are so far from being innate, that it is not every studious or thinking man, much less every one that is born, in whom they are to be found clear and distinct; and that one of them, which of all others seems most likely to be innate, is not so (I mean the idea of God), I think, in the next chapter, will appear very evident to any considering man.

From what has been said, I think we may safely conclude, that whatever practical rule is in any place generally and with allowance broken, cannot be supposed innate. Principles of actions indeed there are lodged in men's appetites; but these are so far from being innate moral principles, that if they were left to their full swing they would carry men to the overturning of all morality. Moral laws are set as a curb and restraint to these exorbitant desires, which they cannot be but by rewards and punishments that will overbalance the satisfaction anyone shall propose to himself in the breach of the law. If, therefore, anything be imprinted on the minds of all men as a law, all men must have a certain and unavoidable knowledge that certain and unavoidable punishment will attend the breach of it. For if men can be ignorant or doubtful of what is innate, innate principles are insisted on, and urged to no purpose; truth and certainty (the things pretended) are not at all secured by them; but men are in the same uncertain floating estate with as without them. An evident indubitable knowledge of unavoidable punishment, great enough to make the transgression very ineligible must accompany an innate law; unless with an innate law they can suppose an innate Gospel too. I would not here be mistaken, as if, because I deny an innate law, I thought there were none but positive laws. There is a great deal of difference between an innate law, and a law of nature; between something imprinted on our minds in their very original, and something that we, being ignorant of, may attain to the knowledge of, by the use and due application of our natural faculties. And I think they equally forsake the truth who, running into contrary extremes, either affirm an innate law, or deny that there is a law knowable by the light of nature, i.e. without the help of positive revelation.

[Locke next protests that the champions of innate practical principles never say precisely what those principles are. He finds those suggested by Lord Herbert of Cherburg in his book *De Veritate* platitudinous and ambiguous, and thinks it improbable that God should engrave in men's minds principles of such uncertain meaning.]

I easily grant that there are great numbers of opinions which, by men of different countries, educations, and tempers, are received and embraced as first and unquestionable principles; many whereof, both for their absurdity as well as oppositions to one another, it is impossible should be true. But yet all those propositions, how remote soever from reason, are so sacred somewhere or other, that men even of good understanding in other matters, will sooner part with their lives, and whatever is dearest to them, than suffer themselves to doubt, or others to question, the truth of them.

This, however strange it may seem, is that which every day's experience confirms; and will not, perhaps, appear so wonderful, if we consider the ways and steps by which it is brought about; and how really it may come to pass, that doctrines that have been derived from no better original than the superstitition of a nurse, or the authority of an old woman, may, by length of time and consent of neighbors, grow up to the dignity of *principles* in religion or morality. For such, who are careful (as they call it) to principle children well (and few there be who have not a set of those principles for them, which they believe in), instill into the unwary, and as yet unprejudiced, understanding (for white paper receives any characters) those doctrines they would have them retain and profess. These being taught them as soon as they have any apprehension; and still as they grow up confirmed to them, either by the open profession or tacit consent of all they have to do with; or at least by those of whose wisdom, knowledge, and piety they have an opinion, who never suffer those propositions to be otherwise mentioned but as the basis and foundation on which they build their religion and manners, come, by these means, to have the reputation of unquestionable, self-evident, and innate truths.

To which we may add, that when men so instructed are grown up, and reflect on their own minds, they cannot find anything more ancient there than those opinions, which were taught them before their memory began to keep a register of their actions, or date the time when any new thing appeared to them; and therefore make no scruple to conclude, that those propositions of whose knowledge they can find in themselves no original, were certainly the impress of God and nature upon their minds, and not taught them by anyone else. These they entertain and submit to, as many do to their parents with veneration; not because it is natural; nor do children do it where they are not so taught; but because, having been always so educated, and having no remembrance of the beginning of this respect, they think it is natural.

This will appear very likely, and almost unavoidable to come to pass, if we consider the nature of mankind and the constitution of human affairs; wherein most men cannot live without employing their time in the daily labors of their callings; nor be at quiet in their minds without *some* foundation or principle to rest their thoughts on. There is scarcely anyone so floating and superficial in his understanding, who hath not some reverenced propositions, which are to him the principles on which he bottoms his reasonings, and by which he judgeth of truth and falsehood, right and wrong; which some wanting skill and leisure, and others the inclination, and some being taught that they ought not to examine, there are few to be found who are not exposed by their ignorance, laziness, education, or precipitancy, to *take them upon trust.*

This is evidently the case of all children and young folk; and custom, a greater power than nature, seldom failing to make them worship for divine what she hath inured them to bow their minds and submit their understandings to, it is no wonder that grown men, either perplexed in the necessary affairs of life, or hot in the pursuit of pleasures, should *not* seriously sit down to examine their own tenets; especially when one of their principles is, that principles ought not to be questioned. And had men leisure, parts, and will, who is there almost that dare shake the foundations of all his past thoughts and actions, and endure to bring upon himself the shame of having been a long time wholly in mistake and error? Who is there hardy enough to contend with the reproach which is everywhere prepared for those who dare venture to dissent from the received opinions of their country or party? And where is the man to be found that can patiently prepare himself to bear the name of whimsical, skeptical, or atheist; which he is sure to meet with, who does in the least scruple any of the common opinions? And he will be much more afraid to question those principles, when he shall think them, as most men do, the standards set up by God in his mind, to be the rule and touchstone of all other opinions. And what can hinder him from thinking them sacred, when he finds them the earliest of all his own thoughts, and the most reverenced by others?

It is easy to imagine how, by these means, it comes to pass that men worship the idols that have been set up in their minds; grow fond of the notions they have been long acquainted with there; and stamp the characters of divinity upon absurdities and errors; become zealous votaries to bulls and monkeys, and contend too, fight, and die in defense of their opinions. *Dum solos credit habendos esse deos, quos ipse colit.* For, since the reasoning faculties of the soul, which are almost constantly, though not always warily nor wisely employed, would not know how to move, for want of a foundation and footing, in most men, who through laziness or avocation do not, or for want of time, or true helps, or for other causes, cannot penetrate into the principles of knowledge, and trace truth to its fountain and original, it is natural for them, and almost unavoidable, to take up with some borrowed principles; which being reputed and presumed to be the evident proofs of other things, are thought not to need any other proof themselves. Whoever shall receive any of these into his mind, and entertain them there with the reverence usually paid to principles, never venturing to examine them, but accustoming himself to believe them, because they are to be believed, may take up, from his education and the fashions of his country, any absurdity for innate principles; and by long poring on the same objects, so dim his sight as to take monsters lodged in his own brain for the images of the Deity, and the workmanship of his hands.

By this progress, how many there are who arrive at principles which they believe innate may be easily observed, in the variety of opposite principles held and contended for by all sorts and degrees of men. And he that shall deny this to be the method wherein most men proceed to the assurance they have of the truth and evidence of their principles, will perhaps find it a hard matter any other way to account for the contrary tenets, which are firmly believed, confidently asserted and which great numbers are ready at any time to seal with their blood. And, indeed, if it be the privilege of innate principles to be received upon their own authority, without examination, I know not what may not be believed, or how anyone's principles can be questioned. If they may and ought to be examined and tried, I desire to know how first and innate principles can be tried; or at least it is reasonable to demand the *marks* and *characters* whereby the genuine innate principles may be distinguished from others: that so, amidst the great variety of pretenders, I may be kept from mistakes in so material a point as this. When this is done, I shall be ready to embrace such welcome and useful propositions; and till then I may with modesty doubt; since I fear universal consent, which is the only one produced, will scarcely prove a sufficient mark to direct my choice, and assure me of any innate principles.

From what has been said, I think it past doubt, that there are no practical principles wherein all men agree; and therefore none innate.

III

Other Considerations Concerning Innate Principles, Both Speculative and Practical

HAD THOSE WHO WOULD PERSUADE US that there are innate principles not taken them together in gross, but considered separately the parts out of which those propositions are made, they would not, perhaps, have been so forward to believe they were innate. Since, if the *ideas* which made up those truths were not, it was impossible that the *propositions* made up of them should be innate, or our knowledge of them be born with us. For, if the ideas be not innate, there was a time when the mind was without those principles; and then they will not be innate, but be derived from some other original. For, where the ideas themselves are not, there can be no knowledge, no assent, no mental or verbal propositions about them.

If we will attentively consider new-born children, we shall have little reason to think that they bring many ideas into the world with them. For, bating perhaps some faint ideas of hunger, and thirst, and warmth, and some pains, which they may have felt in the womb, there is not the least appearance of any settled ideas at all in them; especially of *ideas answering the terms which make up those universal propositions that are esteemed innate principles*. One may perceive how, by degrees, afterwards, ideas come into their minds; and that they get no more, nor other, than what experience, and the observation of things that come in their way, furnish them with; which might be enough to satisfy us that they are not original characters stamped on the mind.

[Locke goes on to deny that such concepts as "impossibility" and "identity" are innate, and declares that many grown men do not have them in their heads. Even the idea of God is not innate; not all men have an idea of Him, and if they did this would not prove it to be an innate idea. And if the idea of God is not innate no other idea can pretend to be.]

Whatever then we talk of innate, either speculative or practical, principles, it may with as much probability be said, that a man hath £100 sterling in his pocket, and yet denied that he hath there either penny, shilling, crown, or other coin out of which the sum is to be made up; as to think that certain *propositions* are innate when the *ideas* about which they are can by no means be supposed to be so. The general reception and assent that is given doth not at all prove, that the ideas expressed in them are innate; for in many cases, however the ideas came there, the assent to words expressing the agreement or disagreement, of such ideas, will necessarily follow. Everyone that hath a true idea of *God* and *worship*, will assent to this proposition, "That God is to be worshipped," when expressed in a language he understands; and every rational man that hath not thought on it today, may be ready to assent to this proposition tomorrow; and yet millions of men may be well supposed to want one or both those ideas today. For, if we will allow savages, and most country people, to have ideas of God and worship (which conversation with them will not make one forward to believe), yet I think few children can be supposed to have those ideas, which therefore they must begin to have some time or other; and then they will also begin to assent to that proposition, and make very little question of it ever after. But such an assent upon hearing, no more proves the *ideas* to be innate, than it does that one born blind (with cataracts which will be couched tomorrow) had the innate ideas of the sun, or light, or saffron, or yellow; because, when his sight is cleared, he will certainly assent to this proposition, "That the sun is lucid, or that saffron is yellow." And therefore, if such an assent upon hearing cannot prove the ideas innate, it can much less the *propositions* made up of those ideas. If they have any innate ideas, I would be glad to be told what, and how many, they are.

Besides what I have already said, there is another reason why I doubt that neither these nor any other principles are innate. I that am fully persuaded that the infinitely wise God made all things in perfect wisdom, cannot satisfy myself why he should be supposed to print upon the minds of men some universal principles; whereof those that are pretended innate, and concern *speculation,* are of no great use; and those that concern *practice,* not self-evident; and neither of them distinguishable from some other truths not allowed to be innate. For, to what purpose should characters be graven on the mind by the finger of God, which are not clearer there than those which are afterward introduced, or cannot be distinguished from them? If anyone thinks there are such innate ideas and propositions, which by their clearness and usefulness are distinguishable from all that is adventitious in the mind and acquired, it will not be a hard matter for him to tell us *which they are;* and then everyone will be a fit judge whether they be so or no. Since if there be such innate ideas and impressions, plainly different from all other perceptions and knowledge, everyone will find it true in himself. Of the evidence of these supposed innate maxims, I have spoken already: of their usefulness I shall have occasion to speak more hereafter.

To conclude: some ideas forwardly offer themselves to all men's understanding; and some sorts of truths result from any ideas, as soon as the mind puts them into propositions: other truths require a train of ideas placed in order, a due comparing of them, and deductions made with attention, before they can be discovered and assented to. Some of the first sort, because of their general and easy reception, have been mistaken for innate: but the truth is, ideas and notions are no more born with us than arts and sciences; though some of them indeed offer themselves to our faculties more readily than others; and therefore are more generally received: though that too be according as the organs of our bodies and powers of our minds happen to be employed; God having fitted men with faculties and means to discover, receive, and retain truths, according as they are employed. The great difference that is to be found in the notions of mankind is, from the different use they put their faculties to. Whilst some (and those the most) taking things upon trust, misemploy their power of assent, by lazily enslaving their minds to the dictates and dominion of others, in doctrines which it is their duty carefully to examine, and not blindly, with an implicit faith, to swallow; others, employing their thoughts only about some few things, grow acquainted sufficiently with them, attain great degrees of knowledge in them, and are ignorant of all other, having never let their thoughts loose in the search of other inquiries. Thus, that the three angles of a triangle are quite equal to two right ones is a truth as certain as anything can be, and I think more evident than many of those propositions that go for principles; and yet there are millions, however expert in other things, who know not this at all, because they never set their thoughts on work about such angles. And he that certainly knows this proposition may yet be utterly ignorant of the truth of other propositions, in mathematics itself, which are as clear and evident as this; because, in his search of those mathematical truths, he stopped his thoughts short and went not so far. The same may happen concerning the notions we have of the being of a Deity. For, though there be no truth which a man may more evidently make out to himself than the existence of a God, yet he that shall content himself with things as he finds them in this world, as they minister to his pleasures and passions, and not make inquiry a little further into their causes, ends, and admirable contrivances, and pursue the thoughts thereof with diligence and attention, may live long without any notion of such a Being. And if any person hath by talk put such a notion into his head, he may perhaps believe it; but if he hath never examined it, his knowledge of it will be no perfecter than his, who having been told, that the three angles of a triangle are equal to two right ones, takes it upon trust, without examining the demonstration; and may yield his assent as a probable opinion, but hath no knowledge of the truth of it; which yet his faculties, if carefully employed, were able to make clear and evident to him. But this only, by the by, to show how much *our knowledge depends upon the right use of those powers nature hath bestowed upon us,* and how little upon *such innate principles as are in vain supposed to be in all mankind for their direction;* which all men could not but know if they were there, or else they would be there to no purpose. And which since all men do not know, nor can distinguish from other adventitious truths, we may well conclude there are no such.

What censure doubting thus of innate principles may deserve from men, who will be apt to call it pulling up the old foundations of knowledge and certainty, I cannot tell;—I persuade myself at least that the way I have pursued, being conformable to truth, lays those foundations surer. This I am certain, I have not made it my business either to quit or follow any authority in the ensuing Discourse. Truth has been my only aim; and wherever that has appeared to lead, my thoughts have impartially followed, without minding whether the footsteps of any other lay that way or not. Not that I want a due respect to other men's opinions; but, after all, the greatest reverence is due to truth: and I hope it will not be thought arrogance to say, that perhaps we should make greater progress in the discovery of rational and contemplative knowledge, if we sought it in the fountain, *in the consideration of things themselves;* and made use rather of our own thoughts than other men's to find it. For I think we may as rationally hope to see with other men's eyes, as to know by other men's understandings. So much as we ourselves consider and comprehend of truth and reason, so much we possess of real and true knowledge. The floating of other men's opinions in our brains, makes us not one jot the more knowing, though they happen to be true. What in them was science, is in us but opiniatrety; whilst we give up our assent only to reverend names, and do not, as they did, employ our own reason to understand those truths which gave them reputation. Aristotle was certainly a knowing man, but nobody ever thought him so because he blindly embraced, and confidently vented the opinions of another. And if the taking up of another's principles, without examining them, made not him a philosopher, I suppose it will hardly make anybody else so. In the sciences, everyone has so much as he really knows and comprehends. What he believes only, and takes upon trust, are but shreds; which, however well in the whole piece, make no considerable addition to his stock who gathers them. Such borrowed wealth, like fairy money, though it were gold in the hand from which he received it, will be but leaves and dust when it comes to use.

When men have found some general propositions that could not be doubted of as soon as understood, it was, I know, a short and easy way to conclude them innate. This being once received, it eased the lazy from the pains of search, and stopped the inquiry of the doubtful concerning all that was once styled innate. And it was of no small advantage to those who affected to be masters and teachers, to make this the principle of principles,—*that principles must not be questioned*. For, having once established this tenet,—that there are innate principles, it put their followers upon a necessity of receiving *some* doctrines as such; which was to take them off from the use of their own reason and judgment, and put them on believing and taking them upon trust without further examination: in which posture of blind credulity, they might be more easily governed by, and made useful to some sort of men, who had the skill and office to principle and guide them. Nor is it a small power it gives one man over another, to have the authority to be the dictator of principles, and teacher of unquestionable truths; and to make a man swallow that for an innate principle which may serve to his purpose who teacheth them. Whereas had they examined the ways whereby men came to the knowledge of many universal truths, they would have found them to result in the minds of men from the being of things themselves, when duly considered; and that they were discovered by the application of those faculties that were fitted by nature to receive and judge of them, when duly employed about them.

To show *how* the understanding proceeds herein is the design of the following Discourse; which I shall proceed to when I have first premised, that hitherto,—to clear my way to those foundations which I conceive are the only true ones, whereon to establish those notions we can have of our own knowledge,—it hath been necessary for me to give an account of the reasons I had to doubt of innate principles. And since the arguments which are against them do, some of them, rise from common received opinions, I have been forced to take several things for granted; which is hardly avoidable to any one, whose task is to show the falsehood or improbability of any tenet;—it happening in controversial discourses as it does in assaulting of towns; where, if the ground be but firm whereon the batteries are erected, there is no further inquiry of whom it is borrowed, nor whom it belongs to, so it affords but a fit rise for the present purpose. But in the future part of this Discourse, designing to raise an edifice uniform and consistent with itself, as far as my own experience and observation will assist me, I hope to erect it on such a basis that I shall not need to shore it up with props and buttresses, leaning on borrowed or begged foundations: or at least, if mine prove a castle in the air, I will endeavor it shall be all of a piece and hang together.

BOOK TWO

OF IDEAS

I

Of Ideas in General, and Their Original

EVERY MAN BEING CONSCIOUS to himself that he thinks; and that which his mind is applied about whilst thinking being the *ideas* that are there, it is past doubt that men have in their minds several ideas,—such as are those expressed by the words *whiteness, hardness, sweetness, thinking, motion, man, elephant, army, drunkenness,* and others: it is in the first place then to be inquired, *How he comes by them?*

I know it is a received doctrine, that men have native ideas, and original characters, stamped upon their minds in their very first being. This opinion I have at large examined already; and, I suppose what I have said in the foregoing Book will be much more easily admitted, when I have shown whence the understanding may get all the ideas it has; and by what ways and degrees they may come into the mind;—for which I shall appeal to everyone's own observation and experience.

Let us then suppose the mind to be, as we say, white paper, void of all characters, without any ideas:—How comes it to be furnished? Whence comes it by that vast store which the busy and boundless fancy of man has painted on it with an almost endless variety? Whence has it all the *materials* of reason and knowledge? To this I answer, in one word, from EXPERIENCE. In that all our knowledge is founded; and from that it ultimately derives itself. Our observation employed either, about external sensible objects, or about the internal operations of our minds perceived and reflected on by ourselves, is that which supplies our understandings with all the *materials* of thinking. These two are the fountains of knowledge, from whence all the ideas we have, or can naturally have, do spring.

First, our Senses, conversant about particular sensible objects, do convey into the mind several distinct perceptions of things, according to those various ways wherein those objects do affect them. And thus we come by those *ideas* we have of *yellow, white, heat, cold, soft, hard, bitter, sweet,* and all those which we call sensible qualities; which when I say the senses convey into the mind, I mean, they from external objects convey into the mind what produces there those perceptions. This great source of most of the ideas we have, depending wholly upon our senses, and derived by them to the understanding, I call SENSATION.

Secondly, the other fountain from which experience furnisheth the understanding with ideas is,—the perception of the operations of our own mind within us, as it is employed about the ideas it has got;—which operations, when the soul comes to reflect on and consider, do furnish the understanding with another set of ideas, which could not be had from things without. And such are *perception, thinking, doubting, believing, reasoning, knowing, willing,* and all the different actings of our own minds;—which we being conscious of, and observing in ourselves, do from these receive into our understandings as distinct ideas as we do from bodies affecting our senses. This source of ideas every man has wholly in himself; and though it be not sense, as having nothing to do with external objects, yet it is very like it, and might properly enough be called *internal sense.* But as I call the other Sensation, so I call this REFLECTION, the ideas it affords being such only as the mind gets by reflecting on its own operations within itself. By reflection then, in the following part of this discourse, I would be understood to mean, that notice which the mind takes of its own operations, and the manner of them, by reason whereof there come to be ideas of these operations in the understanding. These two, I say, viz. external material things, as the objects of SENSATION, and the operations of our own minds within, as the objects of REFLECTION, are to me the only originals from whence all our ideas take their beginnings. The term *operations* here I use in a large sense, as comprehending not barely the actions of the mind about its ideas, but some sort of passions arising sometimes from them, such as is the satisfaction or uneasiness arising from any thought.

The understanding seems to me not to have the least glimmering of any ideas which it doth not receive from one of these two. *External objects* furnish the mind with the ideas of sensible qualities, which are all those different perceptions they produce in us; and *the mind* furnishes the understanding with ideas of its own operations.

These, when we have taken a full survey of them, and their several modes, combinations, and relations, we shall find to contain all our whole stock of ideas; and that we have nothing in our minds which did not come in one of these two ways. Let any one examine his own thoughts, and thoroughly search into his understanding; and then let him tell me, whether all the original ideas he has there, are any other than of the objects of his senses, or of the operations of his mind, considered as objects of his reflection. And how great a mass of knowledge soever he imagines to be lodged there, he will, upon taking a strict view, see that he has not any idea in his mind but what one of these two have imprinted;—though perhaps, with infinite variety compounded and enlarged by the understanding, as we shall see hereafter.

He that attentively considers the state of a child, at his first coming into the world, will have little reason to think him stored with plenty of ideas, that are to be the matter of his future knowledge. It is *by degrees* he comes to be furnished with them. And though the ideas of obvious and familiar qualities imprint themselves before the memory begins to keep a register of time or order, yet it is often so late before some unusual qualities come in the way, that there are few men that cannot recollect the beginning of their acquaintance with them. And if it were worthwhile, no doubt a child might be so ordered as to have but a very few, even of the ordinary ideas, till he were grown up to a man. But all that are born into the world, being surrounded with bodies that perpetually and diversely affect them, variety of ideas, whether care be taken of it or not, are imprinted on the minds of children. Light and colors are busy at hand everywhere, when the eye is but open; sounds and some tangible qualities fail not to solicit their proper senses, and force an entrance to the mind;—but yet, I think, it will be granted easily, that if a child were kept in a place where he never saw any other but black and white till he were a man, he would have no more ideas of scarlet or green, than he that from his childhood never tasted an oyster, or a pineapple, has of those particular relishes.

Men then come to be furnished with fewer or more simple ideas from without, according as the objects they converse with afford greater or less variety; and from the operations of their minds within, according as they more or less reflect on them. For, though he that contemplates the operations of his mind, cannot but have plain and clear ideas of them; yet, unless he turn his thoughts that way, and considers them *attentively,* he will no more have clear and distinct ideas of all the operations of his mind, and all that may be observed therein, than he will have all the particular ideas of any landscape, or of the parts and motions of a clock, who will not turn his eyes to it, and with attention heed all the parts of it. The picture, or clock may be so placed, that they may come in his way every day; but yet he will have but a confused idea of all the parts they are made up of, till he applies himself with attention, to consider them each in particular.

And hence we see the reason why it is pretty late before most children get ideas of the operations of their own minds; and some have not any very clear or perfect ideas of the greatest part of them all their lives. Because, though they pass there continually, yet, like floating visions, they make not deep impressions enough to leave in their minds clear, distinct, lasting ideas, till the understanding turns inward upon itself, reflects on its own operations, and makes them the objects of its own contemplation. Children when they come first into it, are surrounded with a world of new things, which, by a constant solicitation of their senses, draw the mind constantly to them; forward to take notice of new, and apt to be delighted with the variety of changing objects. Thus the first years are usually employed and diverted in looking abroad. Men's business in them is to acquaint themselves with what is to be found without; and so growing up in a constant attention to outward sensations, seldom make any considerable reflection on what passes within them, till they come to be of riper years; and some scarce ever at all.

To ask, at what *time* a man has first any ideas, is to ask, when he begins to perceive;—*having ideas,* and *perception,* being the same thing. I know it is an opinion, that the soul always thinks, and that it has the actual perception of ideas in itself constantly, as long as it exists; and that actual thinking is as inseparable from the soul as actual extension is from the body; which if true, to inquire after the beginning of a man's ideas is the same as to inquire after the beginning of his soul. For, by this account, soul and its ideas, as body and its extension, will begin to exist both at the same time.

But whether the soul be supposed to exist antecedent to, or coeval with, or some time after the first rudiments of organization, or the beginnings of life in the body, I leave to be disputed by those who have better thought of that matter. I confess myself to have one of those dull souls, that doth not perceive itself always to contemplate ideas; nor can conceive it any more necessary for the soul always to think, than for the body always to move: the perception of ideas being (as I conceive) to the soul, what motion is to the body; not its essence, but one of its operations. And therefore, though thinking be supposed never so much the proper action of the soul, yet it is not necessary to suppose that it should be always thinking, always in action. That, perhaps, is the privilege of the infinite Author and Preserver of all things, who "never slumbers nor sleeps"; but is not competent to any finite being, at least not to the soul of man. We know certainly, by experience, that we *sometimes* think; and thence draw this infallible consequence,—that there is something in us that has a power to think. But whether that substance *perpetually* thinks or no, we can be no further assured than experience informs us. For, to say that actual thinking is essential to the soul, and inseparable from it, is to beg what is in question, and not to prove it by reason;—which is necessary to be done, if it be not a self-evident proposition. But whether this, "That the soul always thinks," be a self-evident proposition, that everybody assents to at first hearing, I appeal to mankind.

I grant that the soul, in a waking man, is never without thought, because it is the condition of being awake. But whether sleeping without dreaming be not an affection of the whole man, mind as well as body, may be worth a waking man's consideration; it being hard to conceive that anything should think and not be conscious of it. If the soul doth think in a sleeping man without being conscious of it, I ask whether, during such thinking, it has any pleasure or pain, or be capable of happiness or misery? I am sure the man is not; no more than the bed or earth he lies on. For to be happy or miserable without being conscious of it, seems to me utterly inconsistent and impossible. Or if it be possible that the *soul* can, whilst the body is sleeping, have its thinking, enjoyments, and concerns, its pleasures or pain, apart, which the *man* is not conscious of nor partakes in,—it is certain that Socrates asleep and Socrates awake is not the same person; but his soul when he sleeps, and Socrates the man, consisting of body and soul, when he is waking, are two persons: since waking Socrates has no knowledge of, or concernment for that happiness or misery of his soul, which it enjoys alone by itself whilst he sleeps, without perceiving anything of it; no more than he has for the happiness or misery of a man in the Indies, whom he knows not. For, if we take wholly away all consciousness of our actions and sensations, especially of pleasure and pain, and the concernment that accompanies it, it will be hard to know wherein to place personal identity.

Thus, methinks, every drowsy nod shakes their doctrine, who teach that the soul is always thinking. Those, at least, who do at any time *sleep without dreaming,* can never be convinced that their thoughts are sometimes for four hours busy without their knowing of it; and if they are taken in the very act, waked in the middle of that sleeping contemplation, can give no manner of account of it.

Those who so confidently tell us that the soul always actually thinks, I would they would also tell us, what those ideas are that are in the soul of a child, before or just at the union with the body, before it hath received any by sensation. The dreams of sleeping men are, as I take it, all made up of the waking man's ideas; though for the most part oddly put together. It is strange, if the soul has ideas of its own that it derived not from sensation or reflection (as it must have, if it thought before it received any impressions from the body), that it should never, in its private thinking (so private, that the man himself perceives it not), retain any of them the very moment it wakes out of them, and then make the man glad with new discoveries. Who can find it reason that the soul should, in its retirement during sleep, have so many hours' thoughts, and yet never light on any of those ideas it borrowed not from sensation or reflection; or at least preserve the memory of none but such, which, being occasioned from the body, must needs be less natural to a spirit? It is strange the soul should never once in a man's whole life recall over any of its pure native thoughts, and those ideas it had before it borrowed anything from the body; never bring into the waking man's view any other ideas but what have a tang of the cask, and manifestly derive their original from that union. If it always thinks, and so had ideas before it was united, or before it received any from the body, it is not to be supposed but that during sleep it recollects its native ideas; and during that retirement from communicating with the body, whilst it thinks by itself, the ideas it is busied about should be, sometimes at least, those more natural and congenial ones which it had in itself, underived from the body, or its own operations about them: which, since the waking man never remembers, we must from this hypothesis conclude either that the soul remembers something that the man does not; or else that memory belongs only to such ideas as are derived from the body, or the mind's operations about them.

I see no reason, therefore, to believe that the soul thinks before the senses have furnished it with ideas to think on; and as those are increased and retained, so it comes, by exercise, to improve its faculty of thinking in the several parts of it; as well as, afterward, by compounding those ideas, and reflecting on its own operations, it increases its stock, as well as facility in remembering, imagining, reasoning, and other modes of thinking.

He that will suffer himself to be informed by observation and experience, and not make his own hypothesis the rule of nature, will find few signs of a soul accustomed to much thinking in a newborn child, and much fewer of any reasoning at all. And yet it is hard to imagine that the rational soul should think so much, and not reason at all. And he that will consider that infants newly come into the world spend the greatest part of their time in sleep, and are seldom awake but when either hunger calls for the teat, or some pain (the most importunate of all sensations), or some other violent impression on the body, forces the mind to perceive and attend to it;—he, I say, who considers this, will perhaps find reason to imagine that a *foetus* in the mother's womb differs not much from the state of a vegetable, but passes the greatest part of its time without perception or thought; doing very little but sleep in a place where it needs not seek for food, and is surrounded with liquor, always equally soft, and near of the same temper; where the eyes have no light, and the ears so shut up are not very susceptible of sounds; and where there is little or no variety, or change of objects, to move the senses.

Follow a child from its birth, and observe the alterations that time makes, and you should find, as the mind by the senses comes more and more to be furnished with ideas, it comes to be more and more awake; thinks more, the more it has matter to think on. After some time it begins to know the objects which, being most familiar with it, have made lasting impressions. Thus it comes by degrees to know the persons it daily converses with, and distinguishes them from strangers; which are instances and effects of its coming to retain and distinguish the ideas the senses convey to it. And so we may observe how the mind, *by degrees,* improves in these; and *advances* to the exercise of those other faculties of enlarging, compounding, and abstracting its ideas, and of reasoning about them, and reflecting upon all these; of which I shall have occasion to speak more hereafter.

If it shall be demanded then, *when* a man *begins* to have any ideas, I think the true answer is,—*when he first has any sensation.* For, since there appear not to be any ideas in the mind before the senses have conveyed any in, I conceive that ideas in the understanding are coeval with *sensation; which is such an impression or motion made in some part of the body, as produces some perception in the understanding.* It is about these impressions made on our senses by outward objects that the mind seems *first* to employ itself, in such operations as we call perception, remembering, consideration, reasoning, etc.

In time the mind comes to reflect on its own operations about the ideas got by sensation, and thereby stores itself with a new set of ideas, which I call ideas of reflection. These are the impressions that are made on our senses by outward objects that are extrinsical to the mind; and its own operations, proceeding from powers intrinsical and proper to itself, which, when reflected on by itself, become also objects of its contemplation—are, as I have said, the original of all knowledge. Thus the first capacity of human intellect is,—that the mind is fitted to receive the impressions made on it; either through the senses by outward objects, or by its own operations when it reflects on them. This is the first step a man makes toward the discovery of anything, and the groundwork whereon to build all those notions which ever he shall have naturally in this world. All those sublime thoughts which tower above the clouds, and reach as high as heaven itself, take their rise and footing here: in all that great extent wherein the mind wanders, in those remote speculations it may seem to be elevated with, it stirs not one jot beyond those ideas which *sense* or *reflection* have offered for its contemplation.

In this part the understanding is merely passive; and

whether or no it will have these beginnings, and as it were materials of knowledge, is not in its own power. For the objects of our senses do, many of them, obtrude their particular ideas upon our minds whether we will or not; and the operations of our minds will not let us be without, at least, some obscure notions of them. No man can be wholly ignorant of what he does when he thinks. These simple ideas, when offered to the mind, the understanding can no more refuse to have, nor alter when they are imprinted, nor blot them out and make new ones itself, than a mirror can refuse, alter, or obliterate the images or ideas which the objects set before it do therein produce. As the bodies that surround us do diversely affect our organs, the mind is forced to receive the impressions; and cannot avoid the perception of those ideas that are annexed to them.

I I

Of Simple Ideas

THE BETTER TO UNDERSTAND the nature, manner, and extent of our knowledge, one thing is carefully to be observed concerning the ideas we have; and that is, that some of them are *simple* and some *complex.*

Though the qualities that affect our senses are, in the things themselves, so united and blended, that there is no separation, no distance between them; yet it is plain, the ideas they produce in the mind enter by the senses simple and unmixed. For, though the sight and touch often take in from the same object, at the same time, different ideas;—as a man sees at once motion and color; the hand feels softness and warmth in the same piece of wax: yet the simple ideas thus united in the same subject, are as perfectly distinct as those that come in by different senses. The coldness and hardness which a man feels in a piece of ice being as distinct ideas in the mind as the smell and whiteness of a lily; or as the taste of sugar, and smell of a rose. And there is nothing can be plainer to a man than the clear and distinct perception he has of those simple ideas; which, being each in itself uncompounded, contains in it nothing but *one uniform appearance, or conception in the mind,* and is not distinguishable into different ideas.

These simple ideas, the materials of all our knowledge, are suggested and furnished to the mind only by those two ways above mentioned, viz. sensation and reflection. When the understanding is once stored with these simple ideas, it has the power to repeat, compare, and unite them, even to an almost infinite variety, and so can make at pleasure new complex ideas. But it is not in the power of the most exalted wit, or enlarged understanding, by any quickness or variety of thought, to *invent* or *frame* one new simple idea in the mind, not taken in by the ways before mentioned; nor can any force of the understanding *destroy* those that are there. The dominion of man, in this little world of his own understanding being muchwhat the same as it is in the great world of visible things; wherein his power, however managed by art and skill, reaches no farther than to compound and divide the materials that are made to his hand; but can do nothing toward the making the least particle of new matter, or destroying one atom of what is already in being. The same inability will everyone find in himself, who shall go about to fashion in his understanding one simple idea, not received in by his senses from external objects, or by reflection from the operations of his own mind about them. I would have anyone try to fancy any taste which had never affected his palate; or frame the idea of a scent he had never smelt: and when he can do this, I will also conclude that a blind man hath ideas of colors, and a deaf man true distinct notions of sounds.

This is the reason why—though we cannot believe it impossible to God to make a creature with other organs, and more ways to convey into the understanding the notice of corporeal things than those five, as they are usually counted, which he has given to man—yet I think it is not possible for any *man* to imagine any other qualities in bodies, howsoever constituted, whereby they can be taken notice of, besides sounds, tastes, smells, visible and tangible qualities. And had mankind been made but with four senses, the qualities then which are the objects of the fifth sense had been as far from our notice, imagination, and conception, as now any belonging to a sixth, seventh, or eighth sense can possibly be;—which, whether yet some other creatures, in some other parts of this vast and stupendous universe, may not have, will be a great presumption to deny. He that will not set himself proudly at the top of all things, but will consider the immensity of this fabric, and the great variety that is to be found in this little and inconsiderable part of it which he has to do with, may be apt to think that, in other mansions of it, there may be other and different intelligent beings, of whose faculties he has as little knowledge or apprehension as a worm shut up in one drawer of a cabinet hath of the senses or understanding of a man; such variety and excellency being suitable to the wisdom and power of the Maker. I have here followed the common opinion of man's having but five senses; though, perhaps, there may be justly counted more;—but either supposition serves equally to my present purpose.

III

Of Simple Ideas of Sense

THE BETTER TO CONCEIVE the ideas we receive from sensation, it may not be amiss for us to consider them, in reference to the different ways whereby they make their approaches to our minds, and make themselves perceivable by us.

First, then, There are some which come into our minds *by one sense only.*

Secondly, There are others that convey themselves into the mind *by more senses than one.*

Thirdly, Others that are had from *reflection only.*

Fourthly, There are some that make themselves way, and are suggested to the mind *by all the ways of sensation and reflection.*

We shall consider them apart under these several heads.

There are some ideas which have admittance only through one sense, which is peculiarly adapted to receive them. Thus light and colors, as white, red, yellow, blue; with their several degrees or shades and mixtures, as green, scarlet, purple, sea-green, and the rest, come in only by the eyes. All kinds of noises, sounds, and tones, only by the ears. The several tastes and smells, by the nose and palate. And if these organs, or the nerves which are the conduits to convey them from without to their audience in the brain,—the mind's presence-room (as I may so call it)—are any of them so disordered as not to perform their functions, they have no postern to be admitted by; no other way to bring themselves into view, and be perceived by the understanding.

The most considerable of those belonging to the touch, are heat and cold, and solidity: all the rest, consisting almost wholly in the sensible configuration, as smooth and rough; or else, more or less firm adhesion of the parts, as hard and soft, tough and brittle, are obvious enough.

IV

Idea of Solidity

THE IDEA OF *solidity* we receive by our touch: and it arises from the resistance which we find in body to the entrance of any other body into the place it possesses, till it has left it. There is no idea which we receive more constantly from sensation than solidity. Whether we move or rest, in what posture soever we are, we always feel something under us that supports us, and hinders our further sinking downward; and the bodies which we daily handle make us perceive that, whilst they remain between them, they do, by an insurmountable force, hinder the approach of the parts of our hands that press them. *That which thus hinders the approach of two bodies, when they are moved one toward another, I call solidity.* I will not dispute whether this acceptation of the word solid be nearer to its original signification than that which mathematicians use it in. It suffices that I think the common notion of solidity will allow, if not justify, this use of it; but if anyone think it better to call it *impenetrability,* he has my consent. Only I have thought the term solidity the more proper to express this idea, not only because of its vulgar use in that sense, but also because it carries something more of positive in it than impenetrability; which is negative, and is perhaps more a consequence of solidity, than solidity itself. This, of all other, seems the idea most intimately connected with, and essential to body; so as nowhere else to be found or imagined, but only in matter. And though our senses take no notice of it, but in masses of matter, of a bulk sufficient to cause a sensation in us: yet the mind, having once got this idea from such grosser sensible bodies, traces it further, and considers it, as well as figure, in the minutest particle of matter that can exist; and finds it inseparably inherent in body, wherever or however modified.

This is the idea which belongs to body, whereby we conceive it to fill space. The idea of which filling of space is,—that where we imagine any space taken up by a solid substance, we conceive it so to possess it, that it excludes all other solid substances; and will forever hinder any other two bodies, that move toward one another in a straight line, from coming to touch one another, unless it removes from between them in a line not parallel to that which they move in. This idea of it, the bodies which we ordinarily handle sufficiently furnish us with.

This resistance, whereby it keeps other bodies out of the space which it possesses, is so great, that no force, how great soever, can surmount it. All the bodies in the world, pressing a drop of water on all sides, will never be able to overcome the resistance which it will make, soft as it is, to their approaching one another, till it be removed out of their way: whereby our idea of solidity is distinguished both from pure space, which is capable neither of resistance nor motion; and from the ordinary idea of hardness. For a man may conceive two bodies at a distance, so as they may approach one another, without touching or displacing any solid thing, till their superficies come to meet; whereby, I think, we have the clear idea of space without solidity. For (not to go so far as annihilation of any particular body) I ask, whether a man cannot have the idea of the motion of one single body alone, without any other succeeding immediately into its place? I think it is evident he can: the idea of motion in one body no more including the idea of motion in another, than the idea of a square figure in one body includes the idea of a square figure in another. I do not ask, whether bodies do so *exist*, that the motion of one body cannot really be without the motion of another. To determine this either way, is to beg the question for or against a *vacuum*. But my question is,—whether one cannot have the *idea* of one body moved, whilst others are at rest? And I think this no one will deny. If so, then the place it deserted gives us the idea of pure space without solidity; whereinto any other body may enter, without either resistance of protrusion of anything. When the sucker in a pump is drawn, the space it filled in the tube is certainly the same whether any other body follows the motion of the sucker or not: nor does it imply a contradiction that, upon the motion of one body, another that is only contiguous to it should not follow it. The necessity of such a motion is built only on the supposition that the world is full; but not on the distinct *ideas* of space and solidity, which are as different as resistance and not resistance, protrusion and not protrusion. And that men have ideas of space without a body, their very disputes about a vacuum plainly demonstrate, as is shown in another place.

Solidity is hereby also differenced from hardness, in that solidity consists in repletion, and so an utter exclusion of other bodies out of the space it possesses: but hardness, in a firm cohesion of the parts of matter, making up masses of a sensible bulk, so that the whole does not easily change its figure. And indeed, hard and soft are names that we give to things only in relation to the constitutions of our own bodies; that being generally called hard by us, which will put us to pain sooner than change figure by the pressure of any part of our bodies; and that, on the contrary, soft, which changes the situation of its parts upon an easy and unpainful touch.

But this difficulty of changing the situation of the sensible parts amongst themselves, or of the figure of the whole, gives no more solidity to the hardest body in the world than to the softest; nor is an adamant one jot more solid than water. For, though the two flat sides of two pieces of marble will more easily approach each other, between which there is nothing but water or air, than if there be a diamond between them; yet it is not that the parts of the diamond are more solid than those of water, or resist more; but because the parts of water, being more easily separable from each other, they will, by a side motion, be more easily removed, and give way to the approach of the two pieces of marble. But if they could be kept from making place by that side motion, they would eternally hinder the approach of these two pieces of marble, as much as the diamond; and it would be as impossible by any force to surmount their resistance, as to surmount the resistance of the parts of a diamond. The softest body in the world will as invincibly resist the coming together of any other two bodies, if it be not put out of the way, but remain between them, as the hardest that can be found or imagined.

If anyone asks me, *What this solidity is*, I send him to his senses to inform him. Let him put a flint or a football between his hands, and then endeavor to join them, and he will know. If he thinks this not a sufficient explication of solidity, what it is, and wherein it consists; I promise to tell him what it is, and wherein it consists, when he tells me what thinking is, or wherein it consists; or explains to me what extension or motion is, which perhaps seems much easier. The simple ideas we have, are such as experience teaches them us; but if, beyond that, we endeavor by words to make them clearer in the mind, we shall succeed no better than if we went about to clear up the darkness of a blind man's mind by talking; and to discourse into him the ideas of light and colors. The reason of this I shall show in another place.

V

Of Simple Ideas of Divers Senses

THE IDEAS WE GET by more than one sense are, of *space* or *extension, figure, rest*, and *motion*. For these make perceivable impressions, both on the eyes and touch; and we can receive and convey into our minds the ideas of the extension, figure, motion, and rest of bodies, both by seeing and feeling. But having occasion to speak more at large of these in another place, I here only enumerate them.

VI

Of Simple Ideas of Reflection

THE MIND RECEIVING THE IDEAS mentioned in the foregoing chapters from without, when it turns its view inward upon itself, and observes its own actions about those ideas it has, takes from thence other ideas, which are as capable to be the objects of its contemplation as any of those it received from foreign things.

The two great and principal actions of the mind, which are most frequently considered, and which are so frequent that everyone that pleases may take notice of them in himself, are these two:——

Perception, or *Thinking;* and
Volition, or *Willing.*

The power of thinking is called the *Understanding,* and the power of volition is called the *Will;* and these two powers or abilities in the mind are denominated faculties.

Of some of the *modes* of these simple ideas of reflection, such as are *remembrance, discerning, reasoning, judging, knowledge, faith,* etc., I shall have occasion to speak hereafter.

VII

Of Simple Ideas of Both Sensation and Reflection

THERE BE OTHER SIMPLE IDEAS which convey themselves into the mind by all the ways of sensation and reflection, viz. *pleasure* or *delight*, and its opposite, *pain*, or *uneasiness; power; existence; unity*.

Delight or uneasiness, one or other of them, join themselves to almost all our ideas both of sensation and reflection: and there is scarce any affection of our senses from without, any retired thought of our mind within, which is not able to produce in us pleasure or pain. By pleasure and pain, I would be understood to signify, whatsoever delights or molests us; whether it arises from the thoughts of our minds, or anything operating on our bodies. For, whether we call it satisfaction, delight, pleasure, happiness, etc., on the one side, or uneasiness, trouble, pain, torment, anguish, misery, etc., on the other, they are still but different degrees of the same thing, and belong to the ideas of pleasure and pain, delight or uneasiness; which are the names I shall most commonly use for those two sorts of ideas.

The infinite wise Author of our being, having given us the power over several parts of our bodies, to move or keep them at rest as we think fit; and also, by the motion of them, to move ourselves and other contiguous bodies, in which consist all the actions of our body: having also given a power to our minds, in several instances, to choose, amongst its ideas, which it will think on, and to pursue the inquiry of this or that subject with consideration and attention, to excite us to these actions of thinking and motion that we are capable of,—has been pleased to join to several thoughts, and several sensations a perception of delight. If this were wholly separated from all our outward sensations, and inward thoughts, we should have no reason to prefer one thought or action to another; negligence to attention, or motion to rest. And so we should neither stir our bodies, nor employ our minds, but let our thoughts (if I may so call it) run adrift, without any direction or design, and suffer the ideas of our minds, like unregarded shadows, to make their appearances there, as it happened, without attending to them. In which state man, however furnished with the faculties of understanding and will, would be a very idle, inactive creature, and pass his time only in a lazy, lethargic dream. It has therefore pleased our wise Creator to annex to several objects, and the ideas which we receive from them, as also to several of our thoughts, a concomitant pleasure, and that in several objects, to several degrees, that those faculties which he had endowed us with might not remain wholly idle and unemployed by us.

Pain has the same efficacy and use to set us on work that pleasure has, we being as ready to employ our faculties to avoid that, as to pursue this: only this is worth our consideration, that pain is often produced by the same objects and ideas that produce pleasure in us. This their near conjunction, which makes us often feel pain in the sensations where we expected pleasure, gives us new occasion of admiring the wisdom and goodness of our Maker, who, designing the preservation of our being, has annexed pain to the application of many things to our bodies, to warn us of the harm that they will do, and as advices to withdraw from them. But He, not designing our preservation barely, but the preservation of every part and organ in its perfection, hath in many cases annexed pain to those very ideas which delight us. Thus heat, that is very agreeable to us in one degree, by a little greater increase of it proves no ordinary torment: and the most pleasant of all sensible objects, light itself, if there be too much of it, if increased beyond a due proportion to our eyes, causes a very painful sensation. Which is wisely and favorably so ordered by nature, that when any object does, by the vehemency of its operation, disorder the instruments of sensation, whose structures cannot but be very nice and delicate, we might, by the pain, be warned to withdraw, before the organ be quite put out of order, and so be unfitted for its proper function for the future.

Though what I have here said may not, perhaps, make the ideas of pleasure and pain clearer to us than our own experience does, which is the only way that we are capable of having them; yet the consideration of the reason why they are annexed to so many other ideas, serving to give us due sentiments of the wisdom and goodness of the Sovereign Disposer of all things, may not be unsuitable to the main end of these inquiries: the knowledge and veneration of Him being the chief end of all our thoughts, and the proper business of all understandings.

Existence and *Unity* are two other ideas that are suggested to the understanding by every object without, and every idea within. When ideas are in our minds, we consider them as being actually there, as well as we consider things to be actually without us;—which is, that they exist, or have existence. And whatever we can consider as one thing, whether a real being or idea, suggests to the understanding the idea of unity.

Power also is another of those simple ideas which we receive from sensation and reflection. For, observing in ourselves that we do and can think, and that we can at pleasure move several parts of our bodies which were at rest; the effects, also, that natural bodies are able to produce in one another, occurring every moment to our senses,—we both these ways get the idea of power.

Besides these there is another idea, which, though suggested by our senses, yet is more constantly offered to us by what passes in our minds; and that is the idea of *succession*. For if we look immediately into ourselves, and reflect on what is observable there, we shall find our ideas always, whilst we are awake, or have any thought, passing in train, one going and another coming, without intermission.

These, if they are not all, are at least (as I think) the most considerable of those simple ideas which the mind has, and out of which is made all its other knowledge; all which it receives only by the two forementioned ways of sensation and reflection.

VIII

Some Further Considerations Concerning Our Simple Ideas of Sensation

CONCERNING THE SIMPLE IDEAS of Sensation, it is to be considered,—that whatsoever is so constituted in nature as to be able, by affecting our senses, to cause any perception in the mind, doth thereby produce in the understanding a simple idea; which, whatever be the external cause of it, when it comes to be taken notice of by our discerning faculty, it is by the mind looked on and considered there to be a real positive idea in the understanding, as much as any other whatsoever; though, perhaps, the cause of it be but a privation of the subject.

Thus the ideas of heat and cold, light and darkness, white and black, motion and rest, are equally clear and positive ideas in the mind; though, perhaps, some of the causes which produce them are barely privations, in those subjects from whence our senses derive those ideas. These the understanding, in its view of them, considers all as distinct positive ideas, without taking notice of the causes that produce them: which is an inquiry not belonging to the idea, as it is in the understanding, but to the nature of the things existing without us. These are two very different things, and carefully to be distinguished; it being one thing to perceive and know the idea of white or black, and quite another to examine what kind of particles they must be, and how ranged in the superficies, to make any object appear white or black.

[Locke next claims that it is possible to have ideas of colors, for example, without any knowledge of the cause of these ideas.]

To discover the nature of our *ideas* the better, and to discourse of them intelligibly, it will be convenient to distinguish them *as they are ideas or perceptions in our minds;* and *as they are modifications of matter in the bodies that cause such perceptions in us:* that so we may not think (as perhaps usually is done) that they are exactly the images and resemblances of something inherent in the subject; most of those of sensation being in the mind no more the likeness of something existing without us, than the names that stand for them are the likeness of our ideas, which yet upon hearing they are apt to excite in us.

Whatsoever the mind perceives *in itself,* or is the immediate object of perception, thought, or understanding, that I call *idea;* and the power to produce any idea in our mind, I call *quality* of the subject wherein that power is. Thus a snowball having the power to produce in us the ideas of white, cold, and round,—the power to produce those ideas in us, as they are in the snowball, I call qualities; and as they are sensations or perceptions in our understandings, I call them ideas; which *ideas,* if I speak of sometimes as in the things themselves, I would be understood to mean those qualities in the objects which produce them in us.

Qualities thus considered in bodies are,

First, such as are utterly inseparable from the body, in what state soever it be; and such as in all the alterations and changes it suffers, all the force can be used upon it, it constantly keeps; and such as sense constantly finds in every particle of matter which has bulk enough to be perceived; and the mind finds inseparable from every particle of matter, though less than to make itself singly be perceived by our senses: v.g. Take a grain of wheat, divide it into two parts; each part has still solidity, extension, figure, and mobility: divide it again, and it retains still the same qualities; and so divide it on, till the parts become insensible: they must retain still each of them all those qualities. For division (which is all that a mill, or pestle, or any other body, does upon another, in reducing it to insensible parts) can never take away either solidity, extension, figure, or mobility from any body, but only makes two or more distinct separate masses of matter, of that which was but one before; all which distinct masses, reckoned as so many distinct bodies, after division, make a certain number. These I call *original* or *primary qualities* of body, which I think we may observe to produce simple ideas in us, viz. solidity, extension, figure, motion or rest, and number.

Secondly, such qualities which in truth are nothing in the objects themselves but powers to produce various sensations in us by their primary qualities, i.e. by the bulk, figure, texture, and motion of their insensible parts, as colors, sounds, tastes, etc. These I call *secondary qualities.* To these might be added a *third* sort, which are allowed to be barely powers;

though they are as much real qualities in the subject as those which I, to comply with the common way of speaking, call qualities, but for distinction, secondary qualities. For the power in fire to produce a new color, or consistency, in *wax* or *clay*, —by its primary qualities, is as much a quality in fire, as the power it has to produce in *me* a new idea or sensation of warmth or burning, which I felt not before,—by the same primary qualities, viz. the bulk, texture, and motion of its insensible parts.

The next thing to be considered is, how bodies produce ideas in us; and that is manifestly by impulse, the only way which we can conceive bodies to operate in.

If then external objects be not united to our minds when they produce ideas therein; and yet we perceive these *original* qualities in such of them as singly fall under our senses, it is evident that some motion must be thence continued by our nerves, or animal spirits, by some parts of our bodies, to the brains or the seat of sensation, there to produce in our minds the particular ideas we have of them. And since the extension, figure, number, and motion of bodies of an observable bigness, may be perceived at a distance by the sight, it is evident some singly imperceptible bodies must come from them to the eyes, and thereby convey to the brain some motion; which produces these ideas which we have of them in us.

After the same manner that the ideas of these original qualities are produced in us, we may conceive that the ideas of *secondary* qualities are also produced, viz. by the operation of insensible particles on our senses. For, it being manifest that there are bodies and good store of bodies, each whereof are so small, that we cannot by any of our senses discover either their bulk, figure, or motion,—as is evident in the particles of the air and water, and others extremely smaller than those; perhaps as much smaller than the particles of air and water, as the particles of air and water are smaller than peas or hailstones;—let us suppose at present that the different motions and figures, bulk and number, of such particles, affecting the several organs of our senses, produce in us those different sensations which we have from the colors and smells of bodies; v.g. that a violet, by the impulse of such insensible particles of matter, of peculiar figures and bulks, and in different degrees and modifications of their motions, causes the ideas of the blue color, and sweet scent of that flower to be produced in our minds. It being no more impossible to conceive that God should annex such ideas to such motions, with which they have no similitude, than that he should annex the idea of pain to the motion of a piece of steel dividing our flesh, with which that idea hath no resemblance.

What I have said concerning colors and smells may be understood also of tastes and sounds, and other the like sensible qualities; which, whatever reality we by mistake attribute to them, are in truth nothing in the objects themselves, but powers to produce various sensations in us; and depend on those primary qualities, viz. bulk, figure, texture, and motion of parts.

From whence I think it easy to draw this observation,—that the ideas of primary qualities of bodies are resemblances of them, and their patterns do really exist in the bodies themselves, but the ideas produced in us by these secondary qualities have no resemblance of them at all. There is nothing like our ideas, existing in the bodies themselves. They are, in the bodies we denominate from them, only a power to produce those sensations in us: and what is sweet, blue, or warm in idea, is but the certain bulk, figure, and motion of the insensible parts, in the bodies themselves, which we call so.

Flame is denominated hot and light; snow, white and cold; and manna, white and sweet, from the ideas they produce in us. Which qualities are commonly thought to be the same in those bodies that those ideas are in us, the one the perfect resemblance of the other, as they are in a mirror, and it would by most men be judged very extravagant if one should say otherwise. And yet he that will consider that the same fire that, at one distance produces in us the sensation of warmth, does, at a nearer approach, produce in us the far different sensation of pain, ought to bethink himself what reason he has to say—that this idea of warmth, which was produced in him by the fire, is *actually in the fire;* and his idea of pain, which the same fire produced in him the same way, is *not* in the fire. Why are whiteness and coldness in snow, and pain not, when it produces the one and the other idea in us; and can do neither, but by the bulk, figure, number, and motion of its solid parts?

The particular bulk, number, figure, and motion of the parts of fire or snow are really in them,—whether anyone's senses perceive them or no: and therefore they may be called *real* qualities, because they really exist in those bodies. But light, heat, whiteness, or coldness, are no more really in them than sickness or pain is in manna. Take away the sensation of them; let not the eyes see light or colors, nor the ears hear sounds; let the palate not taste, nor the nose smell, and all colors, tastes, odors, and sounds, *as they are such particular ideas,* vanish and cease, and are reduced to their causes, i.e. bulk, figure, and motion of parts.

Let us consider the red and white colors in porphyry. Hinder light from striking on it, and its colors vanish; it no longer produces any such ideas in us: upon the return of light it produces these appearances on us again. Can anyone think any real alterations are made in the porphyry by the presence or absence of light; and that those ideas of whiteness and redness are really in porphyry in the light, when it is plain *it has no color in the dark?* It has, indeed, such a configuration of particles, both night and day, as are apt, by the rays of light rebounding from some parts of that hard stone, to produce in us the idea of redness, and from others the idea of whiteness; but whiteness or redness are not in it at any time, but such a texture that hath the power to produce such a sensation in us.

Ideas being thus distinguished and understood, we may be able to give an account how the same water, at the same time, may produce the idea of cold by one hand and of heat by the other: whereas it is impossible that the same water, if those ideas were really in it, should at the same time be both hot and cold. For, if we imagine *warmth,* as it is in our hands, to be nothing but a certain sort and degree of motion in the minute particles of our nerves or animal spirits, we may understand how it is possible that the same water may, at the same time, produce the sensations of heat in one hand and cold in the other; which yet *figure* never does, that never producing the idea of a square by one hand which has produced the idea of a globe by another. But if the sensation of heat and cold be nothing but the increase or diminution of the motion of the minute parts of our bodies, caused by the corpuscles of any other body, it is easy to be understood, that if that motion be greater in one hand than in the other; if a body be applied to the two hands, which has in its minute particles a greater motion than in those of one of the hands, and a less than in those of the other, it will increase the motion of the one hand and lessen it in the other; and so cause the different sensations of heat and cold that depend thereon.

I have in what just goes before been engaged in physical inquiries a little further than perhaps I intended. But, it being necessary to make the nature of sensation a little understood; and to make the difference between the *qualities* in bodies, and the *ideas* produced by them in the mind, to be distinctly conceived, without which it were impossible to discourse intelligibly of them;—I hope I shall be pardoned this little excursion into natural philosophy; it being necessary in our present inquiry to distinguish the *primary* and *real* qualities of bodies, which are always in them (viz. solidity, extension, figure, number, and motion, or rest, and are sometimes perceived by us, viz. when the bodies they are in are big enough singly to be discerned), from those *secondary* and *imputed* qualities, which are but the powers of several combinations of those primary ones, when they operate without being distinctly discerned;—whereby we may also come to know what ideas are, and what are not, resemblances of something really existing in the bodies we denominate from them.

The qualities, then, that are in bodies, rightly considered, are of three sorts:——

First, The bulk, figure, number, situation, and motion or rest of their solid parts. Those are in them, whether we perceive them or not; and when they are of that size that we can discover them, we have by these an idea of the thing as it is in itself; as is plain in artificial things. These I call *primary qualities.*

Secondly, The power that is in any body, by reason of its insensible primary qualities, to operate after a peculiar manner on any of our senses, and thereby produce in *us* the different ideas of several colors, sounds, smells, tastes, etc. These are usually called *sensible qualities.*

Thirdly, The power that is in any body, by reason of the particular constitution of its primary qualities, to make such a change in the bulk, figure, texture, and motion of *another body,* as to make it operate on our senses differently from what it did before. Thus the sun has a power to make wax white, and fire to make lead fluid. These are usually called *powers.*

The first of these, as has been said, I think may be properly called real, original, or primary qualities; because they are in the things themselves, whether they are perceived or not: and upon their different modifications it is that the secondary qualities depend.

The other two are only powers to act differently upon other things: which powers result from the different modifications of those primary qualities.

To conclude. Beside those forementioned primary qualities in bodies, viz. bulk, figure, extension, number, and motion of their solid parts; all the rest, whereby we take notice of bodies, and distinguish them one from another, are nothing else but several powers in them, depending on those primary qualities; whereby they are fitted, either by immediately operating on our bodies to produce several different ideas in us; or else, by operating on other bodies, so to change their primary qualities as to render them capable of producing ideas in us different from what before they did. The former of these, I think, may be called secondary qualities *immediately perceivable:* the latter, secondary qualities, *mediately perceivable.*

IX

Of Perception

PERCEPTION, as it is the first faculty of the mind exercised about our ideas; so it is the first and simplest idea we have from reflection, and is by some called thinking in general. Though thinking, in the propriety of the English tongue, signifies that sort of operation in the mind about its ideas, wherein the mind is active; where it, with some degree of voluntary attention, considers anything. For in bare naked perception, the mind is, for the most part, only passive; and what it perceives, it cannot avoid perceiving.

What perception is, everyone will know better by reflecting on what he does himself, when he sees, hears, feels, etc., or thinks, than by any discourse of mine. Whoever reflects on what passes in his own mind cannot miss it. And if he does not reflect, all the words in the world cannot make him have any notion of it.

This is certain, that whatever alterations are made in the body, if they reach not the mind; whatever impressions are made on the outward parts, if they are not taken notice of within, there is no perception. Fire may burn our bodies with no other effect than it does a billet, unless the motion be continued to the brain, and there the sense of heat, or idea of pain, be produced in the mind; wherein consists actual perception.

How often may a man observe in himself, that whilst his mind is intently employed in the contemplation of some objects, and curiously surveying some ideas that are there, it takes no notice of impressions of sounding bodies made upon the organ of hearing, with the same alteration? A sufficient impulse there may be on the organ; but it not reaching the observation of the mind, there follows no perception: and though the motion that uses to produce the idea of sound be made in the ear, yet no sound is heard. Want of sensation, in this case, is not through any defect in the organ, or that the man's ears are less affected than at other times when he does hear: but that which uses to produce the idea, though conveyed in by the usual organ, not being taken notice of in the understanding, and so imprinting no idea in the mind, there follows no sensation. So that wherever there is sense or perception, there some idea is actually produced, and present in the understanding.

Therefore I doubt not but children, by the exercise of their senses about objects that affect them in the womb, receive some few ideas before they are born, as the unavoidable effects, either of the bodies that environ them, or else of those wants or diseases they suffer; amongst which (if one may conjecture concerning things not very capable of examination) I think the ideas of hunger and warmth are two: which probably are some of the first that children have, and which they scarce ever part with again.

But though it be reasonable to imagine that children receive some ideas before they come into the world, yet these simple ideas are far from those *innate principles* which some contend for, and we, above, have rejected. These here mentioned, being the effects of sensation, are only from some affections of the body, which happen to them there, and so depend on something exterior to the mind; no otherwise differing in their manner of production from other ideas derived from sense, but only in the precedency of time. Whereas those innate principles are supposed to be quite of another nature; not coming into the mind by any accidental alterations in, or operations on the body; but, as it were, original characters impressed upon it, in the very first moment of its being and constitution.

As there are some ideas which we may reasonably suppose may be introduced into the minds of children in the womb, subservient to the necessities of their life and being there: so, after they are born, those ideas are the earliest imprinted which happen to be the sensible qualities which first occur to them; amongst which light is not the least considerable, nor of the weakest efficacy. And how covetous the mind is to be furnished with all such ideas as have no pain accompanying them, may be a little guessed by what is observable in children newborn; who always turn their eyes to that part from whence the light comes, lay them how you please. But the ideas that are most familiar at first, being various, according to the divers circumstances of children's first entertainment in the world, the order wherein the several ideas come at first into the mind is very various, and uncertain also; neither is it much material to know it.

We are further to consider concerning perception, that the

ideas we receive by sensation are often, in grown people, altered by the judgment, without our taking notice of it. When we set before our eyes a round globe of any uniform color, v.g. gold, alabaster, or jet, it is certain that the idea thereby imprinted on our mind is of a flat circle, variously shadowed, with several degrees of light and brightness coming to our eyes. But we having, by use, been accustomed to perceive what kind of appearance convex bodies are wont to make in us; what alterations are made in the reflections of light by the difference of the sensible figures of bodies;—the judgment presently, by a habitual custom, alters the appearances into their causes. So that from that which is truly variety of shadow or color, collecting the figure, it makes it pass for a mark of figure, and frames to itself the perception of a convex figure and an uniform color; when the idea we receive from thence is only a plane variously colored, as is evident in painting. To which purpose I shall here insert a problem of that very ingenious and studious promoter of real knowledge, the learned and worthy Mr. Molyneux, which he was pleased to send me in a letter some months since; and it is this:—"Suppose a man *born* blind, and now adult, and taught by his *touch* to distinguish between a cube and a sphere of the same metal, and nighly of the same bigness, so as to tell, when he felt one and the other, which is the cube, which the sphere. Suppose then the cube and sphere placed on a table, and the blind man be made to see: *quaere*, whether *by his sight, before he touched them,* he could now distinguish and tell which is the globe, which the cube?" To which the acute and judicious proposer answers, "Not. For, though he has obtained the experience of how a globe, how a cube affects his touch, yet he has not yet obtained the experience, that what affects his touch so or so, must affect his sight so or so; or that a protuberant angle in the cube, that pressed his hand unequally, shall appear to his eye as it does in the cube."—I agree with this thinking gentleman, whom I am proud to call my friend, in his answer to this problem; and am of opinion that the blind man, at first sight, would not be able with certainty to say which was the globe, which the cube, whilst he only saw them; though he could unerringly name them by his touch, and certainly distinguish them by the difference of their figures felt. This I have set down, and leave with my reader, as an occasion for him to consider how much he may be beholden to experience, improvement, and acquired notions, where he thinks he had not the least use of, or help from them. And the rather, because this observing gentleman further adds, that "having, upon the occasion of my book, proposed this to divers very ingenious men," he hardly ever met with one that at first gave the answer to it which he thinks true, till by hearing his reasons they were convinced.

But this is not, I think, usual in any of our ideas, but those received by sight. Because sight, the most comprehensive of all our senses, conveying to our minds the ideas of light and colors, which are peculiar only to that sense; and also the far different ideas of space, figure, and motion, the several varieties whereof change the appearances of its proper object, viz. light and colors; we bring ourselves by use to judge of the one by the other. This, in many cases by a settled habit,—in things whereof we have frequent experience, is performed so constantly and so quick, that we take that for the perception of our sensation which is an idea formed by our judgment; so that one, viz. that of sensation, serves only to excite the other, and is scarce taken notice of itself;—as a man who reads or hears with attention and understanding, takes little notice of the characters or sounds, but of the ideas that are excited in him by them.

Nor need we wonder that this is done with so little notice, if we consider how quick the actions of the mind are performed. For, as itself is thought to take up no space, to have no extension; so its actions seem to require no time, but many of them seem to be crowded into an instant. I speak this in comparison to the actions of the body. Anyone may easily observe this in his own thoughts, who will take the pains to reflect on them. How, as it were in an instant, do our minds, with one glance, see all the parts of a demonstration, which may very well be called a long one, if we consider the time it will require to put it into words, and step by step show it another? Secondly, we shall not be so much surprised that this is done in us with so little notice, if we consider how the facility which we get of doing things, by a custom of doing, makes them often pass in us without our notice. Habits, especially such as are begun very early, come at last to produce actions in us, which often escape our observation. How frequently do we, in a day, cover our eyes with our eyelids, without perceiving that we are at all in the dark! Men that, by custom, have got the use of a byword, do almost in every sentence pronounce sounds which, though taken notice of by others, they themselves neither hear nor observe. And therefore it is not so strange, that our mind should often change the idea of its sensation into that of its judgment, and make one serve only to excite the other, without our taking notice of it.

Perception then being the *first* step and degree toward knowledge, and the inlet of all the materials of it; the fewer senses any man, as well as any other creature, hath; and the fewer and duller the impressions are that are made by them; and the duller the faculties are that are employed about them,—the more remote are they from that knowledge which is to be found in some men. But this being in great variety of degrees (as may be perceived amongst men) cannot certainly be discovered in the several species of animals, much less in their particular individuals. It suffices me only to have remarked here,—that perception is the first operation of all our intellectual faculties, and the inlet of all knowledge in our minds. And I am apt too to imagine, that it is perception, in the lowest degree of it, which puts the boundaries between animals and the inferior ranks of creatures. But this I mention only as my conjecture by the by; it being indifferent to the matter in hand which way the learned shall determine of it.

X

Of Retention

THE NEXT FACULTY OF THE MIND, whereby it makes a further progress toward knowledge, is that which I call *retention;* or the keeping of those simple ideas which from sensation or reflection it hath received. This is done two ways.

First, by keeping the idea which is brought into it, for some time actually in view, which is called *contemplation.*

The other way of retention is, the power to revive again in our minds those ideas which, after imprinting, have disappeared, or have been as it were laid aside out of sight. And thus we do, when we conceive heat or light, yellow or sweet,—the object being removed. This is *memory,* which is as it were the storehouse of our ideas. For, the narrow mind of man not being capable of having many ideas under view and consideration at once, it was necessary to have a repository, to lay up those ideas which, at another time, it might have use of.

Attention and repetition help much to the fixing any ideas in the memory. But those which naturally at first make the deepest and most lasting impressions, are those which are accompanied with pleasure or pain. The great business of the senses being, to make us take notice of what hurts or advantages the body, it is wisely ordered by nature, as has been shown, that pain should accompany the reception of several ideas; which, supplying the place of consideration and reasoning in children, and acting quicker than consideration in grown men, makes both the old and young avoid painful objects with that haste which is necessary for their preservation; and in both settles in the memory a caution for the future.

In this secondary perception, as I may so call it, or viewing again the ideas that are lodged in the memory, the mind is oftentimes more than barely passive; the appearance of those dormant pictures depending sometimes on the *will.* The mind very often sets itself on work in search of some hidden idea, and turns as it were the eye of the soul upon it; though sometimes too they start up in our minds of their own accord, and offer themselves to the understanding; and very often are roused and tumbled out of their dark cells into open daylight, by turbulent and tempestuous passions; our affections bringing ideas to our memory, which had otherwise lain quiet and unregarded.

Memory, in an intellectual creature, is necessary in the next degree to perception. It is of so great moment, that, where it is wanting, all the rest of our faculties are in a great measure useless. And we in our thoughts, reasonings, and knowledge, could not proceed beyond present objects, were it not for the assistance of our memories; wherein there may be two defects:——

First, That it loses the idea quite, and so far it produces perfect ignorance. For, since we can know nothing further than we have the idea of it, when that is gone, we are in perfect ignorance.

Secondly, That it moves slowly, and retrieves not the ideas that it has, and are laid up in store, quick enough to serve the mind upon occasion. This, if it be to a great degree, is stupidity; and he who, through this default in his memory, has not the ideas that are really preserved there, ready at hand when need and occasion calls for them, were almost as good be without them quite, since they serve him to little purpose. The dull man, who loses the opportunity, whilst he is seeking in his mind for those ideas that should serve his turn, is not much more happy in his knowledge than one that is perfectly ignorant. It is the business therefore of the memory to furnish to the mind those dormant ideas which it has present occasion for; in the having them ready at hand on all occasions, consists that which we call invention, fancy, and quickness of parts.

XI

Of Discerning, and Other Operations of the Mind

ANOTHER FACULTY WE MAY TAKE NOTICE OF in our minds is that of discerning and distinguishing between the several ideas it has. It is not enough to have a confused perception of something in general. Unless the mind had a distinct perception of different objects and their qualities, it would be capable of very little knowledge, though the bodies that affect us were as busy about us as they are now, and the mind were continually employed in thinking. On this faculty of distinguishing one thing from another depends the evidence and certainty of several, even very general, propositions, which have passed for innate truths;—because men, overlooking the true cause why those propositions find universal assent, impute it wholly to native uniform impressions; whereas it in truth depends upon this clear discerning faculty of the mind, whereby it *perceives* two ideas to be the same, or different. But of this more hereafter.

How much the imperfection of accurately discriminating ideas one from another lies, either in the dullness or faults of the organs of sense; or want of acuteness, exercise, or attention in the understanding; or hastiness and precipitancy, natural to some tempers, I will not here examine; it suffices to take notice, that this is one of the operations that the mind may reflect on and observe in itself. It is of that consequence to its other knowledge, that so far as this faculty is in itself dull, or not rightly made use of, for the distinguishing one thing from another,—so far our notions are confused, and our reason and judgment disturbed or misled. If in having our ideas in the memory ready at hand consists quickness of parts; in this, of having them unconfused, and being able nicely to distinguish one thing from another, where there is but the least difference, consists, in a great measure, the exactness of judgment, and clearness of reason, which is to be observed in one man above another. And hence perhaps may be given some reason of that common observation,—that men who have a great deal of wit, and prompt memories, have not always the clearest judgment or deepest reason. For *wit* lying most in the assemblage of ideas, and putting those together with quickness and variety, wherein can be found any resemblance or congruity, thereby to make up pleasant pictures and agreeable visions in the fancy; *judgment,* on the contrary, lies quite on the other side, in separating carefully, one from another, ideas wherein can be found the least difference, thereby to avoid being misled by similitude, and by affinity to take one thing for another. This is a way of proceeding quite contrary to metaphor and allusion; wherein for the most part lies that entertainment and pleasantry of wit, which strikes so lively on the fancy, and therefore is so acceptable to all people, because its beauty appears at first sight, and there is required no labor of thought to examine what truth or reason there is in it. The mind, without looking any further, rests satisfied with the agreeableness of the picture and the gaiety of the fancy. And it is a kind of affront to go about to examine it, by the severe rules of truth and good reason; whereby it appears that it consists in something that is not perfectly conformable to them.

To the well distinguishing our ideas, it chiefly contributes that they be *clear* and *determinate.* And when they are so, it will not breed any confusion or mistake about them, though the senses should (as sometimes they do) convey them from the same object differently on different occasions, and so seem to err. For, though a man in a fever should from sugar have a bitter taste, which at another time would produce a sweet one, yet the idea of bitter in that man's mind would be as clear and distinct from the idea of sweet as if he had tasted only gall. Nor does it make any more confusion between the two ideas of sweet and bitter, that the same sort of body produces at one time one, and at another time another idea by the taste, than it makes a confusion in two ideas of white and sweet, or white and round, that the same piece of sugar produces them both in the mind at the same time. And the ideas of orange color and azure, that are produced in the mind by the same parcel of the infusion of *lignum nephriticum,* are no less distinct ideas than those of the same colors taken from two very different bodies.

The comparing them one with another, in respect of extent, degrees, time, place, or any other circumstances, is another operation of the mind about its ideas, and is that upon which depends all that large tribe of ideas comprehended under *relation;* which, of how vast an extent it is, I shall have occasion to consider hereafter.

The next operation we may observe in the mind about its ideas is COMPOSITION; whereby it puts together several of those simple ones it has received from sensation and reflection, and combines them into complex ones. Under this of composition may be reckoned also that of *enlarging,* wherein, though the composition does not so much appear as in more complex ones, yet it is nevertheless a putting several ideas together, though of the same kind. Thus, by adding several units together, we make the idea of a dozen; and putting together the repeated ideas of several perches, we frame that of a furlong.

When children have, by repeated sensations, got ideas fixed in their memories, they begin by degrees to learn the use of signs. And when they have got the skill to apply the organs of speech to the framing of articulate sounds, they begin to make use of words, to signify their ideas to others. These verbal signs they sometimes borrow from others, and sometimes make themselves, as one may observe among the new and unusual names children often give to things in the first use of language.

The use of words then being to stand as outward marks of our internal ideas, and those ideas being taken from particular things, if every particular idea that we take in should have a distinct name, names must be endless. To prevent this, the mind makes the particular ideas received from particular objects to become general; which is done by considering them as they are in the mind such appearances,—separate from all other existences, and the circumstances of real existence, as time, place, or any other concomitant ideas. This is called ABSTRACTION, whereby ideas taken from particular beings become general representatives of all of the same kind; and their names general names, applicable to whatever exists conformable to such abstract ideas. Such precise, naked appearances in the mind, without considering how, whence, or with what others they came there, the understanding lays up (with names commonly annexed to them) as the standards to rank real existences into sorts, as they agree with these patterns, and to denominate them accordingly. Thus the same color being observed today in chalk or snow, which the mind yesterday received from milk, it considers that appearance alone, makes it a representative of all of that kind; and having given it the name *whiteness,* it by that sound signifies the same quality, wheresoever to be imagined or met with; and thus universals, whether ideas or terms, are made.

These, I think, are the first faculties and operations of the mind, which it makes use of in understanding; and though they are exercised about all its ideas in general, yet the instances I have hitherto given have been chiefly in simple ideas. And I have subjoined the explication of these faculties of the mind to that of simple ideas, before I come to what I have to say concerning complex ones, for these following reasons:—

First, Because several of these faculties being exercised at first principally about simple ideas, we might, by following nature in its ordinary method, trace and discover them, in their rise, progress, and gradual improvements.

Secondly, Because observing the faculties of the mind, how they operate about simple ideas,—which are usually, in most men's minds, much more clear, precise, and distinct than complex ones,—we may the better examine and learn how the mind extracts, denominates, compares, and exercises, in its other operations about those which are complex, wherein we are much more liable to mistake.

Thirdly, Because these very operations of the mind about ideas received from sensations, are themselves, when reflected on, another set of ideas, derived from that other source of our knowledge, which I call reflection; and therefore fit to be considered in this place after the simple ideas of sensation. Of compounding, comparing, abstracting, etc., I have but just spoken, having occasion to treat of them more at large in other places.

And thus I have given a short, and, I think, true *history of the first beginnings of human knowledge;*—whence the mind has its first objects; and by what steps in makes its progress to the laying in and storing up those ideas, out of which is to be framed all the knowledge it is capable of: wherein I must appeal to experience and observation whether I am in the right: the best way to come to truth being to examine things as really they are, and not to conclude they are, as we fancy of ourselves, or have been taught by others to imagine.

To deal truly, this is the only way that I can discover, whereby the *ideas of things* are brought into the understanding. If other men have either innate ideas or infused principles, they have reason to enjoy them; and if they are sure of it, it is impossible for others to deny them the privilege that they have above their neighbors. I can speak but of what I find in myself, and is agreeable to those notions, which, if we will examine the whole course of men in their several ages, countries, and educations, seem to depend on those foundations which I have laid, and to correspond with this method in all the parts and degrees thereof.

I pretend not to teach, but to inquire; and therefore cannot but confess here again,—that external and internal sensation are the only passages I can find of knowledge to the understanding. These alone, as far as I can discover, are the windows by which light is let into this *dark room*. For, methinks, the understanding is not much unlike a closet wholly shut from light, with only some little openings left, to let in external visible resemblances, or ideas of things without; would the pictures coming into such a dark room but stay there, and lie so orderly as to be found upon occasion, it would very much resemble the understanding of a man, in reference to all objects of sight, and the ideas of them.

These are my guesses concerning the means whereby the understanding comes to have and retain simple ideas, and the modes of them, with some other operations about them.

I proceed now to examine some of these simple ideas and their modes a little more particularly.

XII

Of Complex Ideas

WE HAVE HITHERTO CONSIDERED those ideas, in the reception whereof the mind is only passive, which are those simple ones received from sensation and reflection before mentioned, whereof the mind cannot make one to itself, nor have any idea which does not wholly consist of them. But as the mind is wholly passive in the reception of all its simple ideas, so it exerts several acts of its own, whereby out of its simple ideas, as the materials and foundations of the rest, the others are framed. The acts of the mind, wherein it exerts its power over its simple ideas, are chiefly these three: (1) Combining several simple ideas into one compound one; and thus all *complex ideas* are made. (2) The second is bringing two ideas, whether simple or complex, together, and setting them by one another, so as to take a view of them at once, without uniting them into one; by which way it gets all its *ideas of relations*. (3) The third is separating them from all other ideas that accompany them in their real existence: this is called abstraction: and thus all its *general ideas* are made. This shows man's power, and its ways of operation, to be much the same in the material and intellectual world. For the materials in both being such as he has no power over, either to make or destroy, all that man can do is either to unite them together, or to set them by one another, or wholly separate them. I shall here begin with the first of these in the consideration of complex ideas, and come to the other two in their due places. As simple ideas are observed to exist in several combinations united together, so the mind has a power to consider several of them united together as one idea; and that not only as they are united in external objects, but as itself has joined them together. Ideas thus made up of several simple ones put together, I call *complex;*—such as are beauty, gratitude, a man, an army, the universe; which, though complicated of various simple ideas, or complex ideas made up of simple ones, yet are, when the mind pleases, considered each by itself, as one entire thing, and signified by one name.

In this faculty of repeating and joining together its ideas, the mind has great power in varying and multiplying the objects of its thoughts, infinitely beyond what sensation or reflection furnished it with: but all this still confined to those simple ideas which it received from those two sources, and which are the ultimate materials of all its compositions. For simple ideas are all from things themselves, and of these the mind *can* have no more, nor other than what are suggested to it. It can have no other ideas of sensible qualities than what come from without by the senses; nor any ideas of other kind of operations of a thinking substance, than what it finds in itself. But when it has once got these simple ideas, it is not confined barely to observation, and what offers itself from without; it can, by its own power, put together those ideas it has, and make new complex ones, which it never received so united.

Complex ideas, however compounded and decompounded, though their number be infinite, and the variety endless, wherewith they fill and entertain the thoughts of men; yet I think they may be all reduced under these three heads:——

1. MODES.
2. SUBSTANCES.
3. RELATIONS.

First, Modes I call such complex ideas which, however compounded, contain not in them the supposition of subsisting by themselves, but are considered as dependences on, or affections of substances;—such as are the ideas signified by the words triangle, gratitude, murder, etc. And if in this I use the word mode in somewhat a different sense from its ordinary signification, I beg pardon; it being unavoidable in discourses, differing from the ordinary received notions, either to make new words, or to use old words in somewhat a new signification; the later whereof, in our present case, is perhaps the more tolerable of the two.

Of these *modes,* there are two sorts which deserve distinct consideration:——

First, there are some which are only variations, or different combinations of the same simple idea, without the mixture of any other;—as a dozen, or score; which are nothing but the ideas of so many distinct units added together, and these I call *simple modes* as being contained within the bounds of one simple idea.

Secondly, there are others compounded of simple ideas of several kinds, put together to make one complex one;—v.g. beauty, consisting of a certain composition of color and figure, causing delight to the beholder; theft, which being the concealed change of the possession of anything, without the consent of the proprietor, contains, as is visible, a combination of several ideas of several kinds: and these I call *mixed modes.*

Secondly, the ideas of *substances* are such combinations of simple ideas as are taken to represent distinct *particular* things subsisting by themselves; in which the supposed or confused idea of substance, such as it is, is always the first and chief. Thus if to substance be joined the simple idea of a certain dull whitish color, with certain degrees of weight, hardness, ductility, and fusibility, we have the idea of lead; and a combination of the ideas of a certain sort of figure, with the powers of motion, thought and reasoning, joined to substance, make the ordinary idea of a man. Now of substances also, there are two sorts of ideas:—one of *single* substances, as they exist separately, as of a man or a sheep; the other of several of those put together, as an army of men, or flock of sheep—which *collective* ideas of several substances thus put together are as much each of them one single idea as that of a man or an unit.

Thirdly, the last sort of complex ideas is that we call *relation,* which consists in the consideration and comparing one idea with another.

Of these several kinds we shall treat in their order.

If we trace the progress of our minds, and with attention observe how it repeats, adds together, and unites its simple ideas received from sensation or reflection, it will lead us further than at first perhaps we should have imagined. And, I believe, we shall find, if we warily observe the originals of our notions, that *even the most abstruse ideas,* how remote soever they may seem from sense, or from any operations of our own minds, are yet only such as the understanding frames to itself, by repeating and joining together ideas that it had either from objects of sense, or from its own operations about them: so that those even large and abstract ideas are derived from sensation or reflection, being no other than what the mind, by the ordinary use of its own faculties, employed about ideas received from objects of sense, or from the operations it observes in itself about them, may, and does, attain unto.

This I shall endeavor to show in the ideas we have of space, time, and infinity, and some few others that seem the most remote, from those originals.

XIII

Complex Ideas of Simple Modes:—And First, of the Simple Modes of Idea of Space

THOUGH IN THE FOREGOING PART I have often mentioned simple ideas, which are truly the materials of all our knowledge; yet having treated of them there, rather in the way that they come into the mind, than as distinguished from others more compounded, it will not be perhaps amiss to take a view of some of them again under this consideration, and examine those different modifications of the *same* idea; which the mind either finds in things existing, or is able to make within itself without the help of any extrinsical object, or any foreign suggestion.

Those modifications of any *one* simple idea (which, as has been said, I call *simple modes*) are as perfectly different and distinct ideas in the mind as those of the greatest distance or contrariety. For the idea of two is as distinct from that of one, as blueness from heat, or either of them from any number: and yet it is made up only of that simple idea of an unit repeated; and repetitions of this kind joined together make those distinct simple modes, of a dozen, a gross, a million.

I shall begin with the simple idea of *space*. I have showed above, Chapter 4, that we get the idea of space, both by our sight and touch; which, I think, is so evident, that it would be as needless to go to prove that men perceive, by their sight, a distance between bodies of different colors, or between the parts of the same body, as that they see colors themselves: nor is it less obvious, that they can do so in the dark by feeling and touch.

This space, considered barely in length between any two beings, without considering anything else between them, is called *distance:* if considered in length, breadth, and thickness, I think it may be called *capacity*.

Each different distance is a different modification of space; and each idea of any different distance, or space, is a *simple mode* of this idea. Men, for the use and by the custom of measuring, settle in their minds the ideas of certain stated lengths,—such as are an inch, foot, yard, fathom, mile, diameter of the earth, etc., which are so many distinct ideas made up only of space. When any such stated lengths or measures of space are made familiar to men's thoughts, they can, in their minds, repeat them as often as they will, without mixing or joining to them the idea of body, or anything else; and frame to themselves the ideas of long, square, or cubic feet, yards or fathoms, here amongst the bodies of the universe, or else beyond the utmost bounds of all bodies; and, by adding these still to one another, enlarge their ideas of space as much as they please. The power of repeating or doubling any idea we have of any distance, and adding it to the former as often as we will, without being ever able to come to any stop or stint, let us enlarge it as much as we will, is that which gives us the idea of *immensity*.

There is another modification of this idea, which is nothing but the relation which the parts of the termination of extension, or circumscribed space, have amongst themselves. This the touch discovers in sensible bodies, whose extremities come within our reach; and the eye takes both from bodies and colors, whose boundaries are within its view: where, observing how the extremities terminate,—either in straight lines which meet at discernible angles, or in crooked lines wherein no angles can be perceived; by considering these as they relate to one another, in all parts of the extremities of any body or space, it has that idea we call *figure*, which affords to the mind infinite variety. For, besides the vast number of different figures that do really exist in the coherent masses of matter, the stock that the mind has in its power, by varying the idea of space, and thereby making still new compositions, by repeating its own ideas, and joining them as it pleases, is perfectly inexhaustible. And so it can multiply figures *in infinitum*.

For the mind having a power to repeat the idea of any length directly stretched out, and join it to another in the same direction, which is to double the length of that straight line; or else join another with what inclination it thinks fit, and so make what sort of angle it pleases; and being able also to shorten any line it imagines, by taking from it one half, one fourth, or what part it pleases, without being able to come to an end of any such divisions, it can make an angle of any bigness. So also the lines that are its sides, of what length it pleases, which joining again to other lines, of different lengths, and at different angles, till it has wholly enclosed any space, it is evident that it can multiply figures, both in their shape and capacity, *in infinitum;* all which are but so many different simple modes of space.

The same that it can do with straight lines, it can also do with crooked, or crooked and straight together; and the same it can do in lines, it can also in superficies; by which we may be led into farther thoughts of the endless variety of figures that the mind has a power to make, and thereby to multiply the simple modes of space.

Another idea coming under this head, and belonging to this tribe, is that we call *place*. As in simple space, we consider the relation of distance between any two bodies or points; so in our idea of place, we consider the relation of distance betwixt anything, and any two or more points, which are considered as keeping the same distance one with another, and so considered as at rest. For when we find anything at the same distance now which it was yesterday, from any two or more points, which have not since changed their distance one with another, and with which we then compared it, we say it hath kept the same place: but if it hath sensibly altered its distance with either of those points, we say it hath changed its place: though, vulgarly speaking, in the common notion of place, we do not always exactly observe the distance from these precise points, but from larger portions of sensible objects, to which we consider the thing placed to bear relation, and its distance from which we have some reason to observe.

Thus, a company of chessmen, standing on the same squares of the chessboard where we left them, we say they are all in the *same* place, or unmoved, though perhaps the chessboard hath been in the meantime carried out of one room into another; because we compared them only to the parts of the chessboard, which keep the same distance one with another. The chessboard, we also say, is in the same place it was, if it remain in the same part of the cabin, though perhaps the ship which it is in sails all the while. And the ship is said to be in the same place, supposing it kept the same distance with the parts of the neighboring land; though perhaps the earth hath turned round, and so both chessmen, and board, and ship, have every one changed place, in respect of remoter bodies, which have kept the same distance one with another. But yet the distance from certain parts of the board being that which determines the place of the chessmen; and the distance from the fixed parts of the cabin (with which we made the comparison) being that which determined the place of the chessboard; and the fixed parts of the earth that by which we determined the place of the ship,—these things may be said to be in the same place in those respects: though their distance from some other things, which in this matter we did not consider, being varied, they have undoubtedly changed place in that respect; and we ourselves shall think so, when we have occasion to compare them with those other.

But this modification of distance we call place, being made by men for their common use, that by it they might be able to design the particular position of things, where they had occasion for such designation; men consider and determine of this place by reference to those adjacent things which best served to their present purpose, without considering other things which, to another purpose, would better determine the place of the same thing. Thus in the chessboard, the use of the designation of the place of each chessman being determined only within that checkered piece of wood, it would cross that purpose to measure it by anything else; but when these very chessmen are put up in a bag, if any one should ask where the black king is, it would be proper to determine the place by the part of the room it was in, and not by the chessboard; there being another use of designing the place it is now in, than when in play it was on the chessboard, and so must be determined by other bodies.

That our idea of place is nothing else but such a relative position of anything as I have before mentioned, I think is plain, and will be easily admitted, when we consider that we can have no idea of the place of the universe, though we can of all the parts of it; because beyond that we have not the idea of any fixed, distinct, particular beings, in reference to which we can imagine it to have any relation of distance; but all beyond it is one uniform space or expansion, wherein the mind finds no variety, no marks. For to say that the world is somewhere, means no more than that it does exist; this, though a phrase borrowed from place, signifying only its existence, not location: and when one can find out, and frame in his mind, clearly and distinctly, the place of the universe, he will be able to tell us whether it moves or stands still in the undistinguishable inane of infinite space: though it be true that the word place has sometimes a more confused sense, and stands for that space which anybody takes up; and so the universe is in a place.

The idea, therefore, of place we have by the same means that we get the idea of space (whereof this is but a particular limited consideration), viz. by our sight and touch; by either of which we receive into our minds the ideas of extension or distance.

There are some that would persuade us, that body and extension are the same thing, who either change the signification of words, which I would not suspect them of,—they having so severely condemned the philosophy of others, because it hath been too much placed in the uncertain meaning, or deceitful obscurity of doubtful or insignificant terms. If, therefore, they mean by body and extension the same that other people do, viz. by *body* something that is solid and extended, whose parts are separable and movable different ways; and by *extension,* only the space that lies between the extremities of those solid coherent parts, and which is possessed by them,—they confound very different ideas one with another; for I appeal to every man's own thoughts, whether the idea of space be not as distinct from that of solidity, as it is from the idea of scarlet color? It is true, solidity cannot exist without extension, neither can scarlet color exist without extension, but this hinders not, but that they are distinct ideas. Many ideas require others, as necessary to their existence or conception, which yet are very distinct ideas. Motion can neither be, nor be conceived, without space; and yet motion is not space, nor space motion; space can exist without it, and they are very distinct ideas; and so, I think, are those of space and solidity. Solidity is so inseparable an idea from body, that upon that depends its filling of space, its contact, impulse, and communication of motion upon impulse. And if it be a reason to prove that spirit is different from body, because thinking includes not the idea of extension in it; the same reason will be as valid, I suppose, to prove that space is not body, because it includes not the idea of solidity in it; *space* and *solidity* being as distinct ideas as *thinking* and *extension,* and as wholly separable in the mind one from another. Body then and extension, it is evident, are two distinct ideas. For,

First, Extension includes no solidity, nor resistance to the motion of body, as body does.

Secondly, The parts of pure space are inseparable one from the other; so that the continuity cannot be separated, neither really nor mentally. For I demand of anyone to remove any part of it from another, with which it is continued, even so much as in thought. To divide and separate actually is, as I think, by removing the parts one from another, to make two superficies, where before there was a continuity: and to divide mentally is, to make in the mind two superficies, where before there was a continuity, and consider them as removed one from the other; which can only be done in things considered by the mind as capable of being separated; and by separation, of acquiring new distinct superficies, which they then have not, but are capable of. But neither of these ways of separation, whether real or mental, is, as I think, compatible to pure space.

Thirdly, The parts of pure space are immovable, which follows from their inseparability; motion being nothing but change of distance between any two things; but this cannot be between parts that are inseparable, which, therefore, must needs be at perpetual rest one amongst another.

Thus the determined idea of simple space distinguishes it plainly and sufficiently from body; since its parts are inseparable, immovable, and without resistance to the motion of body.

If anyone ask me *what* this space I speak of *is,* I will tell him when he tells me what his extension is. For to say, as is usually done, that extension is to have *partes extra partes,* is to say only, that extension is extension. For what am I the better informed in the nature of extension, when I am told that extension is to have parts that are extended, exterior to parts that are extended, i.e. extension consists of extended parts? As if one, asking what a fiber was, I should answer him,—that it was a thing made up of several fibers. Would he thereby be enabled to understand what a fiber was better than he did before? Or rather, would he not have reason to think that my design was to make sport with him, rather than seriously to instruct him?

Those who contend that space and body are the same, bring this dilemma:—either this space is something or nothing; if nothing be between two bodies, they must necessarily touch; if it be allowed to be something, they ask, Whether it be body or spirit? To which I answer by another question,

Who told them that there was, or could be, nothing but *solid beings, which could not think,* and *thinking beings that were not extended?*—which is all they mean by the terms *body* and *spirit.*

If it be demanded (as usually it is) whether this space, void of body, be *substance* or *accident,* I shall readily answer I know not; nor shall be ashamed to own my ignorance, till they that ask show me a clear, distinct idea of substance.

I endeavor as much as I can to deliver myself from those fallacies which we are apt to put upon ourselves, by taking words for things. It helps not our ignorance to feign a knowledge where we have none, by making a noise with sounds, without clear and distinct significations. Names made at pleasure, neither alter the nature of things, nor make us understand them, but as they are signs of and stand for determined ideas. And I desire those who lay so much stress on the sound of these two syllables, *substance,* to consider whether applying it, as they do, to the infinite, incomprehensible God, to finite spirits, and to body, it be in the same sense; and whether it stands for the same idea, when each of those three so different beings are called substances. If so, whether it will thence follow—that God, spirits, and body, agreeing in the same common nature of substance, differ not any otherwise than in a bare different *modification* of that substance; as a tree and a pebble, being in the same sense body, and agreeing in the common nature of body, differ only in a bare modification of that common matter, which will be a very harsh doctrine. If they say, that they apply it to God, finite spirit, and matter, in three different significations and that it stands for one idea when God is said to be a substance; for another when the soul is called substance; and for a third when body is called so;—if the name substance stands for three several distinct ideas, they would do well to make known those distinct ideas, or at least to give three distinct names to them, to prevent in so important a notion the confusion and errors that will naturally follow from the promiscuous use of so doubtful a term; which is so far from being suspected to have three distinct, that in ordinary use it has scarce one clear distinct signification. And if they can thus make three distinct ideas of substance, what hinders why another may not make a fourth?

They who first ran into the notion of *accidents,* as a sort of real beings that needed something to inhere in, were forced to find out the word *substance* to support them. Had the poor Indian philosopher (who imagined that the earth also wanted something to bear it up) but thought of this word substance, he needed not to have been at the trouble to find an elephant to support it, and a tortoise to support his elephant: the word substance would have done it effectually. And he that inquired might have taken it for as good an answer from an Indian philosopher,—that substance, without knowing what it is, is that which supports the earth, as we take it for a sufficient answer and good doctrine from our European philosophers,—that substance, without knowing what it is, is that which supports accidents. So that of substance, we have no idea of what it is, but only a confused, obscure one of what it does.

Whatever a learned man may do here, an intelligent American, who inquired into the nature of things, would scarce take it for a satisfactory account, if, desiring to learn our architecture, he should be told that a pillar is a thing supported by a base, and a base something that supported a pillar. Would he not think himself mocked, instead of taught, with such an account as this? And a stranger to them would be very liberally instructed in the nature of books, and the things they contained, if he should be told that all learned books consisted of paper and letters, and that letters were things inhering in paper, and paper a thing that held forth letters: a notable way of having clear ideas of letters and paper. But were the Latin words, *inhaerentia* and *substantio*, put into the plain English ones that answer them, and were called *sticking on* and *underpropping*, they would better discover to us the very great clearness there is in the doctrine of substance and accidents, and show of what use they are in deciding of questions in philosophy.

But to return to our idea of space. If body be not supposed infinite (which I think no one will affirm), I would ask, whether, if God placed a man at the extremity of corporeal beings, he could not stretch his hand beyond his body? If he could, then he would put his arm where there was before space without body; and if there he spread his fingers, there would still be space between them without body. If he could not stretch out his hand, it must be because of some external hindrance; (for we suppose him alive, with such a power of moving the parts of his body that he hath now, which is not in itself impossible, if God so pleased to have it; or at least it is not impossible for God so to move him:) and then I ask,—whether that which hinders his hand from moving outward be substance or accident, something or nothing? And when they have resolved that, they will be able to resolve themselves,—what that is, which is or may be between two bodies at a distance, that is not body, and has no solidity. In the meantime, the argument is at least as good, that, where nothing hinders (as beyond the utmost bounds of all bodies) a body put in motion may move on, as where there is nothing between, there two bodies must necessarily touch. For pure space between is sufficient to take away the necessity of mutual contact; but bare space in the way is not sufficient to stop motion. The truth is, these men must either own that they think body infinite, though they are loath to speak it out, or else affirm that space is not body. For I would fain meet with that thinking man that can in his thoughts set any bounds to space, more than he can to duration; or by thinking hope to arrive at the end of either. And therefore, if his idea of eternity be infinite, so is his idea of immensity; they are both finite or infinite alike.

But the question being here,—Whether the idea of space or extension be the same with the idea of body? it is not necessary to prove the real existence of a *vacuum*, but the idea of it; which it is plain men have when they inquire and dispute whether there be a *vacuum* or no. For if they had not the idea of space without body, they could not make a question about its existence: and if their idea of body did not include in it something more than the bare idea of space, they could have no doubt about the plenitude of the world; and it would be as absurd to demand, whether there were space without body, as whether there were space without space, or body without body, since these were but different names of the same idea.

To conclude: whatever men shall think concerning the existence of a *vacuum*, this is plain to me—that we have as clear an idea of space distinct from solidity, as we have of solidity distinct from motion, or motion from space. We have not any two more distinct ideas; and we can as easily conceive space without solidity, as we can conceive body or space without motion, though it be never so certain that neither body nor motion can exist without space. But whether anyone will take space to be only a *relation* resulting from the existence of other beings at a distance; or whether they will think the words of the most knowing King Solomon, "The heaven, and the heaven of heavens, cannot contain thee"; or those more emphatical ones of the inspired philosopher St. Paul, "In him we live, move, and have our being," are to be understood in a literal sense, I leave everyone to consider: only our idea of space is, I think, such as I have mentioned, and distinct from that of body. For, whether we consider, in matter itself, the distance of its coherent solid parts, and call it, in respect of those solid parts, extension; or whether, considering it as lying between the extremities of any body in its several dimensions, we call it length, breadth, and thickness; or else, considering it as lying between any two bodies or positive beings, without any consideration whether there be any matter or not between, we call it distance;—however named or considered, it is always the same uniform simple idea of space, taken from objects about which our senses have been conversant; whereof, having settled ideas in our minds, we can revive, repeat, and add them one to another as often as we will, and consider the space or distance so imagined, either as filled with solid parts, so that another body cannot come there without displacing and thrusting out the body that was there before; or else as void of solidity, so that a body of equal dimensions to that empty or pure space may be placed in it, without the removing or expulsion of anything that was there.

XIV

Idea of Duration and Its Simple Modes

THERE IS ANOTHER SORT OF DISTANCE, or length, the idea whereof we get not from the permanent parts of space, but from the fleeting and perpetually perishing parts of succession. This we call *duration;* the simple modes whereof are any different lengths of it whereof we have distinct ideas, as *hours, days, years,* etc., *time* and *eternity.*

The answer of a great man, to one who asked what time was: *Si non rogas intelligo,* (which amounts to this; The more I set myself to think of it, the less I understand it), might perhaps persuade one that time, which reveals all other things, is itself not to be discovered. Duration, time, and eternity, are, not without reason, thought to have something very abstruse in their nature. But however remote these may seem from our comprehension, yet if we trace them right to their originals, I doubt not but one of those sources of all our knowledge, viz. sensation and reflection, will be able to furnish us with those ideas, as clear and distinct as many others which are thought much less obscure; and we shall find that the idea of eternity itself is derived from the same common original with the rest of our ideas.

To understand *time* and *eternity* aright, we ought with attention to consider what idea it is we have of *duration,* and how we came by it. It is evident to anyone who will but observe what passes in his own mind, that there is a train of ideas which constantly succeed one another in his understanding, as long as he is awake. Reflection on these appearances of several ideas one after another in our minds, is that which furnishes us with the idea of *succession:* and the distance between any parts of that succession, or between the appearance of any two ideas in our minds, is that we call *duration.* For whilst we are thinking, or whilst we receive successively several ideas in our minds, we know that we do exist; and so we call the existence, or the continuation of the existence of ourselves, or anything else, commensurate to the succession of any ideas in our minds, the duration of ourselves, or any such other thing co-existent with our thinking.

That we have our notion of succession and duration from

this original, viz. from reflection on the train of ideas, which we find to appear one after another in our own minds, seems plain to me, in that we have no perception of duration but by considering the train of ideas that take their turns in our understandings. When that succession of ideas ceases, our perception of duration ceases with it; which everyone clearly experiments in himself, whilst he sleeps soundly, whether an hour or a day, a month or a year; of which duration of things, while he sleeps or thinks not, he has no perception at all, but it is quite lost to him; and the moment wherein he leaves off to think, till the moment he begins to think again, seems to him to have no distance. And so I doubt not it would be to a waking man, if it were possible for him to keep *only one* idea in his mind, without variation and the succession of others. And we see, that one who fixes his thoughts very intently on one thing, so as to take but little notice of the succession of ideas that pass in his mind, whilst he is taken up with that earnest contemplation, lets slip out of his account a good part of that duration, and thinks that time shorter than it is. But if sleep commonly unites the distant parts of duration, it is because during that time we have no succession of ideas in our minds. For if a man, during his sleep, dreams, and variety of ideas make themselves perceptible in his mind one after another, he hath then, during such dreaming, a sense of duration, and of the length of it. By which it is to me very clear, that men derive their ideas of duration from their reflections on the train of the ideas they observe to succeed one another in their own understandings; without which observation they can have no notion of duration, whatever may happen in the world.

Indeed a man having, from reflecting on the succession and number of his own thoughts, got the notion or idea of duration, he can apply that notion to things which exist while he does not think; as he that has got the idea of extension from bodies by his sight or touch, can apply it to distances, where no body is seen or felt. And therefore, though a man has no perception of the length of duration which passed whilst he slept or thought not; yet, having observed the revolution of days and nights, and found the length of their duration to be in appearance regular and constant, he can, upon the supposition that that revolution has proceeded after the same manner whilst he was asleep or thought not, as it used to do at other times, he can, I say, imagine and make allowance for the length of duration whilst he slept. But if Adam and Eve (when they were alone in the world), instead of their ordinary night's sleep, had passed the whole twenty-four hours in one continued sleep, the duration of that twenty-four hours had been irrecoverably lost to them, and been forever left out of their account of time.

Thus by reflecting on the appearing of various ideas one after another in our understandings, we get the notion of succession; which, if anyone should think we did rather get from our observation of motion by our senses, he will perhaps be of my mind when he considers, that even motion produces in his mind an idea of succession no otherwise than as it produces there a continued train of distinguishable ideas. For a man looking upon a body really moving, perceives yet no motion at all unless that motion produces a constant train of successive ideas: v.g. a man becalmed at sea, out of sight of land, in a fair day, may look on the sun, or sea, or ship, a whole hour together, and perceive no motion at all in either; though it be certain that two, and perhaps all of them, have moved during that time a great way. But as soon as he perceives either of them to have changed distance with some other body, as soon as this motion produces any new idea in him, then he perceives that there has been motion. But wherever a man is, with all things at rest about him, without perceiving any motion at all,—if during this hour of quiet he has been thinking, he will perceive the various ideas of his own thoughts in his own mind, appearing one after another, and thereby observe and find succession where he could observe no motion.

So that to me it seems, that the constant and regular succession of *ideas* in a waking man, is, as it were, the measure and standard of all other successions. Whereof, if anyone either exceeds the pace of our ideas, as where two sounds or pains, etc., take up in their succession the duration of but one idea; or else where any motion or succession is so slow, as that it keeps not pace with the ideas in our minds, or the quickness in which they take their turns, as when any one or more ideas in their ordinary course come into our mind, between those which are offered to the sight by the different perceptible distances of a body in motion, or between sounds or smells following one another,—there also the sense of a constant continued succession is lost, and we perceive it not, but with certain gaps of rest between.

If it be so, that the ideas of our minds, whilst we have any there, do constantly change and shift in a continual succession, it would be impossible, may anyone say, for a man to think long of any one thing. By which, if it be meant that a man may have one self-same single idea a long time alone in his mind, without any variation at all, I think, in matter of fact, it is not possible. For which (not knowing how the ideas of our minds are framed, of what materials they are made, whence they have their light, and how they come to make their appearances) I can give no other reason but experience: and I would have anyone try, whether he can keep one unvaried single idea in his mind, without any other, for any considerable time together.

For trial, let him take any figure, any degree of light or whiteness, or what other he pleases, and he will, I suppose, find it difficult to keep all other ideas out of his mind; but that some, either of another kind, or various considerations of that idea (each of which considerations is a new idea), will constantly succeed one another in his thoughts, let him be as wary as he can.

All that is in a man's power in this case, I think, is only to mind and observe what the ideas are that take their turns in his understanding; or else to direct the sort, and call in such as he hath a desire or use of: but hinder the constant succession of fresh ones, I think he cannot, though he may commonly choose whether he will heedfully observe and consider them.

Whether these several ideas in a man's mind be made by certain motions, I will not here dispute; but this I am sure, that they include no idea of motion in their appearance; and if a man had not the idea of motion otherwise, I think he would have none at all, which is enough to my present purpose; and sufficiently shows that the notice we take of the ideas of our own minds, appearing there one after another, is that which gives us the idea of succession and duration, without which we should have no such ideas at all. It is not then *motion,* but the constant train of *ideas* in our minds whilst we are waking, that furnishes us with the idea of duration; whereof motion no otherwise gives us any perception than as it causes in our minds a constant succession of ideas, as I have before showed: and we have as clear an idea of succession and duration, by the train of other ideas succeeding one another in our minds, without the idea of any motion, as by the train of ideas caused by the uninterrupted sensible change of distance between two bodies, which we have from motion; and therefore we should as well have the idea of duration were there no sense of motion at all.

Having thus got the idea of duration, the next thing natural for the mind to do, is to get some *measure* of this common duration, whereby it might judge of its different lengths, and consider the distinct order wherein several things exist; without which a great part of our knowledge would be confused, and a great part of history be rendered very useless. This consideration of duration, as set out by certain periods, and marked by certain measures or epochs, is that, I think, which most properly we call *time*.

In the measuring of extension, there is nothing more required but the application of the standard or measure we make use of to the thing of whose extension we would be informed. But in the measuring of duration this cannot be done, because no two different parts of succession can be put together to measure one another. And nothing being a measure of duration but duration, as nothing is of extension but extension, we cannot keep by us any standing, unvarying measure of duration, which consists in a constant fleeting succession, as we can of certain lengths of extension, as inches, feet, yards, etc., marked out in permanent parcels of matter. Nothing then could serve well for a convenient measure of time, but what has divided the whole length of its duration into apparently equal portions, by constantly repeated periods. What portions of duration are not distinguished, or considered as distinguished and measured, by such periods, come not so properly under the notion of time; as appears by such phrases as these, viz. "Before all time," and "When time shall be no more."

The diurnal and annual revolutions of the sun, as having been, from the beginning of nature, constant, regular, and universally observable by all mankind, and supposed equal to one another, have been with reason made use of for the measure of duration. But the distinction of days and years having depended on the motion of the sun, it has brought this mistake with it, that it has been thought that motion and dura-

:on were the measure one of another. For men, in the measring of the length of time, having been accustomed to the leas of minutes, hours, days, months, years, etc., which they ound themselves upon any mention of time or duration presntly to think on, all which portions of time were measured ut by the motion of those heavenly bodies, they were apt ɔ confound time and motion; or at least to think that they ad a necessary connection one with another. Whereas any onstant periodical appearance, or alteration of ideas, in eemingly equidistant spaces of duration, if constant and niversally observable, would have as well distinguished the ntervals of time, as those that have been made use of. For, upposing the sun, which some have taken to be a fire, had een lighted up at the same distance of time that it now every ay comes about to the same meridian, and then gone out gain about twelve hours after, and that in the space of an nnual revolution it had sensibly increased in brightness and eat, and so decreased again,—would not such regular apearances serve to measure out the distances of duration to ll that could observe it, as well without as with motion? For f the appearances were constant, universally observable, in quidistant periods, they would serve mankind for measure of ime as well were the motion away.

One thing seems strange to me,—that whilst all men maniestly measured time by the motion of the great and visible odies of the world, time yet should be defined to be the measure of motion": whereas it is obvious to everyone who eflects ever so little on it, that to measure motion, space is s necessary to be considered as time; and those who look a ittle farther will find also the bulk of the thing moved necesary to be taken into the computation, by anyone who will stimate or measure motion so as to judge right of it. Nor ndeed does motion any otherwise conduce to the measuring f duration, than as it constantly brings about the return of ertain sensible ideas, in seeming equidistant periods. For if he motion of the sun were as unequal as of a ship driven by nsteady winds, sometimes very slow, and at others irreguarly very swift; or if, being constantly equally swift, it yet vas not circular, and produced not the same appearances,—it vould not at all help us to measure time, any more than the eeming unequal motion of a comet does.

Minutes, hours, days, and years are, then, no more necessary to time or duration, than inches, feet, yards, and miles, marked out in any matter, are to extension. For, though we in this part of the universe, by the constant use of them, as of periods set out by the revolutions of the sun, or as known parts of such periods, have fixed the ideas of such lengths of duration in our minds, which we apply to all parts of time whose lengths we would consider; yet there may be other parts of the universe, where they no more use these measures of ours, than in Japan they do our inches, feet, or miles; but yet something analogous to them there must be. For without some regular periodical returns, we could not measure ourselves, or signify to others, the length of any duration; though at the same time the world were as full of motion as it is now, but no part of it disposed into regular and apparently equidistant revolutions. But the different measures that may be made use of for the account of time, do not at all alter the notion of duration, which is the thing to be measured; no more than the different standards of a foot and a cubit alter the notion of extension to those who make use of those different measures.

The mind having once got such a measure of time as the annual revolution of the sun, can apply that measure to duration wherein that measure itself did not exist, and with which, in the reality of its being, it had nothing to do. For should one say, that Abraham was born in the two thousand seven hundred and twelfth year of the Julian period, it is altogether as intelligible as reckoning from the beginning of the world, though there were so far back no motion of the sun, nor any motion at all. For, though the Julian period be supposed to begin several hundred years before there were really either days, nights, or years, marked out by any revolutions of the sun,—yet we reckon as right, and thereby measure durations as well, as if really at that time the sun had existed, and kept the same ordinary motion it doth now. The idea of duration equal to an annual revolution of the sun, is as easily *applicable* in our thoughts to duration, where no sun or motion was, as the idea of a foot or yard, taken from bodies here, can be applied in our thoughts to distances beyond the confines of the world, where are no bodies at all.

The notion of an hour, day, or year, being only the idea I have of the length of certain periodical regular motions, neither of which motions do ever all at once exist, but only in the ideas I have of them in my memory derived from my senses or reflection; I can with the same ease, and for the same reason, apply it in my thoughts to duration antecedent to all manner of motion, as well as to anything that is but a minute or a day antecedent to the motion that at this very moment the sun is in. All things past are equally and perfectly at rest; and to this way of consideration of them are all one, whether they were before the beginning of the world, or but yesterday: the measuring of any duration by some motion depending not at all on the *real* co-existence of that thing to that motion, or any other periods of revolution, but the having a clear *idea* of the length of some periodical known motion, or other interval of duration, in my mind, and applying that to the duration of the thing I would measure.

And thus I think it is plain, that from those two fountains of all knowledge before mentioned, viz. reflection and sensation, we got the ideas of duration, and the measures of it.

For, *First,* by observing what passes in our minds, how our ideas there in train constantly some vanish and others begin to appear, we come by the idea of *succession.*

Secondly, by observing a distance in the parts of this succession, we get the idea of *duration.*

Thirdly, by sensation observing certain appearances, at certain regular and seeming equidistant periods, we get the ideas of certain *lengths* or *measures of duration,* as minutes, hours, days, years, etc.

Fourthly, by being able to repeat those measures of time, or ideas of stated length of duration, in our minds, as often as we will, we can come to imagine *duration, where nothing does really endure or exist;* and thus we imagine tomorrow, next year, or seven years hence.

Fifthly, by being able to repeat ideas of any length of time, as of a minute, a year, or an age, as often as we will in our own thoughts, and adding them one to another, without ever coming to the end of such addition, any nearer than we can to the end of number, to which we can always add; we come by the idea of *eternity,* as the future eternal duration of our souls, as well as the eternity of that infinite Being which must necessarily have always existed.

Sixthly, by considering any part of infinite duration, as set out by periodical measures, we come by the idea of what we call *time* in general.

XV

Ideas of Duration and Expansion, Considered Together

THOUGH WE HAVE IN THE PRECEDENT CHAPTERS dwelt pretty long on the considerations of space and duration, yet, they being ideas of general concernment, that have something very abstruse and peculiar in their nature, the comparing them one with another may perhaps be of use for their illustration; and we may have the more clear and distinct conception of them by taking a view of them together. Distance or space, in its simple abstract conception, to avoid confusion, I call *expansion,* to distinguish it from extension, which by some is used to express this distance only as it is in the solid parts of matter, and so includes, or at least intimates, the idea of body: whereas the idea of pure distance includes no such thing. I prefer also the word expansion to space, because space is often applied to distance of fleeting successive parts, which never exist together, as well as to those which are permanent. In both these (viz. expansion and duration) the mind has this common idea of continued lengths, capable of greater or less quantities. For a man has as clear an idea of the difference of the length of an hour and a day, as of an inch and a foot.

The mind, having got the idea of the length of any part of expansion, let it be a span, or a pace, or what length you will, *can,* as has been said, repeat that idea, and so, adding it to the former, enlarge its idea of length, and make it equal to two spans, or two paces; and so, as often as it will, till it equals the distance of any parts of the earth one from another, and increase thus till it amounts to the distance of the sun or remotest star. By such a progression as this, setting out from the place where it is, or any other place, it can proceed and pass beyond all those lengths, and find nothing to stop its going on, either in or without body. It is true, we can easily in our thoughts come to the end of *solid* extension; the extremity and bounds of all body we have no difficulty to arrive at: but when the mind is there, it finds nothing to hinder its progress into this endless expansion; of that it can neither find nor conceive any end. Nor let anyone say, that beyond the bounds of body, there is nothing at all; unless he will confine God within the limits of matter. Solomon, whose understanding was filled and enlarged with wisdom, seems to have other thoughts when he says, "Heaven, and the heaven of heavens, cannot contain thee." And he, I think, very much magnifies to himself the capacity of his own understanding, who persuades himself that he can extend his thoughts further than God exists, or imagine any expansion where He is not.

Just so is it in duration. The mind having got the idea of any length of duration, *can* double, multiply, and enlarge it, not only beyond its own, but beyond the existence of all corporeal beings, and all the measures of time, taken from the great bodies of all the world and their motions. But yet everyone easily admits, that, though we make duration boundless, as certainly it is, we cannot yet extend it beyond all being. God, everyone easily allows, fills eternity; and it is hard to find a reason why anyone should doubt that he likewise fills immensity. His infinite being is certainly as boundless one way as another; and methinks it ascribes a little too much to matter to say, where there is no body, there is nothing.

Hence I think we may learn the reason why everyone familiarly and without the least hesitation speaks of and supposes Eternity, and sticks not to ascribe *infinity* to *duration;* but it is with more doubting and reserve that many admit or suppose the *infinity* of *space*. The reason whereof seems to me to be this,—That duration and extension being used as names of affections belonging to other beings, we easily conceive in God infinite duration, and we cannot avoid doing so: but, not attributing to Him extension, but only to matter, which is finite, we are apter to doubt of the existence of expansion without matter; of which alone we commonly suppose it an attribute. And, therefore, when men pursue their thoughts of space, they are apt to stop at the confines of body: as if space were there at an end too, and reached no further. Or if their ideas, upon consideration, carry them further, yet they term what is beyond the limits of the universe, imaginary space: as if *it* were nothing, because there is no body existing in it. Whereas duration, antecedent to all body, and to the motions which it is measured by, they never term imaginary: because it is never supposed void of some other real existence.

And if the names of things may at all direct our thoughts toward the original of men's ideas (as I am apt to think they may very much), one may have occasion to think by the name *duration*, that the continuation of existence, with a kind of resistance to any destructive force, and the continuation of solidity (which is apt to be confounded with, and if we will look into the minute anatomical parts of matter, is little different from, hardness) were thought to have some analogy, and gave occasion to words so near of kin as *durare* and *durum esse*. And that *durare* is applied to the idea of hardness, as well as that of existence, we see in Horace, Epod, XVI *ferro duravit secula*. But, be that as it will, this is certain, that whoever pursues his own thoughts, will find them sometimes launch out beyond the extent of body, into the infinity of space or expansion; the idea whereof is distinct and separate from body and all other things: which may (to those who please), be a subject of further meditation.

Time in general is to duration as place to expansion. They are so much of those boundless oceans of eternity and immensity as is set out and distinguished from the rest, as it were by landmarks; and so are made use of to denote the position of *finite* real beings, in respect one to another, in those uniform infinite oceans of duration and space. These, rightly considered, are only ideas of determinate distances from certain known points, fixed in distinguishable sensible things, and supposed to keep the same distance one from another. From such points fixed in sensible beings we reckon, and from them we measure our portions of those infinite quantities; which, so considered, are that which we call *time* and *place*. For duration and space being in themselves uniform and boundless, the order and position of things, without such known settled points, would be lost in them; and all things would lie jumbled in an incurable confusion.

Time and place, taken thus for determinate distinguishable portions of those infinite abysses of space and duration, set out or supposed to be distinguished from the rest, by marks and known boundaries, have each of them a twofold acceptation.

First, Time in general is commonly taken for so much of infinite duration as is measured by, and co-existent with, the existence and motions of the great bodies of the universe, as far as we know anything of them: and in this sense time begins and ends with the frame of this sensible world, as in these phrases before mentioned, "Before all time," or, "When time shall be no more." Place likewise is taken sometimes for that portion of infinite space which is possessed by and comprehended within the material world; and is thereby distinguished from the rest of expansion; though this may be more properly called extension than place. Within these two are confined, and by the observable parts of them are measured and determined, the particular time or duration, and the particular extension and place, of all corporeal beings.

Secondly, sometimes the word time is used in a larger sense, and is applied to parts of that infinite duration, not that were really distinguished and measured out by this real existence, and periodical motions of bodies, that were appointed from the beginning to be for signs and for seasons and for days and years, and are accordingly our measures of time; but such other portions too of that infinite uniform duration, which we upon any occasion do suppose equal to certain lengths of measured time; and so consider them as bounded and determined. For, if we should suppose the creation, or fall of the angels, was at the beginning of the Julian period, we should speak properly enough, and should be understood if we said, it is a longer time since the creation of angels than the creation of the world, by 7,640 years: whereby we would mark out so much of that undistinguished duration as we suppose equal to, and would have admitted, 7,640 annual revolutions of the sun, moving at the rate it now does. And thus likewise we sometimes speak of place, distance, or bulk, in the great *inane,* beyond the confines of the world, when we consider so much of that space as is equal to, or capable to receive, a body of any assigned dimensions, as a cubic foot; or do suppose a point in it, at such a certain distance from any part of the universe.

Where and *when* are questions belonging to all finite existences, and are by us always reckoned from some known parts of this sensible world, and from some certain epochs marked out to us by the motions observable in it. Without some such fixed parts or periods, the order of things would be lost, to our finite understandings, in the boundless invariable oceans of duration and expansion, which comprehend in them all finite beings, and in their full extent belong only to the Deity.

There is one thing more wherein space and duration have

a great conformity, and that is, though they are justly reckoned amongst our *simple ideas,* yet none of the distinct ideas we have of either is without all manner of composition: it is the very nature of both of them to consist of parts: but their parts being all of the same kind, and without the mixture of any other idea, hinder them not from having a place amongst simple ideas. Could the mind, as in number, come to so small a part of extension or duration as excluded divisibility, *that* would be, as it were, the indivisible unit or idea; by repetition of which, it would make its more enlarged ideas of extension and duration. But, since the mind is not able to frame an idea of *any* space without parts, instead thereof it makes use of the common measures, which, by familiar use in each country, have imprinted themselves on the memory (as inches and feet; or cubits and parasangs; and so seconds, minutes, hours, days, and years in duration);—the mind makes use, I say, of such ideas as these, as simple ones: and these are the component parts of larger ideas, which the mind upon occasion makes by the addition of such known lengths which it is acquainted with. On the other side, the ordinary smallest measure we have of either is looked on as an unit in number, when the mind by division would reduce them into less fractions. Though on both sides, both in addition and division, either of space or duration, when the idea under consideration becomes very big or very small, its precise bulk becomes very obscure and confused; and it is the *number* of its repeated additions or divisions that alone remains clear and distinct; as will easily appear to anyone who will let his thoughts loose in the vast expansion of space, or divisibility of matter. Every part of duration is duration too; and every part of extension is extension, both of them capable of addition or division *in infinitum.* But *the least portions of either of them, whereof we have clear and distinct ideas,* may perhaps be fittest to be considered by us, as the *simple ideas* of that kind out of which our complex modes of space, extension, and duration are made up, and into which they can again be distinctly resolved. Such a small part in duration may be called a *moment,* and is the time of one idea in our minds, in the train of their ordinary succession there. The other, wanting a proper name, I know not whether I may be allowed to call a *sensible point,* meaning thereby the least particle of matter or space we can discern, which is ordinarily about a minute, and to the sharpest eyes seldom less than thirty seconds of a circle, whereof the eye is the center.

Expansion and duration have this further agreement, that, though they are both considered by us as having parts, yet their parts are not separable one from another, no not even in thought: though the parts of bodies from whence we take our *measure* of the one; and the parts of motion, or rather the succession of ideas in our minds, from whence we take the *measure* of the other, may be interrupted and separated; as the one is often by rest, and the other is by sleep, which we call rest too.

But there is this manifest difference between them,—That the ideas of length which we have of expansion are turned every way, and so make figure, and breadth, and thickness; but duration is but as it were the length of one straight line, extended *in infinitum,* not capable of multiplicity, variation, or figure; but is one common measure of all existence whatsoever, wherein all things, whilst they exist, equally partake. For this present moment is common to all things that are now in being, and equally comprehends that part of their existence, as much as if they were all but one single being; and we may truly say, they all exist in the *same* moment of time. Whether angels and spirits have any analogy to this, in respect to expansion, is beyond my comprehension: and perhaps for us, who have understandings and comprehensions suited to our own preservation, and the ends of our own being, but not to the reality and extent of all other beings, it is near as hard to conceive any existence, or to have an idea of any real being, with a perfect negation of all manner of expansion, as it is to have the idea of any real existence with a perfect negation of all manner of duration. And therefore, what spirits have to do with space, or how they communicate in it, we know not. All that we know is, that bodies do each singly possess its proper portion of it, according to the extent of solid parts; and thereby exclude all other bodies from having any share in that particular portion of space, whilst it remains there.

Duration, and *time* which is a part of it, is the idea we have of *perishing* distance, of which no two parts exist together, but follow each other in succession; an *expansion* is the idea of *lasting* distance, all whose parts exist together, and are not capable of succession. And therefore, though we cannot conceive any duration without succession, nor can put it together in our thoughts that any being does *now* exist tomorrow, or possess at once more than the present moment of duration; yet we can conceive the eternal duration of the Almighty far different from that of man, or any other finite being. Because man comprehends not in his knowledge or power all past and future things: his thoughts are but of yesterday, and he knows not what tomorrow will bring forth. What is once past he can never recall; and what is yet to come he cannot make present. What I say of man, I say of all finite beings; who, though they may far exceed man in knowledge and power, yet are no more than the meanest creature, in comparison with God himself. Finite or any magnitude holds not any proportion to infinite. God's infinite duration, being accompanied with infinite knowledge and infinite power, He sees all things, past and to come; and they are no more distant from His knowledge, no further removed from His sight, than the present: they all lie under the same view: and there is nothing which He cannot make exist each moment He pleases. For the existence of all things, depending upon His good pleasure, all things exist every moment that He thinks fit to have them exist. To conclude: expansion and duration do mutually embrace and comprehend each other; every part of space being in every part of duration, and every part of duration in every part of expansion. Such a combination of two distinct ideas is, I suppose, scarce to be found in all that great variety we do or can conceive, and may afford matter to further speculation.

XVI

Idea of Number

AMONGST ALL THE IDEAS WE HAVE, as there is none suggested o the mind by more ways, so there is none more simple, han that of *unity*, or one: it has no shadow of variety or omposition in it: every object our senses are employed bout; every idea in our understandings; every thought of our ninds, brings this idea along with it. And therefore it is the nost intimate to our thoughts, as well as it is, in its agree-nent to all other things, *the most universal idea we have.* For umber applies itself to men, angels, actions, thoughts; every-hing that either doth exist, or can be imagined.

By repeating this idea in our minds, and adding the repeti-ions together, we come by the *complex* ideas of the *modes* f it. Thus, by adding one to one, we have the complex idea f a couple; by putting twelve units together, we have the omplex idea of a dozen; and so of a score, or a million, or ny other number.

The *simple modes* of *number* are of all other the most istinct; every the least variation, which is a unit, making ach combination as clearly different from that which ap-roacheth nearest to it, as the most remote; two being as istinct from one, as two hundred; and the idea of two as istinct from the idea of three, as the magnitude of the whole arth is from that of a mite. This is not so in other simple nodes, in which it is not so easy, nor perhaps possible for us o distinguish betwixt two approaching ideas, which yet are eally different. For who will undertake to find a difference etween the white of this paper and that of the next degree o it: or can form distinct ideas of every the least excess in xtension?

The clearness and distinctness of each mode of number rom all others, even those that approach nearest, makes me pt to think that demonstrations in numbers, if they are not nore evident and exact than in extension, yet they are more eneral in their use, and more determinate in their applica-on. Because the ideas of numbers are more precise and istinguishable than in extension; where every equality and ex-ess are not so easy to be observed or measured; because our thoughts cannot in space arrive at any determined smallne beyond which it cannot go, as an unit; and therefore t quantity or proportion of any the least excess cannot be di covered; which is clear otherwise in number, where, as h been said, 91 is as distinguishable from 90 as from 900 though 91 be the next immediate excess to 90. But it is n so in extension, where, whatsoever is more than just a fo or an inch, is not distinguishable from the standard of a fo or an inch; and in lines which appear of an equal length, o may be longer than the other by innumerable parts: nor c anyone assign an angle, which shall be the next biggest to right one.

By the repeating, as has been said, the idea of an unit, ar joining it to another unit, we make thereof one collecti idea, marked by the name two. And whosoever can do thi and proceed on, still adding one more to the last collecti idea which he had of any number, and gave a name to it, m count, or have ideas, for several collections of units, di tinguished one from another, as far as he hath a series names for following numbers, and a memory to retain th series, with their several names: all numeration being but st the adding of one unit more, and giving to the whole togethe as comprehended in one idea, a new or distinct name or sig whereby to know it from those before and after, and di tinguish it from every smaller or greater multitude of unit So that he that can add one to one, and so to two, and so on with his tale, taking still with him the distinct nam belonging to every progression; and so again, by subtracti a unit from each collection, retreat and lessen them, is ca able of all the ideas of numbers within the compass of h language, or for which he hath names, though not perhaps more. For, the several simple modes of numbers being our minds but so many combinations of units, which have variety, nor are capable of any other difference but more less, names or marks for each distinct combination seem mo necessary than in any other sort of ideas. For, without su names or marks, we can hardly well make use of numbers reckoning, especially where the combination is made up any great multitude of units; which put together, without name or mark to distinguish that precise collection, will hard be kept from being a heap in confusion.

This further is observable in number, that it is that whi

the mind makes use of in measuring all things that by us are measurable, which principally are *expansion* and *duration;* and our idea of infinity, even when applied to those, seems to be nothing but the infinity of number. For what else are our ideas of Eternity and Immensity, but the repeated additions of certain ideas of imagined parts of duration and expansion, with the infinity of number; in which we can come to no end of addition? For such an inexhaustible stock, number (of all other our ideas) most clearly furnishes us with, as is obvious to everyone. For let a man collect into one sum as great a number as he pleases, this multitude, how great soever, lessens not one jot the power of adding to it, or brings him any nearer the end of the inexhaustible stock of number; where still there remains as much to be added, as if none were taken out. And this *endless addition* or *addibility* (if anyone like the word better) of numbers, so apparent to the mind, is that, I think, which gives us the clearest and most distinct idea of infinity: of which more in the following chapter.

XVII

Of Infinity

He that would know what kind of idea it is to which w give the name of *infinity*, cannot do it better than by con sidering to what infinity is by the mind more immediatel attributed; and then how the mind comes to frame it.

Finite and *infinite* seem to me to be looked upon by th mind as the *modes of quantity*, and to be attributed primaril in their first designation only to those things which have parts and are capable of increase or diminution by the addition o subtraction of any the least part: and such are the ideas o space, duration, and number, which we have considered i the foregoing chapters. It is true, that we cannot but be as sured, that the great God, of whom and from whom are a things, is incomprehensibly infinite: but yet, when we apply t that first and supreme Being our idea of infinite, in our wea and narrow thoughts, we do it primarily in respect to Hi duration and ubiquity; and, I think, more figuratively to Hi power, wisdom, and goodness, and other attributes, which ar properly inexhaustible and incomprehensible, etc. For, whe we call *them* infinite, we have no other idea of this infinit but what carries with it some reflection on, and imitation o that number or extent of the acts or objects of God's powe wisdom, and goodness, which can never be supposed so grea or so many, which these attributes will not always surmour and exceed, let us multiply them in our thoughts as far as w can, with all the infinity of endless number. I do not preten to say how these attributes are in God, who is infinitely b yond the reach of our narrow capacities: they do, withou doubt, contain in them all possible perfection: but this, I sa is our way of conceiving them, and these our ideas of the infinity.

Finite then, and infinite, being by the mind looked on *modifications* of expansion and duration, the next thing to b considered, is,—*How the mind comes by them*. As for th idea of finite, there is no great difficulty. The obvious portio of extension that affect our senses, carry with them into th mind the idea of finite: and the ordinary periods of succe sion, whereby we measure time and duration, as hours, day and years, are bounded lengths. The difficulty is, how we come by those *boundless ideas* of eternity and immensity; since the objects we converse with come so much short of any approach or proportion to that largeness.

Everyone that has any idea of any stated lengths of space, as a foot, finds that he can repeat that idea; and joining it to the former, make the idea of two feet; and by the addition of a third, three feet; and so on, without ever coming to an end of his additions, whether of the same idea of a foot, or, if he pleases, of doubling it, or any other idea he has of any length, as a mile, or diameter of the earth, or of the *orbis magnus:* for whichever of these he takes, and how often soever he doubles, or any otherwise multiplies it, he finds, that, after he has continued his doubling in his thought, and enlarged his idea as much as he pleases, he has no more reason to stop, nor is one jot nearer the end of such addition, than he was at first setting out: the power of enlarging his idea of space by further additions remaining still the same, he hence takes the idea of infinite space.

This, I think, is the way whereby the mind gets the *idea* of infinite space. It is a quite different consideration, to examine whether the mind has the idea of such a boundless space *actually existing;* since our ideas are not always proofs of the existence of things: but yet, since this comes here in our way, I suppose I may say, that we are *apt to think* that space in itself is actually boundless, to which imagination the idea of space or expansion of itself naturally leads us. For, it being considered by us, either as the extension of body, or as existing by itself, without any solid matter taking it up (for of such a void space we have not only the idea, but I have proved, as I think, from the motion of body, its necessary existence), it is impossible the mind should be ever able to find or suppose any end of it, or be stopped anywhere in its progress in this space, how far soever it extends its thoughts. Any bounds made with body, even adamantine walls, are so far from putting a stop to the mind in its further progress in space and extension that it rather facilitates and enlarges it. For so far as that body reaches, so far no one can doubt of extension; and when we are come to the utmost extremity of body, what is there that can there put a stop, and satisfy the mind that it is at the end of space, when it perceives that it is not; nay, when it is satisfied that body itself can move into it? For, if it be necessary for the motion of body, that there should be an empty space, though ever so little, here amongst bodies; and if it be possible for body to move in or through that empty space;—nay, it is impossible for any particle of matter to move but into an empty space; the same possibility of a body's moving into a void space, beyond the utmost bounds of body, as well as into a void space interspersed amongst bodies, will always remain clear and evident: the idea of empty pure space, whether within or beyond the confines of all bodies, being exactly the same, differing not in nature, though in bulk; and there being nothing to hinder body from moving into it. So that wherever the mind places itself by any thought, either amongst, or remote from all bodies, it can, in this uniform idea of space, nowhere find any bounds, any end; and so must necessarily conclude it, by the very nature and idea of each part of it, to be actually infinite.

As, by the power we find in ourselves of repeating, as often as we will, any idea of space, we get the idea of *immensity*, so, by being able to repeat the idea of any length of duration we have in our minds, with all the endless addition of number, we come by the idea of *eternity*. For we find in ourselves, we can no more come to an end of such repeated ideas than we can come to the end of number; which everyone perceives he cannot. But here again it is another question, quite different from our having an *idea* of eternity, to know whether there were *any real being*, whose duration has been eternal. And as to this, I say, he that considers something now existing, must necessarily come to Something eternal. But having spoke of this in another place, I shall say here no more of it, but proceed on to some other considerations of our idea of infinity.

If it be so, that our idea of infinity be got from the power we observe in ourselves of repeating, without end, our own ideas, it may be demanded,—Why we do not attribute infinity to other ideas, as well as those of space and duration; since they may be as easily, and as often, repeated in our minds as the other: and yet nobody ever thinks of infinite sweetness, or infinite whiteness, though he can repeat the idea of sweet or white, as frequently as those of a yard or a day? To which I answer,—All the ideas that are considered as having parts, and are capable of increase by the addition of any equal or less parts, afford us, by their repetition, the idea of infinity; because, with this endless repetition, there is continued an enlargement of which there *can* be no end. But in other ideas it is not so. For to the largest idea of extension or duration that I at present have, the addition of any the least part makes an increase; but to the perfectest idea I have of the whitest whiteness, if I add another of a less or equal whiteness, (and of a whiter than I have, I cannot add the idea,) it makes no increase, and enlarges not my idea at all; and therefore the different ideas of whiteness, etc. are called degrees. For those ideas that consist of parts are capable of being augmented by every addition of the least part; but if you take the idea of white, which one parcel of snow yielded yesterday to our sight, and another idea of white from another parcel of snow you see today, and put them together in your mind, they embody, as it were, and run into one, and the idea of whiteness is not at all increased; and if we add a less degree of whiteness to a greater, we are so far from increasing, that we diminish it. Those ideas that consist not of parts cannot be augmented to what proportion men please, or be stretched beyond what they have received by their senses; but space, duration, and number, being capable of increase by repetition, leave in the mind an idea of endless room for more; nor can we conceive anywhere a stop to a further addition or progression: and so those ideas *alone* lead our minds toward the thought of infinity.

Though our idea of infinity arise from the contemplation of quantity, and the endless increase the mind is able to make in quantity, by the repeated additions of what portions thereof it pleases; yet I guess we cause great confusion in our thoughts, when we join infinity to any supposed idea of quantity the mind can be thought to have, and so discourse or reason about an infinite quantity, as an infinite space, or an infinite duration. For, as our idea of infinity being, as I think, *an endless growing idea,* but the idea of any quantity the mind has, being at that time *terminated* in that idea (for be it as great as it will, it can be no greater than it is),—to join infinity to it, is to adjust a standing measure to a growing bulk; and therefore I think it is not an insignificant subtlety, if I say, that we are carefully to distinguish between the idea of the infinity of space, and the idea of a space infinite. The first is nothing but a supposed endless progression of the

mind, over what repeated ideas of space it pleases; but to hav
actually in the mind the idea of a space infinite, is to suppos
the mind already passed over, and actually to have a view c
all those repeated ideas of space which an *endless* repetitio
can never totally represent to it; which carries in it a plai
contradiction.

This, perhaps, will be a little plainer, if we consider it i
numbers. The infinity of numbers, to the end of whose addi
tion everyone perceives there is no approach, easily appear
to anyone that reflects on it. But, how clear soever this ide
of the infinity of number be, there is nothing yet more evider
than the absurdity of the actual idea of an infinite number
Whatsoever *positive* ideas we have in our minds of any space
duration, or number, let them be ever so great, they are sti
finite; but when we suppose an inexhaustible remainder, fro
which we remove all bounds, and wherein we allow the min
an endless progression of thought, without ever completin
the idea, there we have our idea of infinity: which, though
seems to be pretty clear when we consider nothing else in
but the negation of an end, yet, when we would frame in ou
minds the idea of an infinite space or duration, that idea
very obscure and confused, because it is made up of tw
parts, very different, if not inconsistent. For, let a man fram
in his mind an idea of any space or number, as great as h
will; it is plain the mind *rests and terminates* in that ide
which is contrary to the idea of infinity, which *consists in*
supposed endless progression. And therefore I think it is th
we are so easily confounded, when we come to argue and rea
son about infinite space or duration, etc. Because the parts c
such an idea not being perceived to be, as they are, incon
sistent, the one side or other always perplexes, whatever con
sequences we draw from the other; as an idea of motion nc
passing on would perplex anyone who should argue fro
such an idea, which is not better than an idea of motion a
rest. And such another seems to me to be the idea of a spac
or (which is the same thing) a number infinite, i.e. of a spac
or number which the mind actually has, and so views an
terminates in; and of a space or number, which, in a constan
and endless enlarging and progression, it can in thoug
never attain to. For, how large soever an idea of space I hav
in my mind, it is no larger than it is that instant that I hav
it, though I be capable the next instant to double it, and s

on *in infinitum;* for that alone is infinite which has no bounds; and that the idea of infinity, in which our thoughts can find none.

But of all other ideas, it is number, as I have said, which I think furnishes us with the clearest and most distinct idea of infinity we are capable of. For, even in space and duration, when the mind pursues the idea of infinity, it there makes use of the ideas and repetitions of numbers, as of millions and millions of miles, or years, which are so many distinct ideas,—kept best by number from running into a confused heap, wherein the mind loses itself; and when it has added together as many millions, etc., as it pleases, of known lengths of space or duration, the clearest idea it can get of infinity, is the confused incomprehensible remainder of endless addible numbers, which affords no prospect of stop or boundary.

[Locke goes on to suggest that our idea of infinity is nothing but the infinity of number applied to determinate parts, of which we have in our minds the distinct ideas. Locke denies that we have a positive idea of infinite duration or of infinite space; though he remarks that some men speak and dispute about infinite space and duration "as if they had as complete and positive ideas of them as they have of the names they use for them."]

If I have dwelt pretty long on the consideration of duration, space, and number, and what arises from the contemplation of them,—Infinity, it is possibly no more than the matter requires; there being few simple ideas whose *modes* give more exercise to the thoughts of men than those do. I pretend not to treat of them in their full latitude. It suffices to my design to show how the mind receives them, such as they are, from sensation and reflection; and how even the idea we have of infinity, how remote soever it may seem to be from any object of sense, or operation of our mind, has, nevertheless, as all our other ideas, its original there. Some mathematicians perhaps, of advanced speculations, may have other ways to introduce into their minds ideas of infinity. But this hinders not but that they themselves, as well as all other men, got the first ideas which they had of infinity from sensation and reflection, in the method we have here set down.

XVIII

Other Simple Modes

THOUGH I HAVE, in the foregoing chapters, shown how, from simple ideas taken in by sensation, the mind comes to extend itself even to infinity; which, however it may of all others seem most remote from any sensible perception, yet at last hath nothing in it but what is made out of simple ideas: received into the mind by the senses, and afterward there put together, by the faculty the mind has to repeat its own ideas; —Though, I say, these might be instances enough of simple modes of the simple ideas of sensation, and suffice to show how the mind comes by them, yet I shall, for method's sake, though briefly, give an account of some few more, and then proceed to more complex ideas.

To slide, roll, tumble, walk, creep, run, dance, leap, skip, and abundance of others that might be named, are words which are no sooner heard but everyone who understands English has presently in his mind distinct ideas, which are all but the different modifications of motion. Modes of motion answer those of extension; swift and slow are two different ideas of motion, the measures whereof are made of the distances of time and space put together; so they are complex ideas, comprehending time and space with motion.

The like variety have we in sounds. Every articulate word is a different modification of sound; by which we see that, from the sense of hearing, by such modifications, the mind may be furnished with distinct ideas, to almost an infinite number. Sounds also, besides the distinct cries of birds and beasts, are modified by diversity of notes of different length put together, which make that complex idea called a tune, which a musician may have in his mind when he hears or makes no sound at all, by reflecting on the ideas of those sounds, so put together silently in his own fancy.

Those of colors are also very various: some we take notice of as the different degrees, or as they were termed shades, of the same color. But since we very seldom make assemblages of colors, either for use or delight, but figure is taken in also, and has its part in it, as in painting, weaving, needlework, etc.;—those which are taken notice of do most commonly belong to *mixed modes,* as being made up of ideas of divers kinds, viz. figure and color, such as beauty, rainbow, etc.

All compounded tastes and smells are also modes, made up of the simple ideas of those senses. But they, being such as generally we have no names for, are less taken notice of, and cannot be set down in writing; and therefore must be left without enumeration to the thoughts and experience of my reader.

In general it may be observed, that those simple modes which are considered but as different *degrees* of the same simple idea, though they are in themselves many of them very distinct ideas, yet have ordinarily no distinct names, nor are much taken notice of, as distinct ideas, where the difference is but very small between them. Whether men have neglected these modes, and given no names to them, as wanting measures nicely to distinguish them; or because, when they were so distinguished, that knowledge would not be of general or necessary use, I leave it to the thoughts of others. It is sufficient to my purpose to show, that all our simple ideas come to our minds only by sensation and reflection; and that when the mind has them, it can variously repeat and compound them, and so make new complex ideas. But, though white, red, or sweet, etc. have not been modified, or made into complex ideas, by several combinations, so as to be named, and thereby ranked into species; yet some others of the simple ideas, viz. those of unity, duration, and motion, etc., above instanced in, as also power and thinking, have been thus modified to a great variety of complex ideas, with names belonging to them.

The reason whereof, I suppose, has been this,—That the great concernment of men being with men one amongst another, the knowledge of men, and their action, and the signifying of them to one another, was most necessary; and therefore they made ideas of *actions* very nicely modified, and gave those complex ideas names, that they might the more easily record and discourse of those things they were daily conversant in, without long ambages and circumlocutions; and that the things they were continually to give and receive information about might be the easier and quicker understood. That this is so, and that men in framing different complex ideas, and giving them names, have been much governed by the end of speech in general (which is a very short and expedite way of conveying their thoughts one to another), is evident in the names which in several arts have been found out, and applied to several complex ideas of modified actions, belonging to their several trades, for dispatch sake, in their direction or discourses about them. Which ideas are not generally framed in the minds of men not conversant about these operations. And thence the words that stand for them, by the greatest part of men of the same language, are not understood: v.g. *coltshire, drilling, filtration, cohobation*, are words standing for certain complex ideas, which being seldom in the minds of any but those few whose particular employments do at every turn suggest them to their thoughts, those names of them are not generally understood but by smiths and chemists; who, having framed the complex ideas which these words stand for, and having given names to them, or received them from others, upon hearing of these names in communication, readily conceive those ideas in their minds;—as by *cohobation* all the simple ideas of distilling, and the pouring the liquor distilled from anything back upon the remaining matter, and distilling it again. Thus we see that there are great varieties of simple ideas, as of tastes and smells, which have no names; and of modes many more; which either not having been generally enough observed, or else not being of any great use to be taken notice of in the affairs and converse of men, they have not had names given to them, and so pass not for species. This we shall have occasion hereafter to consider more at large, when we come to speak of *words*.

XIX

Of the Modes of Thinking

WHEN THE MIND TURNS ITS VIEW INWARD upon itself, and contemplates its own actions, *thinking* is the first that occurs. In it the mind observes a great variety of modifications, and from thence receives distinct ideas. Thus the perception or thought which actually accompanies, and is annexed to, any impression on the body, made by an external object, being distinct from all other modifications of thinking, furnishes the mind with a distinct idea, which we call *sensation;*—which is, as it were, the actual entrance of any idea into the understanding by the senses. The same idea, when it again recurs without the operation of the like object on the external sensory, is *remembrance:* if it be sought after by the mind, and with pain and endeavor found, and brought again in view, it is *recollection:* if it be held there long under attentive consideration, it is *contemplation:* when ideas float in our mind, without any reflection or regard of the understanding, it is that which the French call *reverie;* our language has scarce a name for it: when the ideas that offer themselves (for, as I have observed in another place, whilst we are awake, there will always be a train of ideas succeeding one another in our minds) are taken notice of, and, as it were, registered in the memory, it is *attention:* when the mind with great earnestness, and of choice, fixes its view on any idea, considers it on all sides, and will not be called off by the ordinary solicitation of other ideas, it is that we call *intention* or *study:* sleep, without dreaming, is rest from all these: and *dreaming* itself is the having of ideas (whilst the outward senses are stopped, so that they receive not outward objects with their usual quickness) in the mind, not suggested by any external objects, or known occasion; nor under any choice or conduct of the understanding at all: and whether that which we call *ecstasy* be not dreaming with the eyes open, I leave to be examined.

These are some few instances of those various modes of thinking, which the mind may observe in itself, and so have as distinct ideas of as it hath of white and red, a square or a circle. I do not pretend to enumerate them all, nor to treat at large of this set of ideas, which are got from reflection:

that would be to make a volume. It suffices to my present purpose to have shown here, by some few examples, of what sort these ideas are, and how the mind comes by them; especially since I shall have occasion hereafter to treat more at large of *reasoning, judging, volition,* and *knowledge,* which are some of the most considerable operations of the mind, and modes of thinking.

X X

Of Modes of Pleasure and Pain

AMONGST THE SIMPLE IDEAS which we receive both from sensation and reflection, *pain* and *pleasure* are two very considerable ones. For as in the body there is sensation barely in itself, or accompanied with pain or pleasure, so the thought or perception of the mind is simply so, or else accompanied also with pleasure or pain, delight or trouble, call it how you please. These, like other simple ideas, cannot be described, nor their names defined; the way of knowing them is, as of the simple ideas of the senses, only by experience. For, to define them by the presence of good or evil, is no otherwise to make them known to us than by making us reflect on what we feel in ourselves, upon the several and various operations of good and evil upon our minds, as they are differently applied to or considered by us.

Things then are good or evil, only in reference to pleasure or pain. That we call *good*, which is apt to cause or increase pleasure, or diminish pain in us; or else to procure or preserve us the possession of any other good or absence of any evil. And, on the contrary, we name that *evil* which is apt to produce or increase any pain, or diminish any pleasure in us: or else to procure us any evil, or deprive us of any good. By pleasure and pain, I must be understood to mean of body or mind, as they are commonly distinguished; though in truth they be only different constitutions of the *mind*, sometimes occasioned by disorder in the body, sometimes by thoughts of the mind.

Pleasure and pain and that which causes them,—good and evil, are the hinges on which our passions turn. And if we reflect on ourselves, and observe how these, under various considerations, operate in us; what modifications or tempers of mind, what internal sensations (if I may so call them) they produce in us we may thence form to ourselves the ideas of our passions.

Thus anyone reflecting upon the thought he has of the delight which any present or absent thing is apt to produce in him, has the idea we call *love*. For when a man declares in autumn when he is eating them, or in spring when there are none, that he loves grapes, it is no more but that the taste of grapes delights him: let an alteration of health or constitution destroy the delight of their taste, and he then can be said to love grapes no longer.

On the contrary, the thought of the pain which anything present or absent is apt to produce in us, is what we call *hatred*. Were it my business here to inquire any further than into the bare ideas of our passions, as they depend on different modifications of pleasure and pain, I should remark, that our love and hatred of inanimate insensible beings is commonly founded on that pleasure and pain which we receive from their use and application any way to our senses, though with their destruction. But hatred or love, to beings capable of happiness or misery, is often the uneasiness or delight which we find in ourselves, arising from a [consideration of] their very being or happiness. Thus the being and welfare of a man's children or friends, producing constant delight in him, he is said constantly to love them. But it suffices to note, that our ideas of love and hatred are but the dispositions of the mind, in respect of pleasure and pain in general, however caused in us.

The uneasiness a man finds in himself upon the absence of anything whose present enjoyment carries the idea of delight with it, is that we call *desire;* which is greater or less, as that uneasiness is more or less vehement. Where, by the by, it may perhaps be of some use to remark, that the chief, if not only spur to human industry and action is *uneasiness.* For whatsoever good is proposed, if its absence carries no displeasure or pain with it, if a man be easy and content without it, there is no desire of it, nor endeavor after it; there is no more but a bare velleity, the term used to signify the lowest degree of desire, and that which is next to none at all, when there is so little uneasiness in the absence of anything, that it carries a man no further than some faint wishes for it, without any more effectual or vigorous use of the means to attain it. Desire also is stopped or abated by the opinion of the impossibility or unattainableness of the good proposed, as far as the uneasiness is cured or allayed by that consideration. This might carry our thoughts further, were it seasonable in this place.

Joy is a delight of the mind, from the consideration of the present or assured approaching possession of a good; and we are then possessed of any good, when we have it so in our power that we can use it when we please. Thus a man almost starved has joy at the arrival of relief, even before he has the pleasure of using it: and a father, in whom the very well-being of his children causes delight, is always, as long as his children are in such a state, in the possession of that good; for he needs but to reflect on it, to have that pleasure.

Sorrow is uneasiness in the mind, upon the thought of a good lost, which might have been enjoyed longer; or the sense of a present evil.

Hope is that pleasure in the mind, which everyone finds in himself, upon the thought of a probable future enjoyment of a thing which is apt to delight him.

Fear is an uneasiness of the mind, upon the thought of future evil likely to befall us.

Despair is the thought of the unattainableness of any good, which works differently in men's minds, sometimes producing uneasiness or pain, sometimes rest and indolency.

Anger is uneasiness or discomposure of the mind, upon the receipt of any injury, with a present purpose of revenge.

Envy is an uneasiness of the mind, caused by the consideration of a good we desire obtained by one we think should not have had it before us.

These two last, *envy* and *anger,* not being caused by pain and pleasure simply in themselves, but having in them some mixed considerations of ourselves and others, are not therefore to be found in all men, because those other parts, of valuing their merits, or intending revenge, is wanting in them. But all the rest, terminating purely in pain and pleasure, are, I think, to be found in all men. For we love, desire, rejoice, and hope, only in respect of pleasure; we hate, fear, and grieve only in respect of pain ultimately. In fine, all these passions are moved by things, only as they appear to be the causes of pleasure and pain, or to have pleasure or pain some way or other annexed to them. Thus we extend our hatred usually to the subject (at least, if a sensible or voluntary agent) which has produced pain in us; because the fear it leaves is a constant pain: but we do not so constantly love what has done us good; because pleasure operates not so strongly on us as pain, and because we are not so ready to have hope it will do so again. But this by the by.

By pleasure and pain, delight and uneasiness, I must all

along be understood (as I have above intimated) to mean n only bodily pain and pleasure, but whatsoever delight or u easiness is felt by us, whether arising from any grateful unacceptable sensation or reflection.

It is further to be considered, that, in reference to the pa sions, the removal or lessening of a pain is considered, a operates, as a pleasure: and the loss or diminishing of pleasure, as a pain.

The passions too have most of them, in most persons, o erations on the body, and cause various changes in it; whi not being always sensible, do not make a necessary part the idea of each passion. For *shame*, which is an uneasine of the mind upon the thought of having done something whi is indecent, or will lessen the valued esteem which othe have for us, has not always blushing accompanying it.

I would not be mistaken here, as if I meant this as a Di course of the Passions; they are many more than those have here named: and those I have taken notice of wou each of them require a much larger and more accurate di course. I have only mentioned these here, as so many i stances of modes of pleasure and pain resulting in our min from various considerations of good and evil. I might perha have instanced in other modes of pleasure and pain, mo simple than these; as the pain of hunger and thirst, and t pleasure of eating and drinking to remove them: the pain teeth set on edge; the pleasure of music; pain from captio uninstructive wrangling, and the pleasure of rational conve sation with a friend, or of well-directed study in the sear and discovery of truth. But the passions being of much mo concernment to us, I rather made choice to instance in the and show how the ideas we have of them are derived fro sensation or reflection.

XXI

Of Power

THE MIND BEING EVERY DAY INFORMED, by the senses, of the alteration of those simple ideas it observes in things without; and taking notice how one comes to an end, and ceases to be, and another begins to exist which was not before; reflecting also on what passes within itself, and observing a constant change of its ideas, sometimes by the impression of outward objects on the senses, and sometimes by the determination of its own choice; and concluding from what it has so constantly observed to have been, that the like changes will for the future be made in the same things, by like agents, and by the like ways,—considers in one thing the possibility of having any of its simple ideas changed, and in another the possibility of making that change; and so comes by that idea which we call *power*. Thus we say, Fire has a power to melt gold, i.e. to destroy the consistency of its insensible parts, and consequently its hardness, and make it fluid; and gold has a power to be melted; that the sun has a power to blanch wax, and wax a power to be blanched by the sun, whereby the yellowness is destroyed, and whiteness made to exist in its room. In which, and the like cases, the power we consider is in reference to the change of perceivable ideas. For we cannot observe any alteration to be made in, or operation upon anything, but by the observable change of its sensible ideas; nor conceive any alteration to be made, but by conceiving a change of some of its ideas.

Power thus considered is two-fold, viz. as able to make, or able to receive any change. The one may be called *active*, and the other *passive* power. Whether matter be not wholly destitute of active power, as its author, God, is truly above all passive power; and whether the intermediate state of created spirits be not that alone which is capable of both active and passive power, may be worth consideration. I shall not now enter into that inquiry, my present business being not to search into the original of power, but how we come by the *idea* of it.

This, at least, I think evident,—That we find in ourselves a power to begin or forbear, continue or end several actions of our minds, and motions of our bodies, barely by a though or preference of the mind ordering, or as it were command ing, the doing or not doing such or such a particular action This power which the mind has thus to order the considera tion of any idea, or the forbearing to consider it; or to prefe the motion of any part of the body to its rest, and *vice versa* in any particular instance, is that which we call the *Will*. Th actual exercise of that power, by directing any particular ac tion, or its forbearance, is that which we call *volition* or *will ing*. The forbearance of that action, consequent to such orde or command of the mind, is called *voluntary*. And whatso ever action is performed without such a thought of the mind is called *involuntary*. The power of perception is that whic we call the *Understanding*. Perception, which we make the ac of the understanding, is of three sorts:—1. The perception o ideas in our minds. 2. The perception of the signification o signs. 3. The perception of the connection or repugnancy agreement or disagreement, that there is between any of ou ideas. All these are attributed to the understanding, or per ceptive power, though it be the two latter only that use allow us to say we understand.

These powers of the mind, viz. of perceiving, and of pre ferring, are usually called by another name. And the ordinar way of speaking is, that the understanding and will are tw *faculties* of the mind; a word proper enough, if it be used, a all words should be, so as not to breed any confusion i men's thoughts, by being supposed (as I suspect it has been to stand for some real beings in the soul that performed thos actions of understanding and volition. For when we say th *will* is the commanding and superior faculty of the soul; tha it is or is not free; that it determines the inferior facultie that it follows the dictates of the understanding, etc.,—thoug these and the like expressions, by those that carefully at tend to their own ideas, and conduct their thoughts more b the evidence of things than the sound of words, may be un derstood in a clear and distinct sense—yet I suspect, I say that this way of speaking of *faculties* has misled many into confused notion of so many distinct agents in us, which ha their several provinces and authorities, and did comman obey, and perform several actions, as so many distinct be ings; which has been no small occasion of wrangling, ob scurity, and uncertainty, in questions relating to them.

Everyone, I think, finds in *himself* a power to begin or forbear, continue or put an end to several actions in himself. From the consideration of the extent of this power of the mind over the actions of the man, which everyone finds in himself, arise the *ideas* of *liberty* and *necessity*.

All the actions that we have any idea of reducing themselves, as has been said, to these two, viz. thinking and motion; so far as a man has power to think or not to think, to move or not to move, according to the preference or direction of his own mind, so far is a man *free*. Wherever any performance or forbearance are not equally in a man's power; wherever doing or not doing will not equally *follow* upon the preference of his mind directing it, there he is not free, though perhaps the action may be voluntary. So that the idea of *liberty* is, the idea of a power in any agent to do or forbear any particular action, according to the determination or thought of the mind, whereby either of them is preferred to the other: where either of them is not in the power of the agent to be produced by him according to his volition, there he is not at liberty; that agent is under *necessity*. So that liberty cannot be where there is no thought, no volition, no will; but there may be thought, there may be will, there may be volition, where there is no liberty. A little consideration of an obvious instance or two may make this clear.

A tennis ball, whether in motion by the stroke of a racket, or lying still at rest, is not by anyone taken to be a free agent. If we inquire into the reason, we shall find it is because we conceive not a tennis ball to think, and consequently not to have any volition, or *preference* of motion to rest, or *vice versa;* and therefore has not liberty, is not a free agent; but all its both motion and rest come under our idea of necessary, and are so called. Likewise a man falling into the water (a bridge breaking under him), has not herein liberty, is not a free agent. For though he has volition, though he prefers his not falling to falling; yet the forbearance of that motion not being in his power, the stop or cessation of that motion follows not upon his volition; and therefore therein he is not free.

Again: suppose a man be carried, whilst fast asleep, into a room where is a person he longs to see and speak with; and be there locked fast in, beyond his power to get out: he awakes, and is glad to find himself in so desirable company, which he stays willingly in, i.e. prefers his stay to going away I ask, is not this stay voluntary? I think nobody will doubt it: and yet, being locked fast in, it is evident he is not at liberty not to stay, he has not freedom to be gone. So that liberty is not an idea belonging to volition, or preferring; but to the person having the power of doing, or forbearing to do, according as the mind shall choose or direct. Our idea of liberty reaches as far as that power, and no farther. For wherever restraint comes to check that power, or compulsion takes away that indifferency of ability to act, or to forbear acting there liberty, and our notion of it, presently ceases.

We have instances enough, and often more than enough, in our own bodies. A man's heart beats, and the blood circulates, which it is not in his power by any thought or volition to stop; and therefore in respect of these motions, where rest depends not on his choice, nor would follow the determination of his mind, if it should prefer it, he is not a free agent. Convulsive motions agitate his legs, so that though he wills it ever so much, he cannot by any power of his mind stop their motion (as in that odd disease called *chorea sancti viti*), but he is perpetually dancing; he is not at liberty in this action, but under as much necessity of moving, as a stone that falls, or a tennis ball struck with a racket. On the other side, a palsy or the stocks hinder his legs from obeying the determination of his mind, if it would thereby transfer his body to another place. In all these there is want of freedom; though the sitting still, even of a paralytic, whilst he prefers it to a removal, is truly voluntary. Voluntary, then, is not opposed to necessary, but to involuntary. For a man may prefer what he can do, to what he cannot do; the state he is in, to its absence or change; though necessity has made it in itself unalterable.

As it is in the motions of the body, so it is in the thoughts of our minds: where anyone is such, that we have power to take it up, or lay it by, according to the preference of the mind, there we are at liberty. A waking man, being under the necessity of having some ideas constantly in his mind, is not at liberty to think or not to think; no more than he is at liberty, whether his body shall touch any other or no: but whether he will remove his contemplation from one idea to another is many times in his choice; and then he is, in respect of his ideas, as much at liberty as he is in respect of bodies he rests on; he can at pleasure remove himself from one to another. But yet some ideas to the mind, like some motions to the body, are such as in certain circumstances it cannot avoid, nor obtain their absence by the utmost effort it can use. A man on the rack is not at liberty to lay by the idea of pain, and divert himself with other contemplations: and sometimes a boisterous passion hurries our thoughts, as a hurricane does our bodies, without leaving us the liberty of thinking on other things, which we would rather choose. But as soon as the mind regains the power to stop or continue, begin or forbear, any of these motions of the body without, or thoughts within, according as it thinks fit to prefer either to the other, we then consider the man as a *free agent* again.

Wherever thought is wholly wanting, or the power to act or forbear according to the direction of thought, there necessity takes place. This, in an agent capable of volition, when the beginning or continuation of any action is contrary to that preference of his mind, is called compulsion; when the hindering or stopping any action is contrary to his volition, it is called restraint. Agents that have no thought, no volition at all, are in everything *necessary agents.*

If this be so (as I imagine it is), I leave it to be considered, whether it may not help to put an end to that long agitated, and, I think, unreasonable, because unintelligible question, viz. *Whether man's will be free or no?* For if I mistake not, it follows from what I have said, that the question itself is altogether improper; and it is as insignificant to ask whether man's *will* be free, as to ask whether his sleep be swift, or his virtue square: liberty being as little applicable to the will, as swiftness of motion is to sleep, or squareness to virtue. Everyone would laugh at the absurdity of such a question as either of these: because it is obvious that the modifications of motion belong not to sleep, nor the difference of figure to virtue; and when anyone well considers it, I think he will as plainly perceive that liberty, which is but a power, belongs only to *agents,* and cannot be an attribute or modification of the will, which is also but a power.

Volition, it is plain, is an act of the mind knowingly exerting that dominion it takes itself to have over any part of the man, by employing it in, or withholding it from, any particular action. And what is the will, but the faculty to do this? And is that faculty anything more in effect than a power;

the power of the mind to determine its thought, to the producing, continuing, or stopping any action, as far as it depends on us? For can it be denied that whatever agent has a power to think on its own actions, and to prefer their doing or omission either to other, has that faculty called will? *Will,* then, is nothing but such a power. *Liberty,* on the other side, is the power a *man* has to do or forbear doing any particular action according as its doing or forbearance has the actual preference in the mind; which is the same thing as to say, according as he himself wills it.

It is plain then that the will is nothing but one power or ability, and *freedom* another power or ability so that, to ask whether the will has freedom, is to ask whether one power has another power, one ability another ability; a question at first sight too grossly absurd to make a dispute, or need an answer. For, who is it that sees not that powers belong only to agents, and are attributes only of substances, and not of powers themselves? So that this way of putting the question (viz. whether the will be free) is in effect to ask, whether the will be a substance, an agent, or at least to suppose it, since freedom can properly be attributed to nothing else. If freedom can with any propriety of speech be applied to power, it may be attributed to the power that is in a man to produce, or forbear producing, motion in parts of his body, by choice or preference; which is that which denominates him free, and is freedom itself. But if anyone should ask, whether freedom were free, he would be suspected not to understand well what he said; and he would be thought to deserve Midas's ears, who, knowing that rich was a denomination for the possession of riches, should demand whether riches themselves were rich.

However, the name *faculty,* which men have given to this power called the will, and whereby they have been led into a way of talking of the will as acting, may, by an appropriation that disguises its true sense, serve a little to palliate the absurdity; yet the will, in truth, signifies nothing but a power or ability to prefer or choose: and when the will, under the name of a faculty, is considered as it is, barely as an ability to do something, the absurdity in saying it is free, or not free, will easily discover itself. For, if it be reasonable to suppose and talk of faculties, as distinct beings that can act (as we do, when we say the will orders, and the will is free), it is fit that we should make a speaking faculty, and a walking faculty, and a dancing faculty, by which these actions are produced, which are but several modes of motion; as well as we make the will and understanding to be faculties, by which the actions of choosing and perceiving are produced, which are but several modes of thinking. And we may as properly say that it is the singing faculty sings, and the dancing faculty dances, as that the will chooses, or that the understanding conceives; or, as is usual, that the will directs the understanding, or the understanding obeys or obeys not the will: it being altogether as proper and intelligible to say that the power of speaking directs the power of singing, or the power of singing obeys or disobeys the power of speaking.

The attributing to faculties that which belonged not to them, has given occasion to this way of talking: but the introducing into discourses concerning the mind, with the name of faculties, a notion of *their* operating, has, I suppose, as little advanced our knowledge in that part of ourselves, as the great use and mention of the like invention of faculties, in the operations of the body, has helped us in the knowledge of physic. Not that I deny there are faculties, both in the body and mind: they both of them have their powers of operating, else neither the one nor the other could operate. For nothing can operate that is not able to operate; and that is not able to operate that has no power to operate. Nor do I deny that those words, and the like, are to have their place in the common use of languages that have made them current. It looks like too much affectation wholly to lay them by: and philosophy itself, though it likes not a gaudy dress, yet, when it appears in public, must have so much complacency as to be clothed in the ordinary fashion and language of the country, so far as it can consist with truth and perspicuity. But the fault has been, that faculties have been spoken of and represented as so many distinct agents. For, it being asked, what it was that digested the meat in our stomachs? it was a ready and very satisfactory answer to say, that it was the *digestive faculty*. What was it that made anything come out of the body? the *expulsive faculty*. What moved? the *motive faculty*. And so in the mind, the *intellectual faculty*, or the understanding, understood; and the *elective faculty*, or the will, willed or commanded. This is, in short, to say, that the ability to digest, digested; and the ability to move, moved; and the ability to understand, understood. For faculty, ability, and power, I think, are but different names of the same things: which ways of speaking, when put into more intelligible words, will, I think, amount to thus much;—That digestion is performed by something that is able to digest, motion by something able to move, and understanding by something able to understand. And, in truth, it would be very strange if it should be otherwise; as strange as it would be for a man to be free without being able to be free.

To return, then, to the inquiry about liberty, I think the question is not proper, *whether the will be free,* but *whether a man be free.* Thus, I think,

First, That so far as any one can, by the direction or choice of his mind, preferring the existence of any action to the non-existence of that action, and *vice versa,* make *it* to exist or not exist, so far *he* is free. For if I can, by a thought directing the motion of my finger, make it move when it was at rest, or *vice versa,* it is evident, that in respect of that I am free: and if I can, by a like thought of my mind, preferring one to the other, produce either words or silence, I am at liberty to speak or hold my peace: and as far as this power reaches, of acting or not acting, by the determination of his own thought preferring either, so far is a man free. For how can we think anyone freer, than to have the power to do what he will? And so far as anyone can, by preferring any action to its not being, or rest to any action, produce that action or rest, so far can he do what he will. For such a preferring of action to its absence, is the willing of it: and we can scarce tell how to imagine any being freer, than to be able to do what he wills. So that in respect of actions within the reach of such a power in him, a man seems as free as it is possible for freedom to make him.

But the inquisitive mind of man, willing to shift off from himself, as far as he can, all thoughts of guilt, though it be by putting himself into a worse state than that of fatal necessity, is not content with this: freedom, unless it reaches further than this, will not serve the turn: and it passes for a good plea, that a man is not free at all, if he be not as *free to will* as he is to *act what he wills.* Concerning a man's liberty, there yet, therefore, is raised this further question, *Whether a man be free to will?* which I think is what is meant, when it is disputed whether the will be free. And as to that I imagine,

Secondly, That willing, or volition, being an action, and freedom consisting in a power of acting or not acting, a man in respect of willing or the act of volition, when any action in his power is once proposed to his thoughts, as presently to be done, cannot be free. The reason whereof is very manifest. For, it being unavoidable that the action depending on his will should exist or not exist, and its existence or not existence following perfectly the determination and preference of his will, he cannot avoid willing the existence or non-existence of that action; it is absolutely necessary that he will the one or the other; i.e. prefer the one to the other: since one of them must necessarily follow: and that which does follow follows by the choice and determination of his mind; that is, by his willing it: for if he did not will it, it would not be. So that, in respect of the act of willing, a man in such a case is not free: liberty consisting in a power to act or not to act; which, in regard of volition, a man, upon such a proposal, has not. For it is unavoidably necessary to prefer the doing or forbearance of an action in a man's power, which is once so proposed to his thoughts; a man must necessarily will the one or the other of them; upon which preference or volition, the action or its forbearance certainly follows, and is truly voluntary. But the act of volition, or preferring one of the two, being that which he cannot avoid, a man, in respect of that act of willing, is under a necessity, and so cannot be free; unless necessity and freedom can consist together, and a man can be free and bound at once.

This, then, is evident, That *a man is not at liberty to will, or not to will, anything in his power that he once considers of:* liberty consisting in a power to act or to forbear acting, and in that only. For a man that sits still is said yet to be at liberty; because he can walk if he wills it. A man that walks is at liberty also, not because he walks or moves; but because he can stand still if he wills it. But if a man sitting still has not a power to remove himself, he is not at liberty; so likewise a man falling down a precipice, though in motion, is not at liberty, because he cannot stop that motion if he would. This being so, it is plain that a man that is walking, to whom it is proposed to give off walking, is not at liberty, whether he will determine himself to walk, or give off walking or not: he must necessarily prefer one or the other of them; walking or not walking. And so it is in regard of all other actions in our power so proposed, which are the far greater number. For, considering the vast number of voluntary actions that succeed one another every moment that we are awake in the course of our lives, there are but few of them that are thought on or proposed to the will, till the time they are to be done; and in all such actions, as I have shown, the mind, in respect of willing, has not a power to act or not to act, wherein consists liberty. The mind, in that case, has not a power to forbear *willing;* it cannot avoid some determination concerning them, let the consideration be as short, the thought as quick as it will, it either leaves the man in the state he was before thinking, or changes it; continues the action, or puts an end to it. Whereby it is manifest, that *it* orders and directs one, in preference to, or with neglect of the other, and thereby either the continuation or change becomes *unavoidably* voluntary.

Since then it is plain that, in most cases, a man is not at liberty, whether he will or no (for, when an action in his power is proposed to his thoughts, he *cannot* forbear volition; he *must* determine one way or the other); the next thing demanded is,—*Whether a man be at liberty to will which of the two he pleases, motion or rest?* This question carries the absurdity of it so manifestly in itself, that one might thereby sufficiently be convinced that liberty concerns not the will. For, to ask whether a man be at liberty to will either motion or rest, speaking or silence, which he pleases, is to ask whether a man can will what he wills, or be pleased with what he is pleased with? A question which, I think, needs no answer: and they who can make a question of it must suppose one will to determine the acts of another, and another to determine that, and so on *in infinitum.*

To return, then, to the inquiry, what is it that determines the will in regard to our actions? And that, upon second thoughts, I am apt to imagine is not, as is generally supposed, the greater good in view; but some (and for the most part the most pressing) *uneasiness* a man is at present under. This is that which successively determines the will, and sets us upon those actions we perform. This uneasiness we may call, as it is, *desire;* which is an uneasiness of the mind for want of some absent good. All pain of the body, of what sort soever, and disquiet of the mind, is uneasiness: and with this is always joined desire, equal to the pain or uneasiness felt; and is scarce distinguishable from it. For desire being nothing but an uneasiness in the want of an absent good, in reference to any pain felt, ease is that absent good; and till that ease be attained, we may call it desire; nobody feeling pain that he wishes not to be eased of, with a desire equal to that pain, and inseparable from it. Besides this desire of ease from pain, there is another of absent positive good; and here also the desire and uneasiness are equal. As much as we desire any absent good, so much are we in pain for it. But here all absent good does not, according to the greatness it has, or is acknowledged to have, cause pain equal to that greatness; as all pain causes desire equal to itself: because the absence of good is not always a pain, as the presence of pain is. And therefore absent good may be looked on and considered without desire. But so much as there is anywhere of desire, so much there is of uneasiness.

That desire is a state of uneasiness, everyone who reflects on himself will quickly find. Who is there that has not felt in desire what the wise man says of hope (which is not much different from it), that it being "deferred makes the heart sick"; and that still proportionable to the greatness of the desire, which sometimes raises the uneasiness to that pitch, that it makes people cry out, "Give me children," give me the thing desired, "or I die." Life itself, and all its enjoyments, is a burden cannot be borne under the lasting and unremoved pressure of such an uneasiness.

Good and evil, present and absent, it is true, work upon the mind. But that which *immediately* determines the will, from time to time, to every voluntary action, is the *uneasiness of desire,* fixed on some absent good: either negative, as indolence to one in pain; or positive, as enjoyment of pleasure. That it is this uneasiness that determines the will to the successive voluntary actions, whereof the greatest part of our lives is made up, and by which we are conducted through different courses to different ends, I shall endeavor to show, both from experience, and the reason of the thing.

It seems so established and settled a maxim, by the general consent of all mankind, that good, the greater good, determines the will, that I do not at all wonder that, when I first published my thoughts on this subject I took it for granted;

and I imagine that, by a great many, I shall be thought more excusable for having then done so, than that now I have ventured to recede from so received an opinion. But yet, upon a stricter inquiry, I am forced to conclude that *good,* the *greater good,* though apprehended and acknowledged to be so, does not determine the will, until our desire, raised proportionably to it, makes us uneasy in the want of it. Convince a man never so much, that plenty has its advantages over poverty; make him see and own, that the handsome conveniences of life are better than nasty penury: yet, as long as he is content with the latter, and finds no uneasiness in it, he moves not; his will never is determined to any action that shall bring him out of it. Let a man be ever so well persuaded of the advantages of virtue, that it is as necessary to a man who has any great aims in this world, or hopes in the next, as food to life: yet, till he hungers or thirsts after righteousness, till he *feels an uneasiness* in the want of it, his *will* will not be determined to any action in pursuit of this confessed greater good; but any other uneasiness he feels in himself shall take place, and carry his will to other actions.

If we inquire into the reason of what experience makes so evident in fact, and examine, why it is uneasiness alone operates on the will, and determines it in its choice, we shall find that, we being capable but of one determination of the will to one action at once, the present uneasiness that we are under does *naturally* determine the will, in order to that happiness which we all aim at in all our actions. For, as much as whilst we are under any uneasiness, we cannot apprehend ourselves happy, or in the way to it; pain and uneasiness being, by everyone, concluded and felt to be inconsistent with happiness, spoiling the relish even of those good things which we have: a little pain serving to mar all the pleasure we rejoiced in. And, therefore, that which of course determines the choice of our will to the next action will always be—the removing of pain, as long as we have any left, as the first and necessary step toward happiness.

Another reason why it is uneasiness alone determines the will, is this: because that alone is present and, it is against the nature of things, that what is absent should operate where it is not. It may be said that absent good may, by contemplation, be brought home to the mind and made present. The idea of it indeed may be in the mind, and viewed as present there; but nothing will be in the mind as a present good, able to counterbalance the removal of any uneasiness which we are under, till it raises our desire; and the uneasiness of that has the prevalency in determining the will.

I have hitherto chiefly instanced in the *uneasiness* of desire, as that which determines the will: because that is the chief and most sensible; and the will seldom orders any action, nor is there any voluntary action performed, without some desire accompanying it; which I think is the reason why the will and desire are so often confounded. But yet we are not to look upon the uneasiness which makes up, or at least accompanies, most of the other passions, as wholly excluded in the case. Aversion, fear, anger, envy, shame, etc. have each their uneasinesses too, and thereby influence the will. These passions are scarce any of them, in life and practice, simple and alone, and wholly unmixed with others; though usually, in discourse and contemplation, that carries the name which operates strongest, and appears most in the present state of the mind. Nay, there is, I think, scarce any of the passions to be found without desire joined with it. I am sure wherever there is uneasiness, there is desire.

If it be further asked,—What it is moves desire? I answer, —happiness, and that alone. Happiness and misery are the names of two extremes, the utmost bounds whereof we know not; it is what "eye hath not seen, ear hath not heard, nor hath it entered into the heart of man to conceive." But of some degrees of both we have very lively impressions; made by several instances of delight and joy on the one side, and torment and sorrow on the other; which, for shortness' sake, I shall comprehend under the names of pleasure and pain; there being pleasure and pain of the mind as well as the body,—"With him is fullness of joy, and pleasure for evermore." Or, to speak truly, they are all of the mind; though some have their rise in the mind from thought, others in the body from certain modifications of motion.

Happiness, then, in its full extent, is the utmost pleasure we are capable of, and *misery* the utmost pain; and the lowest degree of what can be called happiness is so much ease from all pain, and so much present pleasure, as without which anyone cannot be content. Now, because pleasure and pain are produced in us by the operation of certain objects, either on our minds or our bodies, and in different degrees; therefore, what has an aptness to produce pleasure in us is that we call *good,* and what is apt to produce pain in us we call *evil;* For no other reason but for its aptness to produce pleasure and pain in us, wherein consists our happiness and misery. Further, though what is apt to produce any degree of pleasure be in itself good; and what is apt to produce any degree of pain be evil; yet it often happens that we do not call it so when it comes in competition with a greater of its sort; because, when they come in competition, the degrees also of pleasure and pain have justly a preference. So that if we will rightly estimate what we call good and evil, we shall find it lies much in comparison: for the cause of every less degree of pain, as well as every greater degree of pleasure, has the nature of good, and *vice versa.*

Though this be that which is called good and evil, and all good be the proper object of desire in general; yet all good, even seen and confessed to be so, does not necessarily move every particular man's desire; but only that part, or so much of it as is considered and taken to make a necessary part of *his* happiness. All other good, however great in reality or appearance, excites not a man's desires who looks not on it to make a part of that happiness wherewith he, in his present thoughts, can satisfy himself. Happiness, under this view, everyone constantly pursues, and desires what makes any part of it: other things, acknowledged to be good, he can look upon without desire, pass by, and be content without. There is nobody, I think, so senseless as to deny that there is pleasure in knowledge; and for the pleasures of sense, they have too many followers to let it be questioned whether men are taken with them or no. Now, let one man place his satisfaction in sensual pleasures, another in the delight of knowledge: though each of them cannot but confess, there is great pleasure in what the other pursues; yet, neither of them making the other's delight a part of *his* happiness, their desires are not moved, but each is satisfied without what the other enjoys; and so his will is not determined to the pursuit of it. But yet, as soon as the studious man's hunger and thirst make him uneasy, he, whose will was never determined to any pursuit of good cheer, poignant sauces, delicious wine, by the pleasant taste he has found in them, is, by the uneasiness of hunger and thirst, presently determined to eating and drinking, though possibly with great indifferency, what wholesome food comes in his way. And, on the other side, the epicure buckles to study, when shame, or the desire to recommend himself to his mistress, shall make him uneasy in the want of any sort of knowledge. Thus, how much soever men are in earnest and constant in pursuit of happiness, yet they may have a clear view of good, great and confessed good, without being concerned for it, or moved by it, if they think they can make up their happiness without it. Though as to pain, *that* they are always concerned for; they can feel no uneasiness without being moved. And therefore, being uneasy in the want of whatever is judged necessary to their happiness, as soon as any good appears to make a part of their portion of happiness, they begin to desire it.

There being in us a great many uneasinesses, always soliciting and ready to determine the will, it is natural, as I have said, that the greatest and most pressing should determine the will to the next action; and so it does for the most part, but not always. For, the mind having in most cases, as is evident in experience, a power to *suspend* the execution and satisfaction of any of its desires; and so all, one after another; is at liberty to consider the objects of them, examine them on all sides, and weigh them with others. In this lies the liberty man has; and from the not using of it right comes all that variety of mistakes, errors, and faults which we run into in the conduct of our lives, and our endeavors after happiness; whilst we precipitate the determination of our wills, and engage too soon, before due examination. To prevent this, we have a power to suspend the prosecution of this or that desire; as everyone daily may experiment in himself. This seems to me the source of all liberty; in this seems to consist that which is (as I think improperly) called *free will*. For, during this suspension of any desire, before the will be determined to action, and the action (which follows that determination) done, we have opportunity to examine, view, and judge of the good or evil of what we are going to do; and when, upon due examination, we have judged, we have done our duty, all that we can, or ought to do, in pursuit of our happiness; and it is not a fault, but a perfection of our nature, to desire, will, and act according to the last result of a fair examination.

This is so far from being a restraint or diminution of freedom, that it is the very improvement and benefit of it; it is not an abridgment, it is the end and use of our liberty; and the further we are removed from such a determination, the nearer we are to misery and slavery. A perfect indifference in the mind, not determinable by its last judgment of the good or evil that is thought to attend its choice, would be so far from being an advantage and excellency of any intellectual nature, that it would be as great an imperfection, as the want of indifferency to act, or not to act, till determined by the will, would be an imperfection on the other side. A man is at liberty to lift up his hand to his head, or let it rest quiet: he is perfectly indifferent in either; and it would be an imperfection in him, if he wanted that power, if he were deprived of that indifferency. But it would be as great an imperfection, if he had the same indifferency, whether he would prefer the lifting up his hand, or its remaining in rest, when it would save his head or eyes from a blow he sees coming: it is as much a perfection, that desire, or the power of preferring, should be determined by good, as that the power of acting should be determined by the will; and the certainer such determination is, the greater is the perfection.

But to give a right view of this mistaken part of liberty let me ask,—Would anyone be a changeling, because he is less determined by wise considerations than a wise man? Is it worth the name of freedom to be at liberty to play the fool, and draw shame and misery upon a man's self? If to break loose from the conduct of reason, and to want that restraint of examination and judgment which keeps us from choosing or doing the worse, be liberty, true liberty, madmen and fools are the only freemen: but yet, I think, nobody would choose to be mad for the sake of such liberty, but he that is mad already. The constant desire of happiness, and the constraint it puts upon us to act for it, nobody, I think, accounts an abridgment of liberty, or at least an abridgment of liberty to be complained of. God Almighty himself is under the necessity of being happy; and the more any intelligent being is so, the nearer is its approach to infinite perfection and happiness.

As therefore the highest perfection of intellectual nature lies in a careful and constant pursuit of true and solid happiness; so the care of ourselves, that we mistake not imaginary for real happiness, is the necessary foundation of our liberty. The stronger ties we have to an unalterable pursuit of happiness in general, which is our greatest good, and which, as such, our desires always follow, the more are we free from any necessary determination of our will to any particular action, and from a necessary compliance with our desire, set upon any particular, and then appearing preferable good, till we have duly examined whether it has a tendency to, or be inconsistent with, our real happiness: and therefore, till we are as much informed upon this inquiry as the weight of the matter, and the nature of the case demands, we are, by the necessity of preferring and pursuing true happiness as our greatest good, obliged to suspend the satisfaction of our desires in particular cases.

This is the hinge on which turns the *liberty* of intellectual beings, in their constant endeavors after, and a steady prosecution of true felicity,—That they *can suspend* this prosecution in particular cases, till they have looked before them, and informed themselves whether that particular thing which is then proposed or desired lie in the way to their main end, and make a real part of that which is their greatest good. For, the inclination and tendency of their nature to happiness is an obligation and motive to them, to take care not to mistake or miss it; and so necessarily puts them upon caution, deliberation, and wariness, in the direction of their particular actions, which are the means to obtain it. Whatever necessity determines to the pursuit of real bliss, the same necessity, with the same force, establishes suspense, deliberation, and scrutiny of each successive desire, whether the satisfaction of it does not interfere with our true happiness, and mislead us from it. This, as seems to me, is the great privilege of finite intellectual beings; and I desire it may be well considered, whether the great inlet and exercise of all the liberty men have, are capable of, or can be useful to them, and that whereon depends the turn of their actions, does not lie in this, —That they can suspend their desires, and stop them from determining their wills to any action, till they have duly and fairly examined the good and evil of it, as far forth as the weight of the thing requires. This we are able to do; and when we have done it, we have done our duty, and all that is in our power; and indeed all that needs. For, since the will supposes knowledge to guide its choice, all that we can do is to hold our wills undetermined, till we have examined the good and evil of what we desire. What follows after that, follows in a chain of consequences, linked one to another, all depending on the last determination of the judgment, which, whether it shall be upon a hasty and precipitate view, or upon a due and mature examination, is in our power; experience showing us, that in most cases, we are able to suspend the present satisfaction of any desire.

But if any extreme disturbance (as sometimes it happens) possesses our whole mind, as when the pain of the rack, an impetuous uneasiness, as of love, anger, or any other violent passion, running away with us, allows us not the liberty of thought, and we are not masters enough of our own minds to consider thoroughly and examine fairly;—God, who knows our frailty, pities our weakness, and requires of us no more than we are able to do, and sees what was and what was not in our power, will judge as a kind and merciful Father. But the forbearance of a too hasty compliance with our desires, the moderation and restraint of our passions, so that our understandings may be free to examine, and reason unbiased give its judgment, being that whereon a right direction of our conduct to true happiness depends; it is in this we should employ our chief care and endeavors. In this we should take pains to suit the relish of our minds to the true intrinsic good or ill that is in things; and not permit an allowed or supposed possible great and weighty good to slip out of our thoughts, without leaving any relish, any desire of itself there, till, by a due consideration of its true worth, we have formed appetites in our minds suitable to it, and made ourselves uneasy in the want of it, or in the fear of losing it. And how much this is in everyone's power, by making resolutions to himself, such as he may keep, is easy for everyone to try. Nor let anyone say, he cannot govern his passions, nor hinder them from breaking out, and carrying him into action; for what he can do before a prince or a great man, he can do alone, or in the presence of God, if he will.

From what has been said, it is easy to give an account how it comes to pass, that, though all men desire happiness, yet their wills carry them so contrarily; and consequently some of them to what is evil. And to this I say, that the various and contrary choices that men make in the world do not argue that they do not all pursue good; but that the same thing is not good to every man alike. This variety of pursuits shows, that everyone does not place his happiness in the same thing, or choose the same way to it. Were all the concerns of man terminated in this life, why one followed study and knowledge, and another hawking and hunting: why one chose luxury and debauchery, and another sobriety and riches, would not be because every one of these did *not* aim at his own happiness; but because their happiness was placed in different things. And therefore it was a right answer of the physician to his patient that had sore eyes:—If you have more pleasure in the taste of wine than in the use of your sight, wine is good for you; but if the pleasure of seeing be greater to you than that of drinking, wine is naught.

The mind has a different relish, as well as the palate; and you will as fruitlessly endeavor to delight all men with riches or glory (which yet some men place their happiness in) as you would to satisfy all men's hunger with cheese or lobsters; which, though very agreeable and delicious fare to some, are to others extremely nauseous and offensive: and many persons would with reason prefer the griping of an hungry belly to those dishes which are a feast to others. Hence it was, I think, that the philosophers of old did in vain inquire, whether *summum bonum* consisted in riches, or bodily delights, or virtue, or contemplation: and they might have as reasonably disputed, whether the best relish were to be found in apples, plums, or nuts, and have divided themselves into sects upon it. For, as pleasant tastes depend not on the things themselves, but on their agreeableness to this or that particular palate, wherein there is great variety; so the greatest happiness consists in the having those things which produce the greatest pleasure, and in the absence of those which cause any disturbance, any pain. Now these, to different men, are very different things. If, therefore, men in this life only have hope; if in this life only they can enjoy, it is not strange nor unreasonable, that they should seek their happiness by avoiding all things that disease them here, and by pursuing all that delight them; wherein it will be no wonder to find variety and difference. For if there be no prospect beyond the grave, the inference is certainly right—"Let us eat and drink," let us enjoy what we delight in, "for tomorrow we shall die." This, I think, may serve to show us the reason, why, though all men's desires tend to happiness, yet they are not moved by the same object. Men may choose different things, and yet all choose right; supposing them only like a company of poor insects; whereof some are bees, delighted with flowers and their sweetness; others beetles, delighted with other kinds of viands, which having enjoyed for a season, they would cease to be, and exist no more forever.

These things, duly weighed, will give us, as I think, a clear view into the state of human liberty. Liberty, it is plain, consists in a power to do, or not to do; to do, or forbear doing, *as we will.* This cannot be denied. But this seeming to comprehend only the actions of a man consecutive to volition, it is further inquired,—Whether he be at liberty to will or no? And to this it has been answered, that, in most cases, a man is not at liberty to forbear the act of volition: he must exert an act of his will, whereby the action proposed is made to exist or not to exist. But yet there is a case wherein a man is at liberty in respect of willing; and that is the choosing of a *remote* good as an end to be pursued. Here a man may *suspend* the act of his choice from being determined for or against the thing proposed, till he has examined whether it be really of a nature, in itself and consequences, to make him happy or not. For, when he has once chosen it, and thereby it is become a part of his happiness, it raises desire, and that proportionably gives him uneasiness; which determines his will, and sets him at work in pursuit of his choice on all occasions that offer. And here we may see how it comes to pass that a man may justly incur punishment, though it be certain that, in all the particular actions that he wills, he does, and necessarily does, will that which he then judges to be good. For, though his will be always determined by that which is judged good by his understanding, yet it excuses him not; because, by a too hasty choice of his own making, he has imposed on himself wrong measures of good and evil; which, however false and fallacious, have the same influence on all his future conduct, as if they were true and right. He has vitiated his own palate, and must be answerable to himself for the sickness and death that follows from it.

What has been said may also discover to us the reason why men in this world prefer different things, and pursue happiness by contrary courses. But yet, since men are always constant and in earnest in matters of happiness and misery, the question still remains, How men come often to prefer the worse to the better; and to choose that, which, by their own confession, has made them miserable?

To account for the various and contrary ways men take, though all aim at being happy, we must consider whence the *various uneasinesses* that determine the will, in the preference of each voluntary action, have their rise:——

1. Some of them come from causes not in our power; such as are often the pains of the body from want, disease, or outward injuries, as the rack, etc.; which, when present and violent, operate for the most part forcibly on the will, and turn the courses of men's lives from virtue, piety, and religion, and what before they judged to lead to happiness; everyone not endeavoring, or, through disuse, not being able, by the contemplation of remote and future good, to raise in himself desires of them strong enough to counterbalance the uneasiness he feels in those bodily torments, and to keep his will steady in the choice of those actions which lead to future happiness. A neighboring country has been of late a tragical theatre from which we might fetch instances, if there needed any, and the world did not in all countries and ages furnish examples enough to confirm that received observation, *Necessitas cogit ad turpia;* and therefore there is great reason for us to pray, "Lead us not into temptation."

2. Other uneasinesses arise from our desires of absent good; which desires always bear proportion to, and depend on, the judgment we make, and the relish we have of any absent good; in both which we are apt to be variously misled, and that by our own fault.

[Locke next remarks that our judgments go wrong with regard to future good and evil only: as to *present* satisfaction, a man is not mistaken. No one would choose long-term misery willingly: but such is the weak and narrow constitution of men's minds, that they misjudge the consequences of their actions.]

All men desire happiness, that is past doubt: but, as has been already observed, when they are rid of pain, they are apt to take up with any pleasure at hand, or that custom has endeared to them; to rest satisfied in that; and so being happy, till some new desire, by making them uneasy, disturbs that happiness, and shows them that they are not so, they look no further; nor is the will determined to any action in pursuit of any other known or apparent good. For since we find that we cannot enjoy all sorts of good, but one excludes another; we do not fix our desires on every apparent greater good, unless it be judged to be necessary to our happiness: if we think we can be happy without it, it moves us not. This is another occasion to men of judging wrong; when they take not that to be necessary to their happiness which really is so. This mistake misleads us, both in the choice of the good we aim at, and very often in the means to it, when it is a remote good. But, which way ever it be, either by placing it where really it is not, or by neglecting the means as not necessary to it;—when a man misses his great end, happiness, he will acknowledge he judged not right. That which contributes to this mistake is the real or supposed unpleasantness of the actions which are the way to this end; it seeming so preposterous a thing to men, to make themselves unhappy in order to happiness, that they do not easily bring themselves to it.

The last inquiry, therefore, concerning this matter is,—Whether it be in a man's power to change the pleasantness and unpleasantness that accompanies any sort of action? And as to that, it is plain, in many cases he can. Men may and should correct their palates, and give relish to what either has, or they suppose has none. The relish of the mind is as various as that of the body, and like that too may be altered; and it is a mistake to think that men cannot change the displeasingness or indifferency that is in actions into pleasure and desire, if they will do but what is in their power. A due consideration will do it in some cases; and practice, application, and custom in most. Bread or tobacco may be neglected where they are shown to be useful to health, because of an indifferency or disrelish to them; reason and consideration at first recommends, and begins their trial, and use finds, or custom makes them pleasant. That this is so in virtue too, is very certain. Actions are pleasing or displeasing, either in themselves, or considered as a means to a greater and more desirable end. The eating of a well-seasoned dish, suited to a man's palate, may move the mind by the delight itself that accompanies the eating, without reference to any other end; to which the consideration of the pleasure there is in health and strength (to which that meat is subservient) may add a new *gusto*, able to make us swallow an ill-relished potion. In the latter of these, any action is rendered more or less pleasing, only by the contemplation of the end, and the being more or less persuaded of its tendency to it, or necessary connection with it: but the pleasure of the action itself is best acquired or increased by use and practice. Trials often reconcile us to that, which at a distance we looked on with aversion; and by repetitions wear us into a liking of what possibly, in the first essay, displeased us. Habits have powerful charms, and put so strong attractions of easiness and pleasure into what we accustom ourselves to, that we cannot forbear to do, or at least be easy in the omission of, actions, which habitual practice has suited, and thereby recommends to us. Though this be very visible, and everyone's experience shows him he can do so; yet it is a part in the conduct of men toward their happiness, neglected to a degree, that it will be possibly entertained as a paradox, if it be said, that men can *make* things or actions more or less pleasing to themselves; and thereby remedy that, to which one may justly impute a great deal of their wandering. Fashion and the common opinion having settled wrong notions, and education and custom ill habits, the just values of things are misplaced, and the palates of men corrupted. Pains should be taken to rectify these; and contrary habits change our pleasures, and give a relish to that which is necessary or conducive to our happiness. This everyone must confess he can do; and when happiness is lost, and misery overtakes him, he will confess he did amiss in neglecting it, and condemn himself for it; and I ask everyone, whether he has not often done so?

XXII

Of Mixed Modes

HAVING TREATED OF SIMPLE MODES in the foregoing chapters, and given several instances of some of the most considerable of them, to show what they are, and how we come by them; we are now in the next place to consider those we call *mixed modes;* such are the complex ideas we mark by the names *obligation, drunkenness,* a *lie,* etc.; which consisting of several combinations of simple ideas of *different* kinds, I have called mixed modes, to distinguish them from the more simple modes, which consist only of simple ideas of the *same* kind. These mixed modes, being also such combinations of simple ideas as are not looked upon to be characteristical marks of any real beings that have a steady existence, but scattered and independent ideas put together by the mind, are thereby distinguished from the complex ideas of substances.

That the mind, in respect of its simple ideas, is wholly passive, and receives them all from the existence and operations of things, such as sensation or reflection offers them, without being able to *make* any one idea, experience shows us. But if we attentively consider these ideas I call mixed modes, we are now speaking of, we shall find their original quite different. The mind often exercises an *active* power in making these several combinations. For, it being once furnished with simple ideas, it can put them together in several compositions, and so make variety of complex ideas, without examining whether they exist so together in nature. And hence I think it is that these ideas are called *notions:* as if they had their original, and constant existence, more in the thoughts of men, than in the reality of things; and to form such ideas, it sufficed that the mind put the parts of them together, and that they were consistent in the understanding, without considering whether they had any real being: though I do not deny but several of them might be taken from observation, and the existence of several simple ideas so combined, as they are put together in the understanding. For the man who first framed the idea of *hypocrisy,* might have either taken it at first from the observation of one who made show of good qualities which he had not; or else have framed that idea in his mind without having any such pattern to fashion it by. For it is evident that, in the beginning of languages and societies of men, several of those complex ideas, which were consequent to the constitutions established amongst them, must needs have been in the minds of men, before they existed anywhere else; and that many names that stood for such complex ideas were in use, and so those ideas framed, before the combinations they stood for ever existed.

Indeed, now that languages are made, and abound with words standing for such combinations, a usual way of *getting* these complex ideas is, by the explication of those terms that stand for them. For, consisting of a company of simple ideas combined, they may, by words standing for those simple ideas, be represented to the mind of one who understands those words, though that complex combination of simple ideas were never offered to his mind by the real existence of things. Thus a man may come to have the idea of *sacrilege* or *murder,* by enumerating to him the simple ideas which these words stand for; without ever seeing either of them committed.

Every mixed mode consisting of many distinct simple ideas, it seems reasonable to inquire, Whence it has its unity; and how such a precise multitude comes to make but one idea; since that combination does not always exist together in nature? To which I answer, it is plain it has its unity from an act of the mind, combining those several simple ideas together, and considering them as one complex one, consisting of those parts; and the mark of this union, or that which is looked on generally to complete it, is one *name* given to that combination. For it is by their names that men commonly regulate their account of their distinct species of mixed modes, seldom allowing or considering any number of simple ideas to make one complex one, but such collections as there be names for. Thus, though the killing of an old man be as fit in nature to be united into one complex idea, as the killing a man's father; yet, there being no name standing precisely for the one, as there is the name of *parricide* to mark the other, it is not taken for a particular complex idea, nor a distinct species of actions from that of killing a young man, or any other man.

There are therefore three ways whereby we get these complex ideas of mixed modes:—(1) By experience and *observa-*

tion of things themselves: thus, by seeing two men wrestle or fence, we get the idea of wrestling or fencing. (2) By *invention,* or voluntary putting together of several simple ideas in our own minds: so he that first invented printing or etching had an idea of it in his mind before it ever existed. (3) Which is the most usual way, by *explaining the names* of actions we never saw, or motions we cannot see; and by enumerating and thereby, as it were, setting before our imaginations all those ideas which go to the making them up, and are the constituent parts of them. For, having by sensation and reflection stored our minds with simple ideas, and by use got the names that stand for them, we can by those means represent to another any complex idea we would have him conceive so that it has in it no simple ideas but what he knows, and has with us the same name for. For all our complex ideas are ultimately resolvable into simple ideas, of which they are compounded and originally made up, though perhaps their immediate ingredients, as I may so say, are also complex ideas.

Power being the source from whence all action proceeds the substances wherein these powers are, when they exert this power into act, are called *causes,* and the substances which thereupon are produced, or the simple ideas which are introduced into any subject by the exerting of that power, are called *effects.* The *efficacy* whereby the new substance or idea is produced is called, in the subject exerting that power *action;* but in the subject wherein any simple idea is changed or produced, it is called *passion:* which efficacy, however various, and the effects almost infinite, yet we can, I think, conceive it, in intellectual agents, to be nothing else but modes of thinking and willing; in corporeal agents, nothing else but modifications of motion. I say, I think we cannot conceive it to be any other but these two. For whatever sort of action besides these produces any effects, I confess myself to have no notion nor idea of; and so it is quite remote from my thoughts, apprehensions, and knowledge; and as much in the dark to me as five other senses, or as the ideas of colors to a blind man. And therefore many words which seem to express some action, signify nothing of the action or *modus operandi* at all, but barely the effect, with some circumstances of the subject wrought on, or cause operating: v.g. *creation, annihilation,* contain in them no idea of the action or manner whereby they are produced, but barely of the cause, and the thing done.

I think I shall not need to remark here that, though power and action make the greatest part of mixed modes, marked by names, and familiar in the minds and mouths of men, yet other simple ideas, and their several combinations, are not excluded: much less, I think, will it be necessary for me to enumerate all the mixed modes which have been settled, with names to them. That would be to make a dictionary of the greatest part of the words made use of in divinity, ethics, law, and politics, and several other sciences. All that is requisite to my present design, is to show what sort of ideas those are which I call mixed modes; how the mind comes by them; and that they are compositions made up of simple ideas got from sensation and reflection; which I suppose I have done.

XXIII

Of Our Complex Ideas of Substances

THE MIND BEING, as I have declared, furnished with a great number of the simple ideas, conveyed in by the senses as they are found in exterior things, or by reflection on its own operations, takes notice also that a certain number of these simple ideas go constantly together; which being presumed to belong to one thing, and words being suited to common apprehensions, and made use of for quick dispatch, are called, so united in one subject, by one name; which, by inadvertency, we are apt afterward to talk of and consider as one simple idea, which indeed is a complication of many ideas together: because, as I have said, not imagining how these simple ideas *can* subsist by themselves, we accustom ourselves to suppose some *substratum* wherein they do subsist, and from which they do result, which therefore we call *substance*.

So that if anyone will examine himself concerning his notion of pure substance in general, he will find he has no other idea of it at all, but only a supposition of he knows not what *support* of such qualities which are capable of producing simple ideas in us; which qualities are commonly called accidents. If anyone should be asked, what is the subject wherein color or weight inheres, he would have nothing to say, but the solid extended parts; and if he were demanded, what is it that solidity and extension adhere in, he would not be in a much better case than the Indian before mentioned who, saying that the world was supported by a great elephant, was asked what the elephant rested on; to which his answer was—a great tortoise: but being again pressed to know what gave support to the broad-backed tortoise, replied—*something, he knew not what*. And thus here, as in all other cases where we use words without having clear and distinct ideas, we talk like children: who, being questioned what such a thing is, which they know not, readily give this satisfactory answer, that it is *something:* which in truth signifies no more, when so used, either by children or men, but that they know not what; and that the thing they pretend to know, and talk of, is what they have no distinct idea of at all, and so are perfectly ignorant of it, and in the dark. The idea then we have, to which we give the *general* name substance, being nothing but the supposed, but unknown, support of those qualities we find existing, which we imagine cannot subsist *sine re substante,* without something to support them, we call that support *substantia;* which, according to the true import of the word, is, in plain English, standing under or upholding.

An obscure and relative idea of *substance in general* being thus made we come to have the ideas of *particular sorts of substances,* by collecting *such* combinations of simple ideas as are, by experience and observation of men's senses, taken notice of to exist together; and are therefore supposed to flow from the particular internal constitution, or unknown essence of that substance. Thus we come to have the ideas of a man, horse, gold, water, etc.; of which substances, whether anyone has any other *clear* idea, further than of certain simple ideas co-existent together, I appeal to everyone's own experience. It is the ordinary qualities observable in iron, or a diamond, put together, that make the true complex idea of those substances, which a smith or a jeweler commonly knows better than a philosopher; who, whatever *substantial forms* he may talk of, has no other idea of those substances, than what is framed by a collection of those simple ideas which are to be found in them: only we must take notice, that our complex ideas of substances, besides all those simple ideas they are made up of, have always the confused idea of something to which they belong, and in which they subsist: and therefore when we speak of any sort of substance, we say it is a thing having such or such qualities; as body is a thing that is extended, figured, and capable of motion; spirit, a thing capable of thinking; and so hardness, friability, and power to draw iron, we say, are qualities to be found in a loadstone. These, and the like fashions of speaking, intimate that the substance is supposed always *something besides* the extension, figure, solidity, motion, thinking, or other observable ideas, though we know not what it is.

Hence, when we talk or think of any particular sort of corporeal substances, as horse, stone, etc., though the idea we have of either of them be but the complication or collection of those several simple ideas of sensible qualities, which we used to find united in the thing called horse or stone; yet, *because we cannot conceive how they should subsist alone, nor one in another,* we suppose them existing in and supported by some common subject; which support we denote by the name substance, though it be certain we have no clear or distinct idea of that thing we suppose a support.

The same thing happens concerning the operations of the mind, viz. thinking, reasoning, fearing, etc., which we concluding not to subsist of themselves, nor apprehending how they can belong to body, or be produced by it, we are apt to think these the actions of some other *substance,* which we call *spirit;* whereby yet it is evident that, having no other idea or notion of matter, but something wherein those many sensible qualities which affect our senses do subsist; by supposing a substance wherein thinking, knowing, doubting, and a power of moving, etc., do subsist, we have as clear a notion of the substance of spirit, as we have of body; the one being supposed to be (without knowing what it is) the *substratum* to those simple ideas we have from without; and the other supposed (with a like ignorance of what it is) to be the *substratum* to those operations we experiment in ourselves within. It is plain then, that the idea of *corporeal substance* in matter is as remote from our conceptions and apprehensions, as that of *spiritual substance,* or spirit: and therefore, from our not having any notion of the substance of spirit, we can no more conclude its non-existence, than we can, for the same reason, deny the existence of body; it being as rational to affirm there is no body, because we have no clear and distinct idea of the substance of matter, as to say there is no spirit, because we have no clear and distinct idea of the substance of a spirit.

Whatever therefore be the secret abstract nature of substance in general, all the ideas we have of particular distinct sorts of substances are nothing but several combinations of simple ideas, co-existing in such, though unknown, cause of their union, as makes the whole subsist of itself. It is by such combinations of simple ideas, and nothing else, that we represent particular sorts of substances to ourselves; such are the ideas we have of their several species in our minds; and such only do we, by their specific names, signify to others, v.g. man, horse, sun, water, iron: upon hearing which words, everyone who understands the language, frames in his mind a combination of those several simple ideas which he has usually observed, or fancied to exist together under that denomination; all which he supposes to rest in and be, as it were, adherent to that unknown common subject, which inheres not in anything else. Though, in the meantime, it be manifest, and everyone, upon inquiry into his own thoughts, will find, that he has no other idea of any substance, v.g. let it be gold, horse, iron, man, vitriol, bread, but what he has barely of those sensible qualities, which he supposes to inhere; with a supposition of such a *substratum* as gives, as it were, a support to those qualities or simple ideas, which he has observed to exist united together. Thus, the idea of the sun,—what is it but an aggregate of those several simple ideas, bright, hot, roundish, having a constant regular motion, at a certain distance from us, and perhaps some other: as he who thinks and discourses of the sun has been more or less accurate in observing those sensible qualities, ideas, or properties, which are in that thing which he calls the sun.

The ideas that make our complex ones of corporeal substances, are of these three sorts. First, the ideas of the primary qualities of things, which are discovered by our senses, and are in them even when we perceive them not; such are the bulk, figure, number, situation, and motion of the parts of bodies; which are really in them, whether we take notice of them or not. Secondly, the sensible secondary qualities, which, depending on these, are nothing but the powers those substances have to produce several ideas in us by our senses; which ideas are not in the things themselves, otherwise than as anything is in its cause. Thirdly, the aptness we consider in any substance, to give or receive such alterations of primary qualities, as that the substance so altered should produce in us different ideas from what it did before; these are called active and passive powers: all which powers, as far as we have any notice or notion of them, terminate only in sensible simple ideas. For whatever alteration a loadstone has the power to make in the minute particles of iron, we should have no notion of any power it had at all to operate on iron, did not its sensible motion discover it; and I doubt not, but there are a thousand changes, that bodies we daily handle have a power to cause in one another, which we never suspect, because they never appear in sensible effects.

Powers therefore justly make a great part of our complex ideas of substances. He that will examine his complex idea of gold, will find several of its ideas that make it up to be only powers; as the power of being melted, but of not spending itself in the fire; of being dissolved in *aqua regia,* are ideas as necessary to make up our complex idea of gold, as its color and weight: which, if duly considered, are also nothing but different powers. For, to speak truly, yellowness is not actually in gold, but is a power in gold to produce that idea in us by our eyes, when placed in a due light: and the heat, which we cannot leave out of our ideas of the sun, is no more really in the sun, than the white color it introduces into wax. These are both equally powers in the sun, operating, by the motion and figure of its sensible parts, so on a man, as to make him have the idea of heat; and so on wax, as to make it capable to produce in a man the idea of white.

But to return to the matter in hand,—the ideas we have of substances, and the ways we come by them. I say, our *specific* ideas of substances are nothing else but *a collection of a certain number of simple ideas, considered as united in one thing.* These ideas of substances, though they are commonly simple apprehensions, and the names of them simple terms, yet in effect are complex and compounded. Thus the idea which an Englishman signifies by the name swan, is white color, long neck, red beak, black legs, and whole feet, and all these of a certain size, with a power of swimming in the water, and making a certain kind of noise, and perhaps, to a man who has long observed this kind of bird, some other properties: which all terminate in sensible simple ideas, all united in one common subject.

Besides the complex ideas we have of material sensible substances, of which I have last spoken,—by the simple ideas we have taken from those operations of our own minds, which we experiment daily in ourselves, as thinking, understanding, willing, knowing, and power of beginning motion, etc., coexisting in some substance, we are able to frame the *complex idea of an immaterial spirit.* And thus, by putting together the ideas of thinking, perceiving, liberty, and power of moving themselves and other things, we have as clear a perception and notion of immaterial substances as we have of material. For putting together the ideas of thinking and willing, or the power of moving or quieting corporeal motion, joined to substance, of which we have no distinct idea, we have the idea of an immaterial spirit; and by putting together the ideas of coherent solid parts, and a power of being moved, joined with substance, of which likewise we have no positive idea, we have the idea of matter. The one is as clear and distinct an idea as the other: the idea of thinking, and moving a body, being as clear and distinct ideas as the ideas of extension, solidity, and being moved. For our idea of substance is equally obscure, or none at all, in both: it is but a supposed I know not what, to support those ideas we call accidents.

By the complex idea of extended, figured, colored, and all other sensible qualities, which is all that we know of it, we are as far from the idea of the substance of body, as if we knew nothing at all: nor after all the acquaintance and familiarity which we imagine we have with matter, and the many qualities men assure themselves they perceive and know in bodies, will it perhaps upon examination be found, that they have any more or clearer primary ideas belonging to body, than they have belonging to immaterial spirit.

[Locke next suggests that the ideas we have which are peculiar to *body* are cohesion of solid parts and power of impulse while the ideas peculiar to spirit are thinking and power of putting body into motion. But we can no more understand how parts cohere in extension than we can conceive how spirits think and prompt movement.]

To conclude. Sensation convinces us that there are solid extended substances; and reflection, that there are thinking ones: experience assures us of the existence of such beings, and that the one hath a power to move body by impulse, the other by thought; this we cannot doubt of. Experience, I say, every moment furnishes us with the clear ideas both of the one and the other. But beyond these ideas, as received from their proper sources, our faculties will not reach. If we would inquire further into their nature, causes, and manner, we perceive not the nature of extension clearer than we do of thinking. If we would explain them any further, one is as easy as the other; and there is no more difficulty to conceive how *a substance we know not* should, by thought, set body into motion, than how *a substance we know not* should, by impulse, set body into motion. So that we are no more able to discover wherein the ideas belonging to body consist, than those belonging to spirit. From whence it seems probable to me, that the simple ideas we receive from sensation and reflection are the boundaries of our thoughts; beyond which the mind, whatever efforts it would make, is not able to advance one jot; nor can it make any discoveries, when it would pry into the nature and hidden causes of those ideas.

So that, in short, the idea we have of spirit, compared with the idea we have of body, stands thus: the substance of spirits is unknown to us; and so is the substance of body equally unknown to us. Two primary qualities or properties of body, viz. solid coherent parts and impulse, we have distinct clear ideas of: so likewise we know, and have distinct clear ideas, of two primary qualities or properties of spirit, viz. thinking, and a power of action; i.e. a power of beginning or stopping several thoughts or motions. We have also the ideas of several qualities inherent in bodies, and have the clear distinct ideas of them; which qualities are but the various modifications of the extension of cohering solid parts, and their motion. We have likewise the ideas of the several modes of thinking viz. believing, doubting, intending, fearing, hoping; all which are but the several modes of thinking. We have also the ideas of willing, and moving the body consequent to it, and with the body itself too; for, as has been shown, spirit is capable of motion.

Lastly, if this notion of immaterial spirit may have, perhaps, some difficulties in it not easily to be explained, we have therefore no more reason to deny or doubt the existence of such spirits, than we have to deny or doubt the existence of body; because the notion of body is cumbered with some difficulties very hard, and perhaps impossible to be explained or understood by us. For I would fain have instanced anything in our notion of spirit more perplexed, or nearer a contradiction, than the very notion of body includes in it; the divisibility *in infinitum* of any finite extension involving us, whether we grant or deny it, in consequences impossible to be explicated or made in our apprehensions consistent; consequences that carry greater difficulty, and more apparent absurdity, than anything can follow from the notion of an immaterial knowing substance.

Which we are not at all to wonder at, since we having but some few superficial ideas of things, discovered to us only by the senses from without, or by the mind, reflecting on what it experiments in itself within, have no knowledge beyond that, much less of the internal constitution, and true nature of things, being destitute of faculties to attain it. And therefore experimenting and discovering in ourselves knowledge, and the power of voluntary motion, as certainly as we experiment, or discover in things without us, the cohesion and separation of solid parts, which is the extension and motion of bodies; we have as much reason to be satisfied with our notion of immaterial spirit, as with our notion of body, and the existence of the one as well as the other. For it being no more a contradiction that thinking should exist separate and independent from solidity, than it is a contradiction that solidity should exist separate and independent from thinking, they being both but simple ideas, independent one from another: and having as clear and distinct ideas in us of thinking, as of solidity, I know not why we may not as well allow a thinking thing without solidity, i.e. immaterial, to exist, as a solid thing without thinking, i.e. matter, to exist; especially since it is not harder to conceive how thinking should exist without matter, than how matter should think. For whensoever we would proceed beyond these simple ideas we have from sensation and reflection, and dive further into the nature of things, we fall presently into darkness and obscurity, perplexedness and difficulties, and can discover nothing further but our own blindness and ignorance. But whichever of these complex ideas be clearest, that of body, or immaterial spirit, this is evident, that the simple ideas that make them up are no other than what we have received from sensation or reflection: and so is it of all our other ideas of substances, even of God himself.

For if we examine the idea we have of the incomprehensible Supreme Being, we shall find that we come by it the same way; and that the complex ideas we have both of God, and separate spirits, are made of the simple ideas we receive from reflection: v.g. having, from what we experiment in ourselves, got the ideas of existence and duration; of knowledge and power; of pleasure and happiness; and of several other qualities and powers, which it is better to have than to be without; when we would frame an idea the most suitable we can to the Supreme Being, we enlarge every one of these with our idea of infinity; and so putting them together, make our complex idea of God. For that the mind has such a power of enlarging some of its ideas, received from sensation and reflection, has been already shown.

If I find that I know some few things, and some of them, or all, perhaps imperfectly, I can frame an idea of knowing twice as many; which I can double again, as often as I can add to number; and thus enlarge my idea of knowledge, by extending its comprehension to all things existing, or possible. The same also I can do of knowing them more perfectly; i.e. all their qualities, powers, causes, consequences, and relations, etc., till all be perfectly known that is in them, or can any way relate to them: and thus frame the idea of infinite or boundless knowledge. The same may also be done of power, till we come to that we call infinite; and also of the duration of existence, without beginning or end, and so frame the idea of an eternal being. The degrees or extent wherein we ascribe existence, power, wisdom, and all other perfections (which we can have any ideas of) to that sovereign Being, which we call God, being all boundless and infinite, we frame the best idea of Him our minds are capable of: all which is done, I say, by enlarging those simple ideas we have taken from the operations of our own minds, by reflection; or by our senses, from exterior things, to that vastness to which infinity can extend them.

For it is infinity, which, joined to our ideas of existence, power, knowledge, etc., makes that complex idea, whereby we represent to ourselves, the best we can, the Supreme Being. For, though in His own essence (which certainly we do not know, not knowing the real essence of a pebble, or a fly, or of our own selves) God be simple and uncompounded; yet I think I may say we have no other idea of Him, but a complex one of existence, knowledge, power, happiness, etc., infinite and eternal: which are all distinct ideas, and some of them, being relative, are again compounded of others: all which being, as has been shown, originally got from sensation and reflection, go to make up the idea or notion we have of God.

XXIV

Of Collective Ideas of Substances

BESIDES THESE COMPLEX IDEAS of several *single* substances, as of man, horse, gold, violet, apple, etc., the mind hath also complex *collective* ideas of substances; which I so call, because such ideas are made up of many particular substances considered together, as united into one idea, and which so joined are looked on as one; v.g. the idea of such a collection of men as make an *army*, though consisting of a great number of distinct substances, is as much one idea as the idea of a man: and the great collective idea of all bodies whatsoever, signified by the name *world*, is as much one idea as the idea of any the least particle of matter in it; it sufficing to the unity of any idea, that it be considered as one representation or picture, though made up of ever so many particulars.

These collective ideas of substances the mind makes, by its power of composition, and uniting severally either simple or complex ideas into one, as it does, by the same faculty, make the complex ideas of particular substances, consisting of an aggregate of divers simple ideas, united in one substance. And as the mind, by putting together the repeated ideas of unity, makes the collective mode, or complex idea, of any number, as a score, or a gross, etc.,—so, by putting together several particular substances, it makes collective ideas of substances, as a troop, an army, a swarm, a city, a fleet; each of which everyone finds that he represents to his own mind by one idea, in one view; and so under that notion considers those several things as perfectly one, as one ship, or one atom.

X X V

Of Relation

Besides the ideas, whether simple or complex, that the mind has of things as they are in themselves, there are others it gets from their comparison one with another. The understanding, in the consideration of anything, is not confined to that precise object: it can carry any idea as it were beyond itself, or at least look beyond it, to see how it stands in conformity to any other. When the mind so considers one thing, that it does as it were bring it to, and set it by another, and carries its view from one to the other—this is, as the words import, *relation* and *respect;* and the denominations given to positive things, intimating that respect, and serving as marks to lead the thoughts beyond the subject itself denominated, to something distinct from it, are what we call *relatives;* and the things so brought together, *related*. Thus, when the mind considers Caius as such a positive being, it takes nothing into that idea but what really exists in Caius; v.g. when I consider him as a man, I have nothing in my mind but the complex idea of the species, man. So likewise, when I say Caius is a white man, I have nothing but the bare consideration of a man who hath that white color. But when I give Caius the name *husband,* I intimate some other person; and when I give him the name *whiter,* I intimate some other thing: in both cases my thought is led to something beyond Caius, and there are two things brought into consideration. And since any idea, whether simple or complex, may be the occasion why the mind thus brings two things together, and as it were takes a view of them at once, though still considered as distinct: therefore any of our ideas may be the foundation of relation. As in the above mentioned instance, the contract and ceremony of marriage with Sempronia is the occasion of the denomination and relation of husband; and the color white the occasion why he is said to be whiter then freestone.

These and the like relations, expressed by relative terms that have others answering them, with a reciprocal intimation, as father and son, bigger and less, cause and effect, are very obvious to everyone, and everybody at first sight perceives the relation. For father and son, husband and wife, and such other correlative terms, seem so nearly to belong one to another, and, through custom, do so readily chime and answer one another in people's memories, that, upon the naming of either of them, the thoughts are presently carried beyond the thing so named; and nobody overlooks or doubts of a relation, where it is so plainly intimated. But where languages have failed to give correlative names, there the relation is not always so easily taken notice of. *Concubine* is, no doubt, a relative name, as well as wife: but in languages where this and the like words have not a correlative term, there people are not so apt to take them to be so, as wanting that evident mark of relation which is between correlatives, which seem to explain one another, and not to be able to exist, but together. Hence it is, that many of those names, which, duly considered, do include evident relations, have been called *external denominations.* But all names that are more than empty sounds must signify some idea, which is either in the thing to which the name is applied, and then it is positive, and is looked on as united to and existing in the thing to which the denomination is given; or else it arises from the respect the mind finds in it to something distinct from it, with which it considers it, and then it includes a relation.

Concerning relation in general, these things may be considered:

First, That there is no one thing, whether simple idea, substance, mode, or relation, or name of either of them, which is not capable of almost an infinite number of considerations in reference to other things: and therefore this makes no small part of men's thoughts and words: v.g. one single man may at once be concerned in, and sustain all these following relations, and many more, viz. father, brother, son, grandfather, grandson, father-in-law, son-in-law, husband, friend, enemy, subject, general, judge, patron, client, professor, European, Englishman, islander, servant, master, possessor, captain, superior, inferior, bigger, less, older, younger, contemporary, like, unlike, etc., to an almost infinite number: he being capable of as many relations as there can be occasions of comparing him to other things, in any manner of agreement, disagreement, or respect whatsoever.

Secondly, This further may be considered concerning relation, that though it be not contained in the real existence of things, but something extraneous and super-induced, yet the ideas which relative words stand for are often clearer and more distinct than of those substances to which they do belong. The notion we have of a father or brother is a great deal clearer and more distinct than that we have of a man; or, if you will, *paternity* is a thing whereof it is easier to have a clear idea, than of *humanity;* and I can much easier conceive what a friend is, than what God; because the knowledge of one action, or one simple idea, is oftentimes sufficient to give me the notion of a relation; but to the knowing of any substantial being, an accurate collection of sundry ideas is necessary. A man, if he compares two things together, can hardly be supposed not to know what it is wherein he compares them: so that when he compares any things together, he cannot but have a very clear idea of that relation. *The ideas, then, of relations, are capable at least of being more perfect and distinct in our minds than those of substances.*

Thirdly, Though there be a great number of considerations wherein things may be compared one with another, and so a multitude of relations, yet they all terminate in, and are concerned about those simple ideas, either of sensation or reflection, which I think to be the whole materials of all our knowledge. To clear this, I shall show it in the most considerable relations that we have any notion of; and in some that seem to be the most remote from sense or reflection: which yet will appear to have their ideas from thence, and leave it past doubt that the notions we have of them are but certain simple ideas, and so originally derived from sense or reflection.

Fourthly, That relation being the considering of one thing with another which is extrinsical to it, it is evident that all words that necessarily lead the mind to any other ideas than are supposed really to exist in that thing to which the words are applied are relative words: v.g. *a man, black, merry, thoughtful, thirsty, angry, extended;* these and the like are all absolute, because they neither signify nor intimate anything but what does or is supposed really to exist in the man thus denominated; but *father, brother, king, husband, blacker, merrier,* etc., are words which, together with the thing they denominate, imply also something else separate and exterior to the existence of that thing.

Having laid down these premises concerning relation in general, I shall now proceed to show, in some instances, how all the ideas we have of relation are made up, as the others are, only of simple ideas; and that they all, how refined or remote from sense soever they seem, terminate at last in simple ideas. I shall begin with the most comprehensive relation, wherein all things that do, or can exist, are concerned, and that is the relation of *cause* and *effect:* the idea whereof, how derived from the two fountains of all our knowledge, sensation and reflection, I shall in the next place consider.

XXVI

Of Cause and Effect, and Other Relations

In the notice that our senses take of the constant vicissitude of things, we cannot but observe that several particular, both qualities and substances, begin to exist; and that they receive this their existence from the due application and operation of some other being. From this observation we get our ideas of *cause* and *effect. That which produces any simple or complex idea* we denote by the general name, *cause*, and *that which is produced, effect.* Thus, finding that in that substance which we call wax, fluidity, which is a simple idea that was not in it before, is constantly produced by the application of a certain degree of heat we call the simple idea of heat, in relation to fluidity in wax, the cause of it, and fluidity the effect. So also, finding that the substance, wood, which is a certain collection of simple ideas so called, by the application of fire, is turned into another substance, called ashes; i.e., another complex idea, consisting of a collection of simple ideas quite different from that complex idea which we call wood; we consider fire, in relation to ashes, as cause, and the ashes, as effect. So that whatever is considered by us to conduce or operate to the producing any particular simple idea, or collection of simple ideas, whether substance or mode, which did not before exist, hath thereby in our minds the relation of a cause, and so is denominated by us.

Having thus, from what our senses are able to discover in the operations of bodies on one another, got the notion of cause and effect, viz. that a cause is that which makes any other thing, either simple idea, substance, or mode, begin to be; and an effect is that which had its beginning from some other thing; the mind finds no great difficulty to distinguish the several originals of things into two sorts:——

First, When the thing is wholly made new, so that no part thereof did ever exist before; as when a new particle of matter doth begin to exist, *in rerum natura,* which had before no being, and this we call *creation.*

Secondly, When a thing is made up of particles, which did all of them before exist; but that very thing, so constituted of pre-existing particles, which, considered all together, make up such a collection of simple ideas, had not any existence be-more, as this man, this egg, rose, or cherry, etc. And this, when referred to a substance, produced in the ordinary course of nature by internal principle, but set on work by, and received from, some external agent, or cause, and working by insensible ways which we perceive not, we call *generation.* When the cause is extrinsical, and the effect produced by a sensible separation, or juxtaposition of discernible parts, we call it *making*; and such are all artificial things. When any simple idea is produced, which was not in that subject before, we call it *alteration*. Thus a man is generated, a picture made; and either of them altered, when any new sensible quality or simple idea is produced in either of them, which was not there before: and the things thus made to exist, which were not there before, are effects; and those things which operated to the existence, causes. In which, and all other cases, we may observe, that the notion of cause and effect has its rise from ideas received by sensation or reflection; and that this relation, how comprehensive soever, terminates at last in them. For to have the idea of cause and effect, it suffices to consider any simple idea or substance, as beginning to exist, by the operation of some other, without knowing the manner of that operation.

Time and place are also the foundations of very large relations; and all finite beings at least are concerned in them. But having already shown in another place how we get those ideas, it may suffice here to intimate, that most of the denominations of things received from *time* are only relations. Thus, when anyone says that Queen Elizabeth lived sixty-nine, and reigned forty-five years, these words import only the relation of that duration to some other, and mean no more than this, That the duration of her existence was equal to sixty-nine, and the duration of her government to forty-five annual revolutions of the sun; and so are all words, answering, *How long?* Again, William the Conqueror invaded England about the year 1066; which means this, That, taking the duration from our Saviour's time till now for one entire great length of time, it shows at what distance this invasion was from the two extremes; and so do all words of time answering to the question, *When,* which show only the distance of any point of time from the period of a longer duration, from which we measure, and to which we thereby consider it as related.

The relation also that things have to one another in their

places and distances is very obvious to observe; as above below, a mile distant from Charing Cross, in England, an in London. But as in duration, so in extension and bulk there are some ideas that are relative which we signify b names that are thought positive; as *great* and *little* are trul relations. For here also, having, by observation, settled in ou minds the ideas of the bigness of several species of thing from those we have been most accustomed to, we make then as it were the standards, whereby to denominate the bulk o others. Thus we call a great apple, such a one as is bigge than the ordinary sort of those we have been used to; and little horse, such a one as comes not up to the size of tha idea which we have in our minds to belong ordinarily t horses; and that will be a great horse to a Welshman, whic is but a little one to a Fleming; they two having, from th different breed of their countries, taken several-sized ideas t which they compare, and in relation to which they denomi- nate their great and their little.

So likewise weak and strong are but relative denomination of power, compared to some ideas we have at that time c greater or less power. Thus, when we say a weak man, w mean one that has not so much strength or power to move a usually men have, or usually those of his size have; which i a comparing his strength to the idea we have of the usua strength of men, or men of such a size. All which relation how they are confined to, and terminate in ideas derive from sensation or reflection, is too obvious to need any ex- plication.

XXVII

Of Identity and Diversity

ANOTHER OCCASION THE MIND OFTEN TAKES of comparing, is the very being of things, when, considering *anything as existing at any determined time and place,* we compare it with *itself existing at another time,* and thereon form the ideas of *identity* and *diversity.* When we see anything to be in any place in any instant of time, we are sure (be it what it will) that it is that very thing, and not another which at that same time exists in another place, how like and undistinguishable soever it may be in all other respects: and in this consists *identity,* when the ideas it is attributed to vary not at all from what they were that moment wherein we consider their former existence, and to which we compare the present. For we never finding, nor conceiving it possible, that two things of the same kind should exist in the same place at the same time, we rightly conclude, that, whatever exists anywhere at any time, excludes all of the same kind, and is there itself alone. When therefore we demand whether anything be the *same* or no, it refers always to something that existed such a time in such a place, which it was certain, at that instant, was the same with itself, and no other. From whence it follows, that one thing cannot have two beginnings of existence, nor two things one beginning; it being impossible for two things of the same kind to be or exist in the same instant, in the very same place; or one and the same thing in different places. That, therefore, that had one beginning, is the same thing; and that which had a different beginning in time and place from that, is not the same, but diverse. That which has made the difficulty about this relation has been the little care and attention used in having precise notions of the things to which it is attributed.

We have the ideas but of three sorts of substances: 1. *God.* 2. *Finite intelligences.* 3. *Bodies.*

First, God is without beginning, eternal, unalterable, and everywhere, and therefore concerning His identity there can be no doubt.

Secondly, Finite spirits having had each its determinate time and place of beginning to exist, the relation to that time and place will always determine to each of them its identity as long as it exists.

Thirdly, The same will hold of every *particle of matter* to which no addition or subtraction of matter being made, i is the same. For, though these three sorts of substances, as w term them, do not exclude one another out of the same place yet we cannot conceive but that they must necessarily each of them exclude any of the same kind out of the same place or else the notions and names of identity and diversity woul be in vain, and there could be no such distinctions of sub stances, or anything else one from another. For example could two bodies be in the same place at the same time; the those two parcels of matter must be one and the same, tak them great or little; nay, all bodies must be one and th same. For, by the same reason that two particles of matte may be in one place, all bodies may be in one place: which when it can be supposed, takes away the distinction of iden tity and diversity of one and more, and renders it ridiculous But it being a contradiction that two or more should be one identity and diversity are relations and ways of comparin well founded, and of use to the understanding.

All other things being but modes or relations ultimatel terminated in substances, the identity and diversity of each particular existence of them too will be by the same way de termined: only as to things whose existence is in succession such as are the actions of finite beings, v.g. *motion* an *thought*, both which consist in a continued train of succes sion, concerning *their* diversity there can be no question: be cause each perishing the moment it begins, they cannot exis in different times, or in different places, as permanent being can at different times exist in distant places; and therefore n motion or thought, considered as at different times, can b the same, each part thereof having a different beginning o existence.

This being premised, to find wherein personal identity con sists, we must consider what *person* stands for;—which, think, is a thinking intelligent being, that has reason and re flection, and can consider itself as itself, the same thinkin thing, in different times and places; which it does only b that consciousness which is inseparable from thinking, and as it seems to me, essential to it: it being impossible for any one to perceive without *perceiving* that he does perceive

When we see, hear, smell, taste, feel, meditate, or will any-hing, we know that we do so. Thus it is always as to our present sensations and perceptions: and by this everyone is o himself that which he calls *self;*—it not being considered, in his case, whether the same self be continued in the same or livers substances. For, since consciousness always accom-panies thinking, and it is that which makes everyone to be what he calls self, and thereby distinguishes himself from all other thinking things, in this alone consists personal identity, .e. the sameness of a rational being: and as far as this con-sciousness can be extended backwards to any past action or hought, so far reaches the identity of that person; it is the same self now it was then; and it is by the same self with his present one that now reflects on it, that that action was lone.

But it is further inquired, whether it be the same identical substance. This few would think they had reason to doubt of, f these perceptions, with their consciousness, always re-nained present in the mind, whereby the same thinking thing vould be always consciously present, and, as would be hought, evidently the same to itself. But that which seems to nake the difficulty is this, that this consciousness being in-errupted always by forgetfulness, there being no moment of our lives wherein we have the whole train of all our past actions before our eyes in one view, but even the best memo-ies losing the sight of one part whilst they are viewing an-other; and we sometimes, and that the greatest part of our ives, not reflecting on our past selves, being intent on our present thoughts, and in sound sleep having no thoughts at all, or at least none with that consciousness which remarks our waking thoughts,—I say, in all these cases, our con-ciousness being interrupted, and we losing the sight of our past selves, doubts are raised whether we are the same think-ng thing, i.e. the same *substance* or no. Which, however rea-onable or unreasonable, concerns not *personal* identity at ll. The question being what makes the same person; and not whether it be the same identical substance, which always hinks in the same person, which, in this case, matters not at ll: different substances, by the same consciousness (where hey do partake in it) being united into one person, as well s different bodies by the same life are united into one ani-nal, whose identity is preserved in that change of substances

by the unity of one continued life. For, it being the sam
consciousness that makes a man be himself to himself, per
sonal identity depends on that only, whether it be annexe
solely to one individual substance, or can be continued in
succession of several substances. For as far as any intelligen
being *can* repeat the idea of any past action with the sam
consciousness it had of it at first, and with the same con
sciousness it has of any present action; so far it is the sam
personal self. For it is by the consciousness it has of it
present thoughts and actions, that it is *self to itself* now, an
so will be the same self, as far as the same consciousness ca
extend to actions past or to come; and would be by distanc
of time, or change of substance, no more two persons, tha
a man be two men by wearing other clothes today than h
did yesterday, with a long or a short sleep between: the sam
consciousness uniting those distant actions into the same per
son, whatever substances contributed to their production.

Self is that conscious thinking thing,—whatever substanc
made up of (whether spiritual or material, simple or com
pounded, it matters not)—which is sensible or conscious o
pleasure and pain, capable of happiness or misery, and so i
concerned for itself, as far as that consciousness extends. Thu
everyone finds that, whilst comprehended under that con
sciousness, the little finger is as much a part of himself a
what is most so. Upon separation of this little finger, shoul
this consciousness go along with the little finger, and leav
the rest of the body, it is evident the little finger would be th
person, the same person; and self then would have nothing t
do with the rest of the body. As in this case it is the con
sciousness that goes along with the substance, when one par
is separate from another, which makes the same person, an
constitutes this inseparable self: so it is in reference to sub
stances remote in time. That with which the consciousnes
of this present thinking thing *can* join itself, makes the sam
person, and is one self with it, and with nothing else; and s
attributes to itself, and owns all the actions of that thing, a
its own, as far as that consciousness reaches, and no further
as everyone who reflects will perceive.

In this personal identity is founded all the right and justic
of reward and punishment; happiness and misery being tha
for which everyone is concerned for *himself*, and not mat
tering what becomes of any *substance*, not joined to, or af

ected with that consciousness. For, as it is evident in the istance I gave but now, if the consciousness went along with ie little finger when it was cut off, that would be the same elf which was concerned for the whole body yesterday, as aking part of itself, whose actions then it cannot but admit s its own now. Though, if the same body should still live, nd immediately from the separation of the little finger have s own peculiar consciousness, whereof the little finger knew othing, it would not at all be concerned for it, as a part of self, or could own any of its actions, or have any of them nputed to him.

This may show us wherein personal identity consists: not the identity of substance, but, as I have said, in the identity f consciousness, wherein if Socrates and the present mayor f Queensborough agree, they are the same person: if the me Socrates waking and sleeping do not partake of the me consciousness, Socrates waking and sleeping is not the me person. And to punish Socrates waking for what sleepg Socrates thought, and waking Socrates was never conious of, would be no more of right, than to punish one twin or what his brother-twin did, whereof he knew nothing, beause their outsides were so like, that they could not be stinguished; for such twins have been seen.

But yet possibly it will still be objected,—Suppose I wholly se the memory of some parts of my life, beyond a possibility f retrieving them, so that perhaps I shall never be conious of them again; yet am I not the same person that did iose actions, had those thoughts that I once was conscious , though I have now forgot them? To which I answer, that e must here take notice what the word *I* is applied to; hich, in this case, is the *man* only. And the same man being esumed to be the same person, I is easily here supposed to and also for the same person. But if it be possible for the me man to have distinct incommunicable consciousness at fferent times, it is past doubt the same man would at differt times make different persons; which, we see, is the sense mankind in the solemnest declaration of their opinions, iman laws not punishing the mad man for the sober man's tions, nor the sober man for what the mad man did,— ereby making them two persons: which is somewhat exained by our way of speaking in English when we say such one is "not himself," or is "beside himself"; in which

phrases it is insinuated, as if those who now, or at least firs
used them, thought that self was changed; the self-same per
son was no longer in that man.

But yet it is hard to conceive that Socrates, the same in
dividual man, should be two persons. To help us a little in
this, we must consider what is meant by Socrates, or the sam
individual *man*.

First, it must be either the same individual, immaterial
thinking substance; in short, the same numerical soul, an
nothing else.

Secondly, or the same animal, without any regard to an
immaterial soul.

Thirdly, or the same immaterial spirit united to the sam
animal.

Now, take which of these suppositions you please, it i
impossible to make personal identity to consist in anythin
but consciousness; or reach any further than that does.

For, by the first of them, it must be allowed possible tha
a man born of different women, and in distant times, ma
be the same man. A way of speaking which, whoever admits
must allow it possible for the same man to be two distinc
persons, as any two that have lived in different ages withou
the knowledge of one another's thoughts.

By the second and third, Socrates, in this life and after it
cannot be the same man any way, but by the same conscious
ness; and so making human identity to consist in the sam
thing wherein we place personal identity, there will be n
difficulty to allow the same man to be the same person. Bu
then they who place human identity in consciousness only
and not in something else, must consider how they will mak
the infant Socrates the same man with Socrates after th
resurrection. But whatsoever to some men makes a man, an
consequently the same individual man, wherein perhaps fe
are agreed, personal identity can by us be placed in nothin
but consciousness (which is that alone which makes what w
call *self*), without involving us in great absurdities.

But is not a man drunk and sober the same person? Wh
else is he punished for the fact he commits when drunk
though he be never afterwards conscious of it? Just as muc
the same person as a man that walks, and does other thing
in his sleep, is the same person, and is answerable for an
mischief he shall do in it. Human laws punish both, with

ıstice suitable to *their* way of knowledge;—because, in these ases, they cannot distinguish certainly what is real, what ounterfeit: and so the ignorance in drunkenness or sleep is ıot admitted as a plea. For, though punishment be annexed ɔ personality, and personality to consciousness, and the runkard perhaps be not conscious of what he did, yet human judicatures justly punish him; because the fact is proved gainst him, but want of consciousness cannot be proved for ım. But in the Great Day, wherein the secrets of all hearts hall be laid open, it may be reasonable to think, no one shall e made to answer for what he knows nothing of; but shall eceive his doom, his conscience accusing or excusing him.

Nothing but consciousness can unite remote existences into he same person: the identity of substance will not do it; for vhatever substance there is, however framed, without conciousness there is no person: and a carcass may be a person, s well as any sort of substance be so, without consciousness.

Wherever a man finds what he calls himself, there, I think, nother may say is the same person. It is a forensic term, ppropriating actions and their merit; and so belongs only to ntelligent agents, capable of a law, and happiness, and misry. This personality extends itself beyond present existence o what is past, only by consciousness,—whereby it becomes oncerned and accountable; owns and imputes to itself past ctions, just upon the same ground and for the same reason s it does the present. All which is founded in a concern for appiness, the unavoidable concomitant of consciousness; that vhich is conscious of pleasure and pain, desiring that that elf that is conscious should be happy. And therefore whatver past actions it cannot reconcile or *appropriate* to that resent self by consciousness, it can be no more concerned n than if they had never been done: and to receive pleasure r pain, i.e. reward or punishment, on the account of any uch action, is all one as to be made happy or miserable in ts first being, without any demerit at all. For, supposing a *nan* punished now for what he had done in another life, vhereof he could be made to have no consciousness at all, vhat difference is there between that punishment and being *reated* miserable? And therefore, conformable to this, the postle tells us, that, at the great day, when everyone shall 'receive according to his doings, the secrets of all hearts shall e laid open." The sentence shall be justified by the consciousness all persons shall have, that *they themselves,* in what bodies soever they appear, or what substances soever that consciousness adheres to, are the *same* that committed those actions, and deserve that punishment for them.

To conclude: Whatever substance begins to exist, it must during its existence, necessarily be the same: whatever compositions of substances begin to exist, during the union of those substances, the concrete must be the same: whatsoever mode begins to exist, during its existence it is the same: and so if the composition be of distinct substances and different modes, the same rule holds. Whereby it will appear, that the difficulty or obscurity that has been about this matter rather rises from the names ill-used, than from any obscurity in things themselves. For whatever makes the specific idea to which the name is applied, if that idea be steadily kept to the distinction of anything into the same and divers will easily be conceived, and there can arise no doubt about it.

For, supposing a rational spirit be the idea of a *man,* it is easy to know what is the same man, viz. the same spirit—whether separate or in a body—will be the *same man.* Supposing a rational spirit vitally united to a body of a certain conformation of parts to make a man; whilst that rational spirit, with that vital conformation of parts, though continued in a fleeting successive body, remains, it will be the *same man.* But if to anyone the idea of a man be but the vital union of parts in a certain shape; as long as that vital union and shape remain in a concrete, no otherwise the same but by a continued succession of fleeting particles, it will be the *same man.* For, whatever be the composition whereof the complex idea is made, whenever existence makes it one particular thing under any denomination, *the same existence continued* preserves it the *same* individual under the same denomination.

X X V I I I

Of Other Relations

ESIDES THE BEFORE-MENTIONED OCCASIONS of time, place, nd causality of comparing or referring things one to another, ere are, as I have said, infinite others, some whereof I shall ention.

First, The first I shall name is some one simple idea, which, ing capable of parts or degrees, affords an occasion of mparing the subjects wherein it is to one another, in reect of that simple idea, v.g. whiter, sweeter, equal, more, c. These relations depending on the equality and excess of e same simple idea, in several subjects, may be called, if ne will, *proportional;* and that these are only conversant out those simple ideas received from sensation or reflection so evident that nothing need be said to evince it.

Secondly, Another occasion of comparing things together, considering one thing, so as to include in that consideration me other thing, is the circumstances of their origin or beinning; which being not afterwards to be altered, make the lations depending thereon as lasting as the subjects to which ey belong, v.g. father and son, brothers, cousin-germans, c., which have their relations by one community of blood, herein they partake in several degrees: countrymen, i.e. ose who were born in the same country or tract of ground; nd these I call *natural relations:* wherein we may observe, at mankind have fitted their notions and words to the use f common life, and not to the truth and extent of things. or it is certain, that, in reality, the relation is the same etwixt the begetter and the begotten, in the several races of ther animals as well as men; but yet it is seldom said, this ull is the grandfather of such a calf, or that two pigeons are ousin-germans. It is very convenient that, by distinct names, nese relations should be observed and marked out in manind, there being occasion, both in laws and other communiations one with another, to mention and take notice of men nder these relations: from whence also arise the obligations f several duties amongst men: whereas, in brutes, men havng very little or no cause to mind these relations, they have ot thought fit to give them distinct and peculiar names.

Thirdly, Sometimes the foundation of considering things with reference to one another, is some act whereby anyone comes by a moral right, power, or obligation to do something. Thus, a general is one that hath power to command an army: and an army under a general is a collection of armed men obliged to obey one man. A citizen, or a burgher, is one who has a right to certain privileges in this or that place. All this sort depending upon men's wills, or agreement in society, I call *instituted,* or *voluntary;* and may be distinguished from the natural, in that they are most, if not all of them, some way or other alterable, and separable from the persons to whom they have sometimes belonged, though neither of the substances, so related, be destroyed. Now, though these are all reciprocal, as well as the rest, and contain in them a reference of two things one to the other; yet, because one of the two things often wants a relative name, importing that reference, men usually take no notice of it, and the relation is commonly overlooked: v.g. a patron and client are easily allowed to be relations, but a constable or dictator are not so readily at first hearing considered as such. Because there is no peculiar name for those who are under the command of a dictator or constable, expressing a relation to either of them; though it be certain that either of them hath a certain power over some others, and so is so far related to them, as well as a patron is to his client, or general to his army.

Fourthly, There is another sort of relation, which is the conformity or disagreement men's *voluntary actions* have to a *rule* to which they are referred, and by which they are judged of; which, I think, may be called *moral relation,* as being that which denominates our moral actions, and deserves well to be examined; there being no part of knowledge wherein we should be more careful to get determined ideas, and avoid, as much as may be, obscurity and confusion. Human actions, when with their various ends, objects, manners, and circumstances, they are framed into distinct complex ideas, are, as has been shown, so many *mixed modes,* a great part whereof have names annexed to them. Thus, supposing gratitude to be a readiness to acknowledge and return kindness received; polygamy to be the having more wives than one at once: when we frame these notions thus in our minds, we have there so many determined ideas of mixed modes. But this is not all that concerns our actions: it is not enough to have determined ideas of them, and to know what names belong to such and such combinations of ideas. We have a further and greater concernment, and that is, to know whether such actions, so made up, are morally good or bad.

Good and evil, as hath been shown (Book II. Chapter 20 and Chapter 21) are nothing but pleasure or pain, or that which occasions or procures pleasure or pain to us. *Moral good and evil,* then, is only *the conformity or disagreement of our voluntary actions to some law, whereby good or evil is drawn on us, from the will and power of the lawmaker;* which good and evil, pleasure or pain, attending our observance or breach of the law by the decree of the lawmaker, is that we call *reward* and *punishment.*

Of these moral rules or laws, to which men generally refer, and by which they judge of the rectitude or pravity of their actions, there seem to me to be *three sorts,* with their three different enforcements, or rewards and punishments. For, since it would be utterly in vain to suppose a rule set to the free actions of men, without annexing to it some enforcement of good and evil to determine his will, we must, wherever we suppose a law, suppose also some reward or punishment annexed to that law. It would be in vain for one intelligent being to set a rule to the actions of another, if he had it not in his power to reward the compliance with, and punish deviation from his rule, by some good and evil, that is not the natural product and consequence of the action itself. For that, being a natural convenience or inconvenience, would operate of itself, without a law. This, if I mistake not, is the true nature of all law, properly so called.

The laws that men generally refer their actions to, to judge of their rectitude or obliquity, seem to me to be these three:—1. The *divine* law. 2. The *civil* law. 3. The law of *opinion* or *reputation,* if I may so call it. By the relation they bear to the first of these, men judge whether their actions are sins or duties; by the second, whether they be criminal or innocent; and by the third, whether they be virtues or vices.

First, the *divine law,* whereby that law which God has set to the actions of men,—whether promulgated to them by the light of nature, or the voice of revelation. That God has given a rule whereby men should govern themselves, I think there is nobody so brutish as to deny. He has a right to do it; we are His creatures: He has goodness and wisdom to direct our actions to that which is best: and He has power to enforce it by rewards and punishments of infinite weight and duration in another life; for nobody can take us out of His hands. This is the only true touchstone of moral rectitude; and, by comparing them to this law, it is that men judge of the most considerable moral good or evil of their actions; that is, whether, as duties or sins, they are like to procure them happiness or misery from the hands of the ALMIGHTY.

Secondly, the *civil law*—the rule set by the Commonwealth to the actions of those who belong to it—is another rule to which men refer their actions; to judge whether they be criminal or no. This law nobody overlooks: the rewards and punishments that enforce it being ready at hand, and suitable to the power that makes it: which is the force of the Commonwealth, engaged to protect the lives, liberties, and possessions of those who live according to its laws, and has power to take away life, liberty, or goods, from him who disobeys; which is the punishment of offenses committed against his law.

Thirdly, the *law of opinion or reputation.* Virtue and vice are names pretended and supposed everywhere to stand for actions in their own nature right and wrong: and as far as they really are so applied, they so far are coincident with the divine law above mentioned. But yet, whatever is pretended, this is visible, that these names, virtue and vice, in the particular instances of their application, through the several nations and societies of men in the world, are constantly attributed only to such actions as in each country and society are in reputation or discredit. Nor is it to be thought strange, that men everywhere should give the name of virtue to those actions, which amongst them are judged praiseworthy; and call that vice, which they account blamable: since otherwise they would condemn themselves, if they should think anything right, to which they allowed not commendation, anything wrong, which they let pass without blame. Thus the measure of what is everywhere called and esteemed virtue and vice is this approbation or dislike, praise or blame, which, by a secret and tacit consent, establishes itself in the several societies, tribes, and clubs of men in the world: whereby several actions come to find credit or disgrace amongst them, according to the judgment, maxims, or fashion of that place. For, though men uniting into politic societies, have resigned up to the public the disposing of all their force, so that they cannot employ it against any fellow citizens any further than the law of the country directs: yet they retain still the power of thinking well or ill, approving or disapproving of the actions of those whom they live amongst, and converse with: and by this approbation and dislike they establish amongst themselves what they will call virtue and vice.

[Locke next maintains that virtue is nothing other than what is thought praiseworthy. It is enforced by public commendation and disapproval. Morality is the relation of voluntary actions to rules of rectitude. Whether an action is good or bad is relative to the rule that public opinion upholds. This sort of relation of actions to a law Locke calls "moral relations."]

It would make a volume to go over all sorts of *relations:* it is not, therefore, to be expected that I should here mention them all. It suffices to our present purpose to show by these, what the ideas are we have of this comprehensive consideration called *relation.* Which is so various, and the occasions of it so many (as many as there can be of comparing things one to another), that it is not very easy to reduce it to rules, or under just heads. Those I have mentioned, I think, are some of the most considerable; and such as may serve to let us see from whence we get our ideas of relations, and wherein they are founded. But before I quit this argument, from what has been said give me leave to observe:

First, That it is evident, that all relation terminates in, and is ultimately founded on, those simple ideas we have got from sensation or reflection: so that all we have in our thoughts ourselves (if we think of anything, or have any meaning), or would signify to others, when we use words standing for relations, is nothing but some simple ideas, or collections of simple ideas, compared one with another. This is so manifest in that sort called proportional, that nothing can be more. For when a man says "honey is sweeter than wax," it is plain that his thoughts in this relation terminate in this simple idea, sweetness; which is equally true of all the rest: though, where they are compounded, or decompounded, the simple ideas they are made up of, are, perhaps, seldom taken notice of: v.g. when the word father is mentioned: first, there is meant that particular species, or collective idea, signified by the word man; secondly, those sensible simple ideas, signified by the word generation; and, thirdly, the effects of it, and all the simple ideas signified by the word child. So the word friend, being taken for a man who loves and is ready to do good to another, has all these following ideas to the making of it up: first, all the simple ideas, comprehended in the word man, or intelligent being; secondly, the idea of love; thirdly, the idea of readiness or disposition; fourthly, the idea of action, which is any kind of thought or motion; fifthly, the idea of good, which signifies anything that may advance his happiness, and terminates at last, if examined, in particular simple ideas, of which the word good in general signifies any one; but, if removed from all simple ideas quite, it signifies nothing at all. And thus also all moral words terminate at last, though perhaps more remotely, in a collection of simple ideas: the immediate signification of relative words, being very often other supposed known relations; which, if traced one to another, still end in simple ideas.

Secondly, That in relations, we have for the most part, if not always, as clear a notion of *the relation* as we have of *those simple ideas wherein it is founded:* agreement or disagreement, whereon relation depends, being things whereof we have commonly as clear ideas as of any other whatsoever; it being but the distinguishing simple ideas, or their degrees one from another, without which we could have no distinct knowledge at all.

Thirdly, That in these I call *moral relations,* I have a true notion of relation, by comparing the action with the rule, whether the rule be true or false. For if I measure anything by a yard, I know whether the thing I measure be longer or shorter than that supposed yard, though perhaps the yard I measure by be not exactly the standard: which indeed is another inquiry. For though the rule be erroneous, and I mistaken in it; yet the agreement or disagreement observable in that which I compare with, makes me perceive the relation. Though, measuring by a wrong rule, I shall thereby be brought to judge amiss of its moral rectitude; because I have tried it by that which is not the true rule: yet I am not mistaken in the relation which that action bears to that rule I compare it to, which is agreement or disagreement.

XXIX

Of Clear and Obscure, Distinct and Confused Ideas

HAVING SHOWN THE ORIGINAL OF OUR IDEAS, and taken a view of their several sorts; considered the difference between the simple and the complex; and observed how the complex ones are divided into those of modes, substances, and relations—all which, I think, is necessary to be done by anyone who would acquaint himself thoroughly with the progress of the mind, in its apprehension and knowledge of things—it will, perhaps, be thought I have dwelt long enough upon the examination of *ideas*. I must, nevertheless, crave leave to offer some few other considerations concerning them.

The first is, that some are *clear* and others *obscure;* some *distinct* and others *confused*.

The perception of the mind being most aptly explained by words relating to the sight, we shall best understand what is meant by *clear* and *obscure* in our ideas, by reflecting on what we call clear and obscure in the objects of sight. Light being that which discovers to us visible objects, we give the name of *obscure* to that which is not placed in a light sufficient to discover minutely to us the figure and colors which are observable in it, and which, in a better light, would be discernible. In like manner, our simple ideas are *clear,* when they are such as the objects themselves from whence they were taken did or might, in a well-ordered sensation or perception, present them. Whilst the memory retains them thus, and can produce them to the mind whenever it has occasion to consider them, they are clear ideas. So far as they either want anything of the original exactness, or have lost any of their first freshness, and are, as it were, faded or tarnished by time, so far are they obscure. Complex ideas, as they are made up of simple ones, so they are clear, when the ideas that go to their composition are clear, and the number and order of those simple ideas that are the ingredients of any complex one is determinate and certain.

The causes of obscurity, in simple ideas, seem to be either dull organs; or very slight and transient impressions made by the objects; or else a weakness in the memory, not able to retain them as received. For to return again to visible objects, to help us to apprehend this matter: If the organs, or faculties of perception, like wax overhardened with cold, will not receive the impression of the seal, from the usual impulse wont to imprint it; or, like wax of a temper too soft, will not hold it well, when well imprinted; or else supposing the wax of a temper fit, but the seal not applied with a sufficient force to make a clear impression: in any of these cases, the print left by the seal will be obscure. This, I suppose, needs no application to make it plainer.

As a clear idea is that whereof the mind has such a full and evident perception, as it does receive from an outward object operating duly on a well-disposed organ, so a *distinct* idea is that wherein the mind perceives a difference from all other; and a *confused* idea is such a one as is not sufficiently distinguishable from another, from which it ought to be different.

If no idea be confused, but such as is not sufficiently distinguishable from another from which it should be different, it will be hard, may anyone say, to find anywhere a *confused* idea. For, let any idea be as it will, it can be no other but such as the mind perceives it to be; and that very perception sufficiently distinguishes it from all other ideas, which cannot be other, i.e. different, without being perceived to be so. No idea, therefore, can be undistinguishable from another from which it ought to be different, unless you would have it different from itself: for from all other it is evidently different.

To remove this difficulty, and to help us to conceive aright what it is that makes the confusion ideas are at any time chargeable with, we must consider, that things ranked under distinct names are supposed different enough to be distinguished, that so each sort by its peculiar name may be marked, and discoursed of apart upon any occasion: and there is nothing more evident, than that the greatest part of different names are supposed to stand for different things. Now every idea a man has, being visibly what it is, and distinct from all other ideas but itself; that which makes it confused, is, when it is such that it may as well be called by another name as that which it is expressed by; the difference which keeps the things (to be ranked under those two different names) distinct, and makes some of them belong rather to the one and some of them to the other of those names, being left out; and so the distinction, which was intended to be kept up by those different names, is quite lost.

Confusion making it a difficulty to separate two things that should be separated, concerns always two ideas; and those most which most approach one another. Whenever, therefore, we suspect any idea to be confused, we must examine what other it is in danger to be confounded with, or which it cannot easily be separated from; and that will always be found an idea belonging to another name, and so should be a different thing, from which yet it is not sufficiently distinct: being either the same with it, or making a part of it, or at least as properly called by that name as the other it is ranked under; and so keeps not that difference from that other idea which the different names import.

This, I think, is the confusion proper to ideas; which still carries with it a secret reference to names. At least, if there be any other confusion of ideas, this is that which most of all disorders men's thoughts and discourses: ideas, as ranked under names, being those that for the most part men reason of within themselves, and always those which they commune about with others. And therefore where there are supposed two different ideas, marked by two different names, which are not as distinguishable as the sounds that stand for them, there never fails to be confusion; and where any ideas are distinct as the ideas of those two sounds they are marked by, there can be between them no confusion. The way to prevent it is to collect and unite into one complex idea, as precisely as is possible, all those ingredients whereby it is differenced from others; and to them, so united in a determinate number and order, apply steadily the same name. But this neither accommodating men's ease or vanity, nor serving any design but that of naked truth, which is not always the thing aimed at, such exactness is rather to be wished than hoped for. And since the loose application of names, to undetermined, variable, and almost no ideas, serves both to cover our own ignorance, as well as to perplex and confound others, which goes for learning and superiority in knowledge, it is no wonder that most men should use it themselves, whilst they complain of it in others. Though I think no small part of the confusion to be found in the notions of men might, by care and ingenuity, be avoided, yet I am far from concluding it everywhere willful. Some ideas are so complex, and made up of so many parts, that the memory does not easily retain the very same precise combination of simple ideas under one name: much less are we able constantly to divine for what precise complex idea such a name stands in another man's use of it. From the first of these, follows confusion in a man's own reasonings and opinions within himself; from the latter, frequent confusion in discoursing and arguing with others. But having more at large treated of Words, their defects, and abuses, in the following Book, I shall here say no more of it.

XXX

Of Real and Fantastical Ideas

ESIDES WHAT WE HAVE ALREADY MENTIONED concerning leas, other considerations belong to them, in reference to *hings from whence they are taken,* or *which they may be upposed to represent;* and thus, I think, they may come un-er a threefold distinction, and are:——

First, either real or fantastical;

Secondly, adequate or inadequate;

Thirdly, true or false.

First, by *real ideas,* I mean such as have a foundation in ature; such as have a conformity with the real being and xistence of things, or with their archetypes. *Fantastical* or *himerical,* I call such as have no foundation in nature, nor ave any conformity with that reality of being to which they re tacitly referred, as to their archetypes. If we examine the everal sorts of ideas before mentioned, we shall find that,

First, our *simple ideas* are all real, all agree to the reality f things: not that they are all of them the images or rep-esentations of what does exist; the contrary whereof, in all ut the primary qualities of bodies, hath been already shown. ut, though whiteness and coldness are no more in snow than ain is; yet those ideas of whiteness and coldness, pain, etc., eing in us the effects of powers in things without us, or-lained by our Maker to produce in us such sensations; they re real ideas in us, whereby we distinguish the qualities that re really in things themselves. For, these several appear-nces being designed to be the mark whereby we are to know nd distinguish things which we have to do with, our ideas lo as well serve us to that purpose, and are as real distinguish-ng characters, whether they be only *constant effects,* or else *xact resemblances* of something in the things themselves: the eality lying in that steady correspondence they have with the listinct constitutions of real beings. But whether they answer o those constitutions, as to causes or patterns, it matters not; t suffices that they are constantly produced by them. And hus our simple ideas are all real and true, because they nswer and agree to those powers of things which produce hem in our minds; that being all that is requisite to make them real, and not fictions at pleasure. For in simple ide (as has been shown) the mind is wholly confined to the operation of things upon it, and can make to itself no simpl idea, more than what it has received.

Though the mind be wholly passive in respect of its simpl ideas; yet, I think, we may say it is not so in respect of it complex ideas. For those being combinations of simple ide put together, and united under one general name, it is plai that the mind of man uses some kind of liberty in formin those complex ideas: how else comes it to pass that one man' idea of gold, or justice, is different from another's, but becaus he has put in, or left out of his, some simple idea which th other has not? The question then is, Which of these are rea and which barely imaginary combinations? What collection agree to the reality of things, and what not? And to this say that,

Secondly, Mixed modes and *relations,* having no other rea ity but what they have in the minds of men, there is nothin more required to this kind of ideas to make them real, bu that they be so framed, that there be a possibility of existin conformable to them. These ideas themselves, being archetypes, cannot differ from their archetypes, and so cannot b chimerical, unless anyone will jumble together in them inconsistent ideas. Indeed, as any of them have the names of known language assigned to them, by which he that has the in his mind would signify them to others, so bare possibilit of existing is not enough; they must have a conformity t the ordinary signification of the name that is given then that they may not be thought fantastical: as if a man woul give the name of justice to that idea which common us calls liberality. But this fantasticalness relates more to propriety of speech, than reality of ideas. For a man to be undisturbed in danger, sedately to consider what is fittest to b done, and to execute it steadily, is a mixed mode, or a complex idea of an action which may exist. But to be undisturbe in danger, without using one's reason or industry, is what i also possible to be; and so is as real an idea as the othe Though the first of these, having the name *courage* given t it, may, in respect of that name, be a right or wrong ide but the other, whilst it has not a common received name c any known language assigned to it, is not capable of any deformity, being made with no reference to anything but itsel

Thirdly, Our complex ideas of *substances,* being made all f them in reference to things existing without us, and inended to be representations of substances as they really are, re no further real than as they are such combinations of imple ideas as are really united, and co-exist in things withut us. On the contrary, those are fantastical which are made p of such collections of simple ideas as were really never nited, never were found together in any substance: v.g. a ational creature, consisting of a horse's head, joined to a ody of human shape, or such as the *centaurs* are described: r, a body yellow, very malleable, fusible, and fixed, but ghter than common water: or a uniform, unorganized body, onsisting, as to sense, all of similar parts, with perception nd voluntary motion joined to it. Whether such substances s these can possibly exist or no, it is probable we do not now: but be that as it will, these ideas of substances, being nade conformable to no pattern existing that we know; and onsisting of such collections of ideas as no substance ever howed us united together, they ought to pass with us for arely imaginary: but much more are those complex ideas so, vhich contain in them any inconsistency or contradiction of heir parts.

XXXI

Of Adequate and Inadequate Ideas

Of our real ideas, some are adequate, and some are inad quate. Those I call *adequate,* which perfectly represent thos archetypes which the mind supposes them taken from: whic it intends them to stand for, and to which it refers then *Inadequate ideas* are such, which are but a partial or incon plete representation of those archetypes to which they a referred. Upon which account it is plain,

First, that *all our simple ideas are adequate.* Because, bein nothing but the effects of certain powers in things, fitted an ordained by God to produce such sensations in us, they ca not but be correspondent and adequate to those powers: an we are sure they agree to the reality of things. For, if sug produce in us the ideas which we call whiteness and swee ness, we are sure there is a power in sugar to produce thos ideas in our minds, or else they could not have been pr duced by it. And so each sensation answering the power th operates on any of our senses, the idea so produced is a re idea (and not a fiction of the mind, which has no power produce any simple idea); and cannot but be adequate, sin it ought only to answer that power: and so all simple ide are adequate. It is true, the things producing in us these sin ple ideas are but few of them denominated by us, as if the were only the *causes* of them; but as if those ideas were re beings *in* them. For, though fire be called painful to the touc whereby is signified the power of producing in us the idea pain, yet it is denominated also light and hot; as if light an heat were really something in the fire, more than a power excite these ideas in us; and therefore are called qualities or of the fire. But these being nothing, in truth, but powe to excite such ideas in us, I must in that sense be understoo when I speak of secondary qualities as being in things; or their ideas as being the objects that excite them in us. Su ways of speaking, though accommodated to the vulgar n tions, without which one cannot be well understood, yet tru signify nothing but those powers which are in things to exci certain sensations or ideas in us. Since were there no organs to receive the impressions fire makes on the sight a uch, nor a mind joined to those organs to receive the ideas light and heat by those impressions from the fire or sun, ere would yet be no more light or heat in the world than ere would be pain if there were no sensible creature to feel though the sun should continue just as it is now, and ount Etna flame higher than ever it did. Solidity and exten- on, and the termination of it, figure, with motion and rest, hereof we have the ideas, would be really in the world as ey are, whether there were any sensible being to perceive em or no: and therefore we have reason to look on those as e real modifications of matter, and such as are the exciting uses of all our various sensations from bodies. But this ing an inquiry not belonging to this place, I shall enter no rther into it, but proceed to show what complex ideas are lequate, and what not.

Secondly, our complex ideas of modes, being voluntary col- ctions of simple ideas, which the mind puts together, with- it reference to any real archetypes, or standing patterns, isting anywhere, are and cannot but be *adequate ideas.* Be- use they, not being intended for copies of things really exist- g, but for archetypes made by the mind, to rank and enominate things by, cannot want anything; they having each them that combination of ideas, and thereby that perfec- on, which the mind intended they should: so that the mind quiesces in them, and can find nothing wanting. Thus, by ving the idea of a figure with three sides meeting at three igles, I have a complete idea, wherein I require nothing else make it perfect. That the mind is satisfied with the per- ction of this its idea is plain, in that it does not conceive that ny understanding hath, or can have, a more complete or rfect idea of that thing it signifies by the word triangle, pposing it to exist, than itself has, in that complex idea of ree sides and three angles, in which is contained all that is can be essential to it, or necessary to complete it, wherever however it exists. But in our *ideas of substances* it is other- ise. For there, desiring to copy things as they really do exist, nd to represent to ourselves that constitution on which all eir properties depend, we perceive our ideas attain not that rfection we intend: we find they still want something we ould be glad were in them; and so are all inadequate. But *ixed modes* and *relations,* being archetypes without pat- rns, and so having nothing to represent but themselves, can-

not but be adequate, everything being so to itself. He that
first put together the idea of danger perceived, absence of di
order from fear, sedate consideration of what was justly to
done, and executing that without disturbance, or being d
terred by the danger of it, had certainly in his mind that con
plex idea made up of that combination: and intending it
be nothing else but what it is, nor to have in it any other simp
ideas but what it hath, it could not also but be an adequa
idea: and laying this up in his memory, with the name *cou*
age annexed to it, to signify to others, and denominate fro
thence any action he should observe to agree with it, ha
thereby a standard to measure and denominate actions by,
they agreed to it. This idea, thus made and laid up for
pattern, must necessarily be adequate, being referred to not
ing else but itself, nor made by any other original but th
good liking and will of him that first made this combination.

Indeed another coming after, and in conversation learnir
from him the word *courage,* may make an idea, to which
gives the name courage, different from what the first auth
applied it to, and has in his mind when he uses it. And
this case, if he designs that his idea in thinking should
conformable to the other's idea, as the name he uses
speaking is conformable in sound to his from whom
learned it, his idea may be very wrong and inadequate: becau
in this case, making the other man's idea the pattern of h
idea in thinking, as the other man's word or sound is th
pattern of his in speaking, his idea is so far defective an
inadequate, as it is distant from the archetype and pattern
refers it to, and intends to express and signify by the nan
he uses for it; which name he would have to be a sign of th
other man's idea (to which, in its proper use, it is primari
annexed), and of his own, as agreeing to it: to which if h
own does not exactly correspond, it is faulty and inadequate.

Therefore these complex ideas of *modes,* when they a
referred by the mind, and intended to correspond to th
ideas in the mind of some other intelligent being, expressed
the names we apply to them, they may be very deficie
wrong, and inadequate; because they agree not to that whi
the mind designs to be their archetype and pattern: in whi
respect only any idea of modes can be wrong, imperfect,
inadequate. And on this account our ideas of mixed mod
are the most liable to be faulty of any other; but this refe
more to proper speaking than knowing right.

Thirdly, what *ideas we have of substances,* I have above ıown. Now, those ideas have in the mind a double referıce: 1. Sometimes they are referred to a supposed real esnce of each species of things. 2. Sometimes they are only signed to be pictures and representations in the mind of ings that do exist, by ideas of those qualities that are disoverable in them. In both which ways these copies of those iginals and archetypes are imperfect and inadequate.

First, it is usual for men to make the names of substances and for things as supposed to have certain real essences, hereby they are of this or that species: and names standing r nothing but the ideas that are in men's minds, they must onstantly refer their ideas to such real essences, as to their chetypes. That men (especially such as have been bred up the learning taught in this part of the world) do suppose ertain specific essences of substances, which each individual its several kinds is made conformable to and partakes of, so far from needing proof that it will be thought strange if ıyone should do otherwise. And thus they ordinarily apply e specific names they rank particular substances under, to ings as distinguished by such specific real essences. Who is ere almost, who would not take it amiss if it should be oubted whether he called himself a man, with any other eaning than as having the real essence of a man? And yet you demand what those real essences are, it is plain men e ignorant, and know them not. From whence it follows, at the ideas they have in their minds, being referred to real sences, as to archetypes which are unknown, must be so r from being adequate that they cannot be supposed to be y representation of them at all. The complex ideas we have f substances are, as it has been shown, certain collections of mple ideas that have been observed or supposed constantly exist together. But such a complex idea cannot be the real sence of any substance; for then the properties we discover that body would depend on that complex idea, and be educible from it, and their necessary connection with it be nown; as all properties of a triangle depend on, and, as far they are discoverable, are deducible from the complex idea f three lines including a space. But it is plain that in our omplex ideas of substances are not contained such ideas, on hich all the other qualities that are to be found in them do epend. The common idea men have of iron is, a body of a ertain color, weight, and hardness; and a property that they look on as belonging to it, is malleableness. But yet thi property has no necessary connection with that complex idea or any part of it: and there is no more reason to think tha malleableness depends on that color, weight, and hardness than that color or that weight depends on its malleableness And yet, though we know nothing of these real essences there is nothing more ordinary than that men should attribut the sorts of things to such essences. The particular parcel o matter which makes the ring I have on my finger is forwardly by most men supposed to have a real essence, whereby it i gold; and from whence those qualities flow which I find in it viz. its peculiar color, weight, hardness, fusibility, fixedness and change of color upon a slight touch of mercury, etc. Thi essence, from which all these properties flow, when I inquir into it and search after it, I plainly perceive I cannot dis cover: the furthest I can go is, only to presume that, it bein nothing but body, its real essence or internal constitution, o which these qualities depend, can be nothing but the figure size, and connection of its solid parts; of neither of whic having any distinct perception at all can I have any idea o its essence: which is the cause that it has that particular shin ing yellowness; a greater weight than anything I know of th same bulk; and a fitness to have its color changed by th touch of quicksilver. If anyone will say, that the real essenc and internal constitution, on which these properties depend, i not the figure, size, and arrangement or connection of its soli parts, but something else, called its particular *form,* I an further from having any idea of its real essence than I wa before. For I have an idea of figure, size, and situation o solid parts in general, though I have none of the particula figure, size, or putting together of parts, whereby the qualitie above mentioned are produced; which qualities I find in tha particular parcel of matter that is on my finger, and not i another parcel of matter, with which I cut the pen I writ with. But, when I am told that something besides the figure size, and posture of the solid parts of that body in its essence something called *substantial form,* of that I confess I have n idea at all, but only of the sound form; which is far enoug from an idea of its real essence or constitution. The like igno rance as I have of the real essence of this particular sub stance, I have also of the real essence of all other natura ones: of which essences I confess I have no distinct ideas a all; and, I am apt to suppose, others, when they examine their own knowledge, will find in themselves, in this one point, the same sort of ignorance.

Now, then, when men apply to this particular parcel of matter on my finger a general name already in use, and denominate it *gold,* do they not ordinarily, or are they not understood to give it that name, as belonging to a particular species of bodies, having a real internal essence; by having of which essence this particular substance comes to be of that species, and to be called by that name? If it be so, as it is plain it is, the name by which things are marked as having that essence must be referred primarily to that essence; and consequently the idea to which that name is given must be referred also to that essence, and be intended to represent it. Which essence, since they who so use the names know not, their ideas of substances must be all inadequate in that respect, as not containing in them that real essence which the mind intends they should.

Secondly, those who, neglecting that useless supposition of unknown real essences, whereby they are distinguished, endeavor to copy the substances that exist in the world, by putting together the ideas of those sensible qualities which are found co-existing in them, though they come much nearer a likeness of them than those who imagine they know not what real specific essences: yet they arrive not at perfectly adequate ideas of those substances they would thus copy into their minds: nor do those copies exactly and fully contain all that is to be found in their archetypes. Because those qualities and powers of substances, whereof we make their complex ideas, are so many and various, that no man's complex idea contains them all. That our complex ideas of substances do not contain in them *all* the simple ideas that are united in the things themselves is evident, in that men do rarely put into their complex idea of any substance all the simple ideas they do know to exist in it. Because, endeavoring to make the signification of their names as clear and as little cumbersome as they can, they make their specific ideas of the sorts of substance, for the most part, of a few of those simple ideas which are to be found in them: but these having no original precedency, or right to be put in, and make the specific idea, more than others that are left out, it is plain that both these ways our ideas of substances are deficient and inadequate. The simple ideas whereof we make our complex ones of substances are all of them (bating only the figure and bulk of some sorts) powers; which being relations to other substances, we can never be sure that we know *all* the powers that are in any one body, till we have tried what changes it is fitted to give to or receive from other substances in their several ways of application: which being impossible to be tried upon any one body, much less upon all, it is impossible we should have adequate ideas of any substance made up of a collection of all its properties.

Whosoever first lighted on a parcel of that sort of substance we denote by the word *gold*, could not rationally take the bulk and figure he observed in that lump to depend on its real essence, or internal constitution. Therefore those never went into his idea of that species of body; but its peculiar color, perhaps, and weight, were the first he abstracted from it, to make the complex idea of that species. Which both are but powers; the one to affect our eyes after such a manner, and to produce in us that idea we call yellow; and the other to force upwards any other body of equal bulk, they being put into a pair of equal scales, one against another. Another perhaps added to these the ideas of fusibility and fixedness, two other passive powers, in relation to the operation of fire upon it; another, its ductility and solubility in *aqua regia,* two other powers, relating to the operation of other bodies, in changing its outward figure, or separation of it into insensible parts. These, or parts of these, put together, usually make the complex idea in men's minds of that sort of body we call *gold*.

But no one who hath considered the properties of bodies in general, or this sort in particular, can doubt that this, called *gold,* has infinite other properties not contained in that complex idea. Some who have examined this species more accurately could, I believe, enumerate ten times as many properties in gold, all of them as inseparable from its internal constitution, as its color or weight: and it is probable, if anyone knew all the properties that are by divers men known of this metal, there would be an hundred times as many ideas go to the complex idea of gold as any one man yet has in his; and yet perhaps that not be the thousandth part of what is to be discovered in it. The changes that that one body is apt to receive, and make in other bodies, upon a due application, exceeding far not only what we know, but what we are apt to imagine. Which will not appear so much a paradox to anyone who will but consider how far men are yet from knowing all the properties of that one, no very compound figure, a triangle; though it be no small number that are already by mathematicians discovered of it.

So that all our complex ideas of substances are imperfect and inadequate. Which would be so also in mathematical figures, if we were to have our complex ideas of them, only by collecting their properties in reference to other figures. How uncertain and imperfect would our ideas be of an ellipsis, if we had no other idea of it, but some few of its properties? Whereas, having in our plain idea the *whole* essence of that figure, we from thence discover those properties, and demonstratively see how they flow, and are inseparable from it.

Thus the mind has three sorts of abstract ideas or nominal essences:

First, simple ideas, which are ECTYPES or copies; but yet certainly adequate. Because, being intended to express nothing but the power in things to produce in the mind such a sensation, that sensation, when it is produced, cannot but be the effect of that power. So the paper I write on, having the power in the light (I speak according to the common notion of light) to produce in men the sensation which I call white, it cannot but be the effect of such a power in something without the mind; since the mind has not the power to produce any such idea in itself: and being meant for nothing else but the effect of such a power, that simple idea is real and adequate; the sensation of white, in my mind, being the effect of that power which is in the paper to produce it, is perfectly adequate to that power; or else that power would produce a different idea.

Secondly, the *complex* ideas of *substances* are ectypes, copies too; but not perfect ones, not adequate: which is very evident to the mind, in that it plainly perceives, that whatever collection of simple ideas it makes of any substance that exists, it cannot be sure that it exactly answers all that are in that substance. Since, not having tried all the operations of all other substances upon it, and found all the alterations it would receive from, or cause in, other substances, it cannot have an exact adequate collection of all its active and passive capacities; and so not have an adequate complex idea of the powers of any substance existing, and its relations; which is that sort of complex idea of substances we have. And, after all, if we would have, and actually had, in our complex idea, an exact collection of all the secondary qualities or powers of any substance, we should not yet thereby have an idea of the *essence* of that thing. For, since the powers or qualities that are observable by us are not the real essence of that substance, but depend on it, and flow from it, any collection whatsoever of these qualities cannot be the real essence of that thing. Whereby it is plain, that our ideas of substances are not adequate; are not what the mind intends them to be. Besides, a man has no idea of substance in general, nor knows what substance is in itself.

Thirdly, complex ideas of *modes and relations* are originals, and archetypes; are not copies, nor made after the pattern of any real existence, to which the mind intends them to be conformable, and exactly to answer. These being such collections of simple ideas that the mind itself puts together, and such collections that each of them contains in it precisely all that the mind intends that it should, they are archetypes and essences of modes that may exist; and so are designed only for, and belong only to such modes as, when they do exist, have an exact conformity with those complex ideas. The ideas, therefore, of modes and relations cannot but be adequate.

XXXII

Of True and False Ideas

THOUGH TRUTH AND FALSEHOOD BELONG, in propriety of speech, only to *propositions:* yet *ideas* are oftentimes termed true or false (as what words are there that are not used with great latitude, and with some deviation from their strict and proper significations?). Though I think that when ideas themselves are termed true or false, there is still some secret or tacit proposition, which is the foundation of that denomination: as we shall see, if we examine the particular occasions wherein they come to be called true or false. In all which we shall find some kind of affirmation or negation, which is the reason of that denomination. For our ideas, being nothing but bare *appearances,* or perceptions in our minds, cannot properly and simply in themselves be said to be true or false, no more than a single name of anything can be said to be true or false.

Indeed both ideas and words may be said to be true, in a metaphysical sense of the word truth; as all other things that any way exist are said to be true, i.e. really to be such as they exist. Though in things called true, even in that sense, there is perhaps a secret reference to our ideas, looked upon as the standards of that truth; which amounts to a mental proposition, though it be usually not taken notice of.

But it is not in that metaphysical sense of truth which we inquire here, when we examine, whether our ideas are capable of being true or false, but in the more ordinary acceptation of those words: and so I say that the ideas in our minds, being only so many perceptions or appearances there, none of them are false; the idea of a centaur having no more falsehood in it when it appears in our minds, than the name centaur has falsehood in it, when it is pronounced by our mouths, or written on paper. For truth or falsehood lying always in some affirmation or negation, mental or verbal, our ideas are not capable, any of them, of being false, till the mind passes some judgment on them; that is, affirms or denies something of them.

Whenever the mind refers any of its ideas to anything extraneous to them, they are then capable to be called true or false. Because the mind, in such a reference, makes a tacit supposition of their conformity to that thing; which supposition, as it happens to be true or false, so the ideas themselves come to be denominated. The most usual cases wherein this happens, are these following:

First, when the mind supposes any idea it has *conformable* to that in *other men's minds,* called by the same common name; v.g. when the mind intends or judges its ideas of justice, temperance, religion, to be the same with what other men give those names to.

Secondly, when the mind supposes any idea it has in itself to be *conformable* to some *real existence.* Thus the two ideas of a man and a centaur, supposed to be the ideas of real substances, are the one true and the other false; the one having a conformity to what has really existed, the other not.

Thirdly, when the mind *refers* any of its ideas to that *real* constitution and *essence* of anything, whereon all its properties depend: and thus the greatest part, if not all our ideas of substances, are false.

Though, in compliance with the ordinary ways of speaking, I have shown in what sense and upon what ground our ideas may be sometimes called true or false; yet if we will look a little nearer into the matter, in all cases where any idea is called true or false, it is from some *judgment* that the mind makes, or is supposed to make, that is true or false. For truth or falsehood, being never without some affirmation or negation, express or tacit, it is not to be found but where signs are joined or separated, according to the agreement or disagreement of the things they stand for. The signs we chiefly use are either ideas or words; wherewith we make either mental or verbal propositions. Truth lies in so joining or separating these representatives, as the things they stand for do in themselves agree or disagree; and falsehood in the contrary, as shall be more fully shown hereafter.

Any idea, then, which we have in our minds whether conformable or not to the existence of things, or to any idea in the minds of other men, cannot properly for this alone be called false. For these representations, if they have nothing in them but what is really existing in things without, cannot be thought false, being exact representations of something: nor yet if they have anything in them differing from the reality of things, can they properly be said to be false representations, or ideas of things they do not represent. But the mistake and falsehood is:

First, when the mind having any idea, it *judges* and concludes it the same that is in other men's minds, signified by the same name; or that it is conformable to the ordinary received signification or definition of that word, when indeed it is not: which is the most usual mistake in mixed modes, though other ideas also are liable to it.

Secondly, when it having a complex idea made up of such a collection of simple ones as nature never puts together, it *judges* it to agree to a species of creatures really existing; as when it joins the weight of tin to the color, fusibility, and fixedness of gold.

Thirdly, when in its complex idea it has united a certain number of simple ideas that do really exist together in some sort of creatures, but has also left out others as much inseparable, it *judges* this to be a perfect complete idea of a sort of thing which really it is not; v.g. having joined the ideas of substance, yellow, malleable, most heavy, and fusible, it takes that complex idea to be the complete idea of gold, when yet its peculiar fixedness, and solubility in *aqua regia,* are as inseparable from those other ideas, or qualities, of that body as they are one from another.

Fourthly, the mistake is yet greater, when I *judge* that this complex idea contains in it the real essence of any body existing; when at least it contains but some few of those properties which flow from its real essence and constitution. I say only some few of those properties; for those properties consisting mostly in the active and passive powers it has in reference to other things, all that are vulgarly known of any one body, of which the complex idea of that kind of things is usually made, are but a very few, in comparison of what a man that has several ways tried and examined it knows of that one sort of things; and all that the most expert man knows are but a few, in comparison of what are really in that body, and depend on its internal or essential constitution. The essence of a triangle lies in a very little compass, consists in a very few ideas: three lines including a space make up that essence: but the properties that flow from this essence are more than can be easily known or enumerated. So I imagine it is in substances; their real essences lie in a little compass, though the properties flowing from that internal constitution are endless.

To conclude, a man having no notion of anything without him, but by the idea he has of it in his mind (which idea he has a power to call by what name he pleases), he may indeed make an idea neither answering the reason of things, nor agreeing to the idea commonly signified by other people's words; but cannot make a wrong or false idea of a thing which is no otherwise known to him but by the idea he has of it: v.g. when I frame an idea of the legs, arms, and body of a man, and join to this a horse's head and neck, I do not make a false idea of anything; because it represents nothing without me. But when I call it a *man* or *Tartar,* and imagine it to represent some real being without me, or to be the same idea that others call by the same name; in either of these cases I may err. And upon this account it is that it comes to be termed a false idea; though indeed the falsehood lies not in the idea, but in that tacit mental proposition, wherein a conformity and resemblance is attributed to it which it has not. But yet, if, having framed such an idea in my mind, without thinking either that existence, or the name *man* or *Tartar,* belongs to it, I will call it *man* or *Tartar,* I may be justly thought fantastical in the naming; but not erroneous in my judgment; nor the idea any way false.

Upon the whole matter, I think that our ideas, as they are considered by the mind,—either in reference to the proper signification of their names; or in reference to the reality of things,—may very fitly be called *right* or *wrong* ideas, according as they agree or disagree to those patterns to which they are referred. But if anyone had rather call them true or false, it is fit he use a liberty, which everyone has, to call things by those names he thinks best; though, in propriety of speech, *truth* or *falsehood* will, I think scarce agree to them, but as they, some way or other, virtually contain in them some mental proposition. The ideas that are in a man's mind, simply considered, cannot be wrong; unless complex ones, wherein inconsistent parts are jumbled together. All other ideas are in themselves right, and the knowledge about them right and true knowledge; but when we come to refer them to anything, as to their patterns and archetypes, then they are capable of being wrong, as far as they disagree with such archetypes.

Having thus given an account of the original, sorts, and extent of our IDEAS, with several other considerations about these (I know not whether I may say) instruments, or materials of our knowledge, the method I at first proposed to myself would now require that I should immediately proceed to show, what use the understanding makes of them, and what KNOWLEDGE we have by them. This was that which, in the first general view I had of this subject, was all that I thought I should have to do: but, upon a nearer approach, I find that there is so close a connection between ideas and WORDS, and our abstract ideas and general words have so constant a relation one to another, that it is impossible to speak clearly and distinctly of our knowledge, which all consists in propositions, without considering, first, the nature, use, and signification of Language; which, therefore, must be the business of the next Book.

BOOK THREE

OF WORDS

I

Of Words, or Language in General

GOD, HAVING DESIGNED MAN FOR A SOCIABLE CREATURE, made him not only with an inclination, and under a necessity to have fellowship with those of his own kind, but furnished him also with language, which was to be the great instrument and common tie of society. Man, therefore, had by nature his organs so fashioned, as to be fit to frame articulate sounds, which we call words. But this was not enough to produce language; for parrots, and several other birds, will be taught to make articulate sounds distinct enough, which yet by no means are capable of language.

Besides articulate sounds, therefore, it was further necessary that he should be able to use these sounds as signs of internal conceptions; and to make them stand as marks for the ideas within his own mind, whereby they might be made known to others, and the thoughts of men's minds be conveyed from one to another.

But neither was this sufficient to make words so useful as they ought to be. It is not enough for the perfection of language, that sounds can be made signs of ideas, unless those signs can be so made use of as to comprehend several particular things: for the multiplication of words would have perplexed their use, had every particular thing need of a distinct name to be signified by.

Besides these names which stand for ideas, there be other words which men make use of, not to signify any idea, but the want or absence of some ideas, simple or complex, or all ideas together; such as are *nihil* in Latin, and in English, *ignorance* and *barrenness*. All which negative or privative words cannot be said properly to belong to, or signify no ideas: for then they would be perfectly insignificant sounds; but they relate to positive ideas, and signify their absence.

It may also lead us a little toward the original of all our notions and knowledge, if we remark how great a dependence our words have on common sensible ideas; and how those which are made use of to stand for actions and notions quite removed from sense, have their rise from thence, and from obvious sensible ideas are transferred to more abstruse significations, and made to stand for ideas that come not under the cognizance of our senses; v.g. to *imagine, apprehend, comprehend, adhere, conceive, instill, disgust, disturbance, tranquillity,* etc., are all words taken from the operations of sensible things, and applied to certain modes of thinking.

But to understand better the use and force of Language, as subservient to instruction and knowledge, it will be convenient to consider:

First, To what it is that names, in the use of language, are immediately applied.

Secondly, Since all (except proper) names are general, and so stand not particularly for this or that single thing, but for sorts and ranks of things, it will be necessary to consider, in the next place, what the sorts and kinds, or, if you rather like the Latin names, *what the Species and Genera of things are, wherein they consist, and how they come to be made.* These being (as they ought) well looked into, we shall the better come to find the right use of words; the natural advantages and defects of language; and the remedies that ought to be used, to avoid the inconveniences of obscurity or uncertainty in the signification of words: without which it is impossible to discourse with any clearness or order concerning knowledge: which, being conversant about propositions, and those most commonly universal ones, has greater connection with words than perhaps is suspected.

These considerations, therefore, shall be the matter of the following chapters.

11

Of the Signification of Words

MAN, THOUGH HE HAVE GREAT VARIETY OF THOUGHTS, and such from which others as well as himself might receive profit and delight; yet they are all within his own breast, invisible and hidden from others, nor can of themselves be made to appear. The comfort and advantage of society not being to be had without communication of thoughts, it was necessary that man should find out some external sensible signs, whereof those invisible ideas, which his thoughts are made up of, might be made known to others. For this purpose nothing was so fit, either for plenty or quickness, as those articulate sounds, which with so much ease and variety he found himself able to make. Thus we may conceive how *words,* which were by nature so well adapted to that purpose, came to be made use of by men as the signs of their ideas; not by any natural connection that there is between particular articulate sounds and certain ideas, for then there would be but one language amongst all men; but by a voluntary imposition, whereby such a word is made arbitrarily the mark of such an idea. The use, then, of words, is to be sensible marks of ideas; and the ideas they stand for are their proper and immediate signification.

The use men have of these marks being either to record their own thoughts, for the assistance of their own memory; or, as it were, to bring out their ideas, and lay them before the view of others: words, in their primary or immediate signification, stand for nothing but *the ideas in the mind of him that uses them,* how imperfectly soever or carelessly those ideas are collected from the things which they are supposed to represent. When a man speaks to another, it is that he may be understood: and the end of speech is, that those sounds, as marks, may make known his ideas to the hearer. That then which words are the marks of are the ideas of the speaker: nor can anyone apply them as marks, immediately, to anything else but the ideas that he himself hath: for this would be to make them signs of his own conceptions, and yet apply them to other ideas; which would be to make them signs and not signs of his ideas at the same time; and so in effect to have no signification at all. Words being voluntary signs, they cannot be voluntary signs imposed by him on things he knows not. That would be to make them signs of nothing, sounds without signification. A man cannot make his words the signs either of qualities in things, or of conceptions in the mind of another, whereof he has none in his own. Till he has some ideas of his own, he cannot suppose them to correspond with the conceptions of another man; nor can he use any signs for them: for thus they would be the signs of he knows not what, which is in truth to be the signs of nothing. But when he represents to himself other men's ideas by some of his own, if he consent to give them the same names that other men do, it is still to his own ideas; to ideas that he has, and not to ideas that he has not.

But though words, as they are used by men, can properly and immediately signify nothing but the ideas that are in the mind of the speaker; yet they in their thoughts give them a secret reference to two other things.

First, *They suppose their words to be marks of the ideas in the minds also of other men, with whom they communicate:* for else they should talk in vain, and could not be understood, if the sounds they applied to one idea were such as by the hearer were applied to another, which is to speak two languages. But in this men stand not usually to examine, whether the idea they, and those they discourse with have in their minds be the same: but think it enough that they use the word, as they imagine, in the common acceptation of that language; in which they suppose that the idea they make it a sign of is precisely the same to which the understanding men of that country apply that name.

Secondly, Because men would not be thought to talk barely of their own imagination, but of things as really they are; therefore they often suppose the *words to stand also for the reality of things.* But this relating more particularly to substances and their names, as perhaps the former does to simple ideas and modes, we shall speak of these two different ways of applying words more at large, when we come to treat of the names of mixed modes and substances in particular: though give me leave here to say, that it is a perverting the use of words, and brings unavoidable obscurity and confusion into their signification, whenever we make them stand for anything but those ideas we have in our own minds.

Words, by long and familiar use, as has been said, come to

excite in men certain ideas so constantly and readily, that they are apt to suppose a natural connection between them. But that they signify only men's peculiar ideas, and that *by a perfect arbitrary imposition,* is evident, in that they often fail to excite in others (even that use the same language) the same ideas we take them to be signs of: and every man has so inviolable a liberty to make words stand for what ideas he pleases, that no one hath the power to make others have the same ideas in their minds that he has, when they use the same words that he does. And therefore the great Augustus himself, in the possession of that power which ruled the world, acknowledged he could not make a new Latin word: which was as much as to say, that he could not arbitrarily appoint what idea any sound should be a sign of, in the mouths and common language of his subjects. It is true, common use, by a tacit consent, appropriates certain sounds to certain ideas in all languages, which so far limits the signification of that sound, that unless a man applies it to the same idea, he does not speak properly: and let me add, that unless a man's words excite the same ideas in the hearer which he makes them stand for in speaking, he does not speak intelligibly. But whatever be the consequence of any man's using of words differently, either from their general meaning, or the particular sense of the person to whom he addresses them; this is certain, their signification, in his use of them, is limited to his ideas, and they can be signs of nothing else.

III

Of General Terms

ALL THINGS THAT EXIST BEING PARTICULARS, it may perhaps be thought reasonable that words, which ought to be conformed to things, should be so too,—I mean in their signification: but yet we find quite the contrary. The far greatest part of words that make all languages are general terms: which has not been the effect of neglect or chance, but of reason and necessity.

First, It is impossible that every particular thing should have a distinct peculiar name. For, the signification and use of words depending on that connection which the mind makes between its ideas and the sounds it uses as signs of them, it is necessary, in the application of names to things, that the mind should have distinct ideas of the things, and retain also the particular name that belongs to every one, with its peculiar appropriation to that idea. But it is beyond the power of human capacity to frame and retain distinct ideas of all the particular things we meet with: every bird and beast men saw; every tree and plant that affected the senses, could not find a place in the most capacious understanding.

Secondly, If it were possible, it would yet be useless; because it would not serve to the chief end of language. Men would in vain heap up names of particular things, that would not serve them to communicate their thoughts. Men learn names, and use them in talk with others, only that they may be understood: which is then only done when, by use or consent, the sound I make by the organs of speech, excites in another man's mind who hears it, the idea I apply it to in mine, when I speak it. This cannot be done by names applied to particular things; whereof I alone having the ideas in my mind, the names of them could not be significant or intelligible to another, who was not acquainted with all those very particular things which had fallen under my notice.

Thirdly, But yet, granting this also feasible (which I think is not), yet a distinct name for every particular thing would not be of any great use for the improvement of knowledge: which, though founded in particular things, enlarges itself by general views; to which things reduced into sorts, under general names, are properly subservient. These, with the names belonging to them, come within some compass, and do not multiply every moment, beyond what either the mind can contain, or use requires. And therefore, in these, men have for the most part stopped: but yet not so as to hinder themselves from distinguishing particular things by appropriated names, where convenience demands it. And therefore in their own species, which they have most to do with, and wherein they have often occasion to mention particular persons, they make use of proper names; and their distinct individuals have distinct denominations.

Besides persons, countries also, cities, rivers, mountains, and other the like distinctions of place have usually found peculiar names, and that for the same reason; they being such as men have often an occasion to mark particularly, and, as it were, set before others in their discourses with them. And I doubt not but, if we had reason to mention particular horses as often as we have to mention particular men, we should have proper names for the one, as familiar as for the other, and Bucephalus would be a word as much in use as Alexander. And therefore we see that, amongst jockeys, horses have their proper names to be known and distinguished by, as commonly as their servants: because, amongst them, there is often occasion to mention this or that particular horse when he is out of sight.

[Locke goes on to deal with the problem of how general words are made. He suggests that words become general by being made the signs of general ideas. From childhood onward, we enlarge our complex ideas, and then abstract from those complex ideas, general notions. This explains why the *genus* is ordinarily employed in definition: although Locke adds that it is not at all necessary for definitions to consist of *genus* and *differentia*.]

To return to general words: it is plain, by what has been said, that *general* and *universal* belong not to the real existence of things; but are the inventions and creatures of the understanding, made by it for its own use, and concern only signs, whether words or ideas. Words are general, as has been said, when used for signs of general ideas, and so are applicable indifferently to many particular things; and ideas are general when they are set up as the representatives of many particular things: but universality belongs not to things themselves, which are all of them particular in their existence, even those words and ideas which in their signification are general. When therefore we quit particulars, the generals that rest are only creatures of our own making; their general nature being nothing but the capacity they are put into, by the understanding, of signifying or representing many particulars. For the signification they have is nothing but a relation that, by the mind of man, is added to them.

The next thing therefore to be considered is, What kind of signification it is that general words have. For, as it is evident that they do not signify barely one particular thing; for then they would not be general terms, but proper names, so, on the other side, it is as evident they do not signify a plurality; for *man* and *men* would then signify the same; and the distinction of numbers (as the grammarians call them) would be superfluous and useless. That then which general words signify is a *sort* of things; and each of them does that, by being a sign of an abstract idea in the mind; to which idea, as things existing are found to agree, so they come to be ranked under that name, or, which is all one, be of that sort. Whereby it is evident that the *essences* of the sorts, or, if the Latin word pleases better, *species* of things, are nothing else but these abstract ideas. For the having the essence of any species, being that which makes anything to be of that species; and the conformity to the idea to which the name is annexed being that which gives a right to that name; the having the essence, and the having that conformity, must needs be the same thing: since to be of any species, and to have a right to the name of that species, is all one. As, for example, to be a *man*, or of the *species* man, and to have right to the *name* man, is the same thing. Again, to be a man, or of the species man, and have the *essence* of a man, is the same thing. Now, since nothing can be a man, or have a right to the name man, but what has a conformity to the abstract idea the name man stands for, nor anything be a man, or have a right to the species man, but what has the essence of that species; it follows, that the abstract idea for which the name stands, and the essence of the species, is one and the same. From whence it is easy to observe, that the essences of the sorts of things, and, consequently, the sorting of things, is the workmanship of the understanding that abstracts and makes those general ideas.

[Locke next argues that abstract ideas are the workmanship of the understanding, taking occasion from the similitude it observes among things. Each distinct abstract idea has its own essence; but essences may be divided into real and nominal. There is no need for the supposition that species are distinguished by their real essence. We should content ourselves with such essences of the sorts and species of things as come within the reach of our knowledge, i.e. those *abstract* complex ideas to which we have annexed distinct general names.]

To conclude. This is that which in short I would say, viz. that all the great business of *genera* and *species,* and their *essences,* amounts to no more but this:—That men making abstract ideas, and settling them in their minds with names annexed to them, do thereby enable themselves to consider things, and discourse of them, as it were in bundles, for the easier and readier improvement and communication of their knowledge, which would advance but slowly were their words and thoughts confined only to particulars.

I V

Of the Names of Simple Ideas

THOUGH ALL WORDS, as I have shown, signify nothing immediately but the ideas in the mind of the speaker; yet, upon a nearer survey, we shall find the names of *simple ideas, mixed modes* (under which I comprise *relations* too), and *natural substances,* have each of them something peculiar and different from the other. For example:——

First, The names of *simple ideas* and *substances,* with the abstract ideas in the mind which they immediately signify, intimate also some real existence, from which was derived their original pattern. But the names of *mixed modes* terminate in the idea that is in the mind, and lead not the thoughts any further; as we shall see more at large in the following chapter.

Secondly, The names of simple ideas and modes signify always the real as well as nominal essence of their species. But the names of natural substances signify rarely, if ever, anything but barely the nominal essences of those species; as we shall show in the chapter that treats of the names of substances in particular.

Thirdly, The names of simple ideas are not capable of any definition; the names of all complex ideas are.

I will not here trouble myself to prove that all terms are not definable, from that progress *in infinitum,* which it will visibly lead us into, if we should allow that all names could be defined. For, if the terms of one definition were still to be defined by another, where at last should we stop? But I shall, from the nature of our ideas, and the signification of our words, show *why some names can, and others cannot be defined;* and *which they are.*

I think it is agreed, that a *definition* is nothing else but *the showing the meaning of one word by several other not synonymous terms.* The meaning of words being only the ideas they are made to stand for by him that uses them, the meaning of any term is then showed, or the word is defined, when, by other words, the idea it is made the sign of, and annexed to, in the mind of the speaker, is as it were represented, or set before the view of another; and thus its signification ascertained. This is the only use and end of definitions; and therefore the only measure of what is, or is not a good definition.

This being premised, I say that the *names of simple ideas, and those only, are incapable of being defined.* The reason whereof is this, That the several terms of a definition, signifying several ideas, they can all together by no means represent an idea which has no composition at all: and therefore a definition, which is properly nothing but the showing the meaning of one word by several others not signifying each the same thing, can in the names of simple ideas have no place.

Simple ideas, as has been shown, are only to be got by those impressions objects themselves make on our minds, by the proper inlets appointed to each sort. If they are not received this way, all the words in the world, made use of to explain or define any of their names, will never be able to produce in us the idea it stands for. For, words being sounds, can produce in us no other simple ideas than of those very sounds; nor excite any in us, but by that voluntary connection which is known to be between them and those simple ideas which common use has made them the signs of. He that thinks otherwise, let him try if any words can give him the taste of a pineapple, and make him have the true idea of the relish of that celebrated delicious fruit. So far as he is told it has a resemblance with any tastes whereof he has the ideas already in his memory, imprinted there by sensible objects, not strangers to his palate, so far may he approach that resemblance in his mind. But this is not giving us that idea by a definition, but exciting in us other simple ideas by their known names; which will be still very different from the true taste of that fruit itself. In light and colors, and all other simple ideas, it is the same thing: for the signification of sounds is not natural, but only imposed and arbitrary. And no *definition* of light or redness is more fitted or able to produce either of those ideas in us, than the *sound* light or red, by itself. For, to hope to produce an idea of light or color by a sound, however formed, is to expect that sounds should be visible, or colors audible; and to make the ears do the office of all the other senses.

The case is quite otherwise in *complex ideas;* which, consisting of several simple ones, it is in the power of words, standing for the several ideas that make that composition, to imprint complex ideas in the mind which were never there before, and so make their names be understood. In such collections of ideas, passing under one name, definition, or the teaching the signification of one word by several others, has place, and may make us understand the names of things which never came within the reach of our senses; and frame ideas suitable to those in other men's minds, when they use those names: provided that none of the terms of the definition stand for any such simple ideas, which he to whom the explication is made has never yet had in his thought. Thus the word *statue* may be explained to a blind man by other words, when *picture* cannot; his senses having given him the idea of figure, but not of colors, which therefore words cannot excite in him.

Simple ideas, as has been shown, can only be got by experience from those objects which are proper to produce in us those perceptions. When, by this means, we have our minds stored with them, and know the names for them, then we are in a condition to define, and by definition to understand, the names of complex ideas that are made up of them. But when any term stands for a simple idea that a man has never yet had in his mind, it is impossible by any words to make known its meaning to him. When any term stands for an idea a man is acquainted with, but is ignorant that that term is the sign of it, then another name of the same idea, which he has been accustomed to, may make him understand its meaning. But in no case whatsoever is any name of any simple idea capable of a definition.

Fourthly, But though the names of simple ideas have not the help of definition to determine their signification, yet that hinders not but that they are generally less doubtful and uncertain than those of mixed modes and substances; because they, standing only for one simple perception, men for the most part easily and perfectly agree in their signification; and there is little room for mistake and wrangling about their meaning. He that knows once that whiteness is the name of that color he has observed in snow or milk, will not be apt to misapply that word, as long as he retains that idea; which when he has quite lost, he is not apt to mistake the meaning of it, but perceives he understands it not.

To conclude. The names of simple ideas, substances, and mixed modes have also this difference: that those of *mixed modes* stand for ideas perfectly arbitrary; those of *substances* are not perfectly so, but refer to a pattern, though with some latitude; and those of *simple ideas* are perfectly taken from the existence of things, and are not arbitrary at all. Which, what difference it makes in the significations of their names, we shall see in the following chapters.

V

Of the Names of Mixed Modes and Relations

THE NAMES OF MIXED MODES, being general, they stand, as has been shown, for sorts or species of things, each of which has its peculiar essence. The essences of these species also, as has been shown, are nothing but the abstract ideas in the mind, to which the name is annexed. Thus far the names and essences of mixed modes have nothing but what is common to them with other ideas: but if we take a little nearer survey of them, we shall find that they have something peculiar, which perhaps may deserve our attention.

The first particularity I shall observe in them, is, that the abstract ideas, or, if you please, the essences, of the several species of mixed modes, are *made by the understanding,* wherein they differ from those of simple ideas: in which sort the mind has no power to make any one, but only receives such as are presented to it by the real existence of things operating upon it.

In the next place, these essences of the species of mixed modes are not only made by the mind, but *made very arbitrarily, made without patterns, or reference to any real existence.* Wherein they differ from those of substances, which carry with them the supposition of some real being, from which they are taken, and to which they are conformable. But, in its complex ideas of mixed modes, the mind takes a liberty not to follow the existence of things exactly. It unites and retains certain collections, as so many distinct specific ideas; whilst others, that as often occur in nature, and are as plainly suggested by outward things, pass neglected, without particular names or specifications. Nor does the mind, in these of mixed modes, as in the complex idea of substances, examine them by the real existence of things; or verify them by patterns containing such peculiar compositions in nature. To know whether his idea of *adultery* or *incest* be right, will a man seek it anywhere amongst things existing? Or is it true because anyone has been witness to such an action? No: but it suffices here, that men have put together such a collection into one complex idea, that makes the archetype and specific idea;

whether ever any such action were committed *in rerum natura* or no.

To understand this right, we must consider wherein this making of these complex ideas consists; and that is not in the making any new idea, but putting together those which the mind had before. Wherein the mind does these three things: First, It chooses a certain number; Secondly, It gives them connection, and makes them into one idea; Thirdly, It ties them together by a name. If we examine how the mind proceeds in these, and what liberty it takes in them, we shall easily observe how these essences of the species of mixed modes are the workmanship of the mind; and, consequently, that the species themselves are of men's making.

Nobody can doubt but that these ideas of mixed modes are made by a voluntary collection of ideas, put together in the mind, independent from any original patterns in nature, who will but reflect that this sort of complex ideas may be made, abstracted, and have names given them, and so a species be constituted, before any one individual of that species ever existed. Who can doubt but the ideas of *sacrilege* or *adultery* might be framed in the minds of men, and have names given them, and so these species of mixed modes be constituted, before either of them was ever committed; and might be as well discoursed of and reasoned about, and as certain truths discovered of them, whilst yet they had no being but in the understanding, as well as now, that they have but too frequently a real existence? Whereby it is plain how much the sorts of mixed modes are the creatures of the understanding, where they have a being as subservient to all the ends of real truth and knowledge, as when they really exist. And we cannot doubt but lawmakers have often made laws about species of actions which were only the creatures of their own understandings; beings that had no other existence but in their own minds. And I think nobody can deny but that the *resurrection* was a species of mixed modes in the mind, before it really existed.

To see how arbitrarily these essences of mixed modes are made by the mind, we need but take a view of almost any of them. A little looking into them will satisfy us, that it is the mind that combines several scattered independent ideas into one complex one; and, by the common name it gives them, makes them the essence of a certain species, without regulating itself by any connection they have in nature. For what greater connection in nature has the idea of a man than the idea of a sheep with killing, that this is made a particular species of action, signified by the word *murder,* and the other not? Or what union is there in nature between the idea of the relation of a father with killing than that of a son or neighbor, that those are combined into one complex idea, and thereby made the essence of the distinct species *parricide,* whilst the other makes no distinct species at all? But, though they have made killing a man's father or mother a distinct species from killing his son or daughter, yet, in some other cases, son and daughter are taken in too, as well as father and mother: and they are all equally comprehended in the same species, as in that of *incest.* Thus the mind in mixed modes arbitrarily unites into complex ideas such as it finds convenient; whilst others that have altogether as much union in nature are left loose, and never combined into one idea, because they have no need of one name. It is evident then that the mind, by its free choice, gives a connection to a certain number of ideas, which in nature have no more union with one another than others that it leaves out: why else is the part of the weapon the beginning of the wound is made with taken notice of, to make the distinct species called *stabbing,* and the figure and matter of the weapon left out? I do not say this is done without reason, as we shall see more by and by; but this I say, that it is done by the free choice of the mind, pursuing its own ends; and that, therefore, these species of mixed modes are the workmanship of the understanding. And there is nothing more evident than that, for the most part, in the framing these ideas, the mind searches not its patterns in nature, nor refers the ideas it makes to the real existence of things, but puts such together as may best serve its own purposes, without tying itself to a precise imitation of anything that really exists.

But, though these complex ideas or essences of mixed modes depend on the mind, and are made by it with great liberty, yet they are not made at random, and jumbled together without any reason at all. Though these complex ideas be not always copied from nature, yet they are always suited to the end for which abstract ideas are made: and though they be combinations made of ideas that are loose enough, and have as little union in themselves as several other to which the mind never gives a connection that combines them into one idea; yet they are always made for the convenience of communication, which is the chief end of language. The use of language is, by short sounds, to signify with ease and dispatch general conceptions; wherein not only abundance of particulars may be contained, but also a great variety of independent ideas collected into one complex one. In the making therefore of the species of mixed modes men have had regard only to such combinations as they had occasion to mention one to another. Those they have combined into distinct complex ideas, and given names to; whilst others, that in nature have as near a union, are left loose and unregarded.

[Locke goes on to suggest that the impossibility of translating some words from one language into another is proof that names do not stand for fixed essences: and shows that different societies have different notions for which each finds a convenient name. In mixed modes, the name ties the ideas together and makes a sort or species. All these mixed modes are the workmanship of the understanding.]

Another thing we may observe from what has been said is, That the names of mixed modes always signify (when they have any determined signification) the *real* essences of their species. For, these abstract ideas being the workmanship of the mind, and not referred to the real existence of things, there is no supposition of anything more signified by that name, but barely that complex idea the mind itself has formed; which is all it would have expressed by it; and is that on which all the properties of the species depend, and from which alone they all flow: and so in these the real and nominal essence is the same; which, of what concernment it is to the certain knowledge of general truth, we shall see hereafter.

This also may show us the reason why for the most part the names of mixed modes are got before the ideas they stand for are perfectly known. Because there being no species of these ordinarily taken notice of but what have names, and those species, or rather their essences, being abstract complex ideas, made arbitrarily by the mind, it is convenient, if not necessary, to know the names, before one endeavor to frame these complex ideas: unless a man will fill his head with a company of abstract complex ideas, which, others having no names for, he has nothing to do with, but to lay by and forget again. I confess that, in the beginning of languages, it was necessary to have the idea before one gave it the name: and so it is still, where, making a new complex idea, one also, by giving it a new name, makes a new word. But this concerns not languages made, which have generally pretty well provided for ideas which men have frequent occasion to have and communicate; and in such, I ask whether it be not the ordinary method, that children learn the names of mixed modes before they have their ideas? What one of a thousand ever frames the abstract ideas of *glory* and *ambition*, before he has heard the names of them? In simple ideas and substances I grant it is otherwise; which, being such ideas as have a real existence and union in nature, the ideas and names are got one before the other, as it happens.

VI

Of the Names of Substances

THE COMMON NAMES OF SUBSTANCES, as well as other general terms, stand for *sorts:* which is nothing else but the being made signs of such complex ideas wherein several particular substances do or might agree, by virtue of which they are capable of being comprehended in one common conception, and signified by one name. I say do or might agree: for though there be but one sun existing in the world, yet the idea of it being abstracted, so that more substances (if there were several) might each agree in it, it is as much a sort as if there were as many suns as there are stars. They want not their reasons who think there are, and that each fixed star would answer the idea the name sun stands for, to one who was placed in a due distance: which, by the way, may show us how much the sorts, or, if you please, *genera* and *species* of things (for those Latin terms signify to me no more than the English word sort) depend on such collections of ideas as men have made, and not on the real nature of things; since it is not impossible but that, in propriety of speech, that might be a sun to one which is a star to another.

The measure and boundary of each sort or species, whereby it is constituted that particular sort, and distinguished from others, is that we call its *essence,* which is nothing but that abstract idea to which the name is annexed; so that everything contained in that idea is essential to that sort. This, though it be all the essence of natural substances that *we* know, or by which we distinguish them into sorts, yet I call it by a peculiar name, the *nominal essence,* to distinguish it from the real constitution of substances, upon which depends this nominal essence, and all the properties of that sort; which, therefore, as has been said, may be called the *real essence:* v.g. the nominal essence of gold is that complex idea the word gold stands for, let it be, for instance, a body yellow, of a certain weight, malleable, fusible, and fixed. But the real essence is the constitution of the insensible parts of that body, on which those qualities and all the other properties of gold depend. How far these two are different, though they are both called essence, is obvious at first sight to discover.

For, though perhaps voluntary motion, with sense and reason, joined to a body of a certain shape, be the complex idea to which I and others annex the name *man,* and so be the nominal essence of the species so called: yet nobody will say that complex idea is the real essence and source of all those operations which are to be found in any individual of that sort. The foundation of all those qualities which are the ingredients of our complex idea, is something quite different: and had we such a knowledge of that constitution of man, from which his faculties of moving, sensation, and reasoning, and other powers flow, and on which his so regular shape depends, as it is possible angels have, and it is certain his Maker has, we should have a quite other idea of his essence than what now is contained in our definition of that species, be it what it will: and our idea of any individual man would be as far different from what it is now, as is his who knows all the springs and wheels and other contrivances within of the famous clock at Strasburg, from that which a gazing countryman has of it, who barely sees the motion of the hand, and hears the clock strike, and observes only some of the outward appearances.

That *essence,* in the ordinary use of the word, relates to sorts, and that it is considered in particular beings no further than as they are ranked into sorts, appears from hence: that, take but away the abstract ideas by which we sort individuals, and rank them under common names, and then the thought of anything essential to any of them instantly vanishes: we have no notion of the one without the other, which plainly shows their relation. It is necessary for me to be as I am God and nature has made me so: but there is nothing I have is essential to me. An accident or disease may very much alter my color or shape; a fever or fall may take away my reason or memory, or both; and an apoplexy leave neither sense, nor understanding, no, nor life. Other creatures of my shape may be made with more and better, or fewer and worse faculties than I have; and others may have reason and sense in a shape and body very different from mine. None of these are essential to the one or the other, or to any individual whatever, till the mind refers it to some sort or species of things; and then presently, according to the abstract idea of that sort, something is found essential. Let anyone examine his own thoughts, and he will find that as soon as he suppose or speaks of essential, the consideration of some species, or the complex idea signified by some general name, comes into his mind; and it is in reference to that that this or that quality is said to be essential. So that if it be asked, whether it be essential to me or any other particular corporeal being, to have reason? I say, no; no more than it is essential to this white thing I write on to have words in it. But if that particular being be to be counted of the sort *man,* and to have the name *man* given it, then reason is essential to it; supposing reason to be a part of the complex idea the name man stands for: as it is essential to this thing I write on to contain words, if I will give it the name *treatise,* and rank it under that species. So that essential and not essential relate only to our abstract ideas, and the names annexed to them; which amounts to no more than this, That whatever particular thing has not in it those qualities which are contained in the abstract idea which any general term stands for, cannot be ranked under that species nor be called by that name; since, that abstract idea is the very essence of that species.

Thus, if the idea of *body* with some people be bare extension or space, then solidity is not essential to body: if others make the idea to which they give the name *body* to be solidity and extension, then solidity is essential to body. That therefore, and that alone, is considered as essential, which makes a part of the complex idea the name of a sort stands for; without which no particular thing can be reckoned of that sort, nor be entitled to that name. Should there be found a parcel of matter that had all the other qualities that are in iron, but wanted obedience to the loadstone, and would neither be drawn by it nor receive direction from it, would any one question whether it wanted anything essential? It would be absurd to ask, Whether a thing really existing wanted anything essential to it. Or could it be demanded, Whether this made an essential or specific difference or no, since *we* have no other measure of essential or specific but our abstract ideas? And to talk of specific differences in *nature,* without reference to general ideas in names, is to talk unintelligibly. For I would ask anyone, What is sufficient to make an essential difference in nature between any two particular beings, without any regard had to some abstract idea, which is looked upon as the essence and standard of a species? All such patterns and standards being quite laid aside, particular beings, considered barely in themselves, will be found to have all their qualities equally essential; and everything in each individual will be essential to it; or, which is more, nothing at all. For, though it may be reasonable to ask, Whether obeying the magnet be essential to iron? yet I think it is very improper and insignificant to ask, whether it be essential to the particular parcel of matter I cut my pen with; without considering it under the name *iron,* or as being of a certain species. And if, as has been said, our abstract ideas, which have names annexed to them, are the boundaries of species, nothing can be essential but what is contained in those ideas.

It is true, I have often mentioned a *real essence,* distinct in substances from those abstract ideas of them, which I call their nominal essence. By this real essence I mean, that real constitution of anything, which is the foundation of all those properties that are combined in, and are constantly found to co-exist with the nominal essence; that particular constitution which everything has within itself, without any relation to anything without it. But essence, even in this sense, *relates to a sort, and supposes a species.* For, being that real constitution on which the properties depend, it necessarily supposes a sort of things, properties belonging only to species, and not to individuals: v.g. supposing the nominal essence of gold to be a body of such a peculiar color and weight, with malleability and fusibility, the real essence is that constitution of the parts of matter on which these qualities and their union depend; and is also the foundation of its solubility in *aqua regia* and other properties, accompanying that complex idea. Here are essences and properties, but all upon supposition of a sort or general abstract idea, which is considered as immutable; but there is no individual parcel of matter to which any of these qualities are so annexed as to be essential to it or inseparable from it. That which is essential belongs to it as a condition whereby it is of this or that sort: but take away the consideration of its being ranked under the name of some abstract idea, and then there is nothing necessary to it, nothing inseparable from it. Indeed, as to the real essences of substances, we only suppose their being, without precisely knowing what they are; but that which annexes them still to the species is the nominal essence, of which they are the supposed foundation and cause.

The next thing to be considered is, by which of those essences it is that substances are determined into sorts or species; and that, it is evident, is by the nominal essence. For it is that alone that the name, which is the mark of the sort, signifies. It is impossible, therefore, that anything should determine the sorts of things, which *we* rank under general names, but that idea which that name is designed as a mark for; which is that, as has been shown, which we call nominal essence. Why do we say this is a horse, and that a mule; this is an animal, that an herb? How comes any particular thing to be of this or that sort, but because it has that nominal essence; or, which is all one, agrees to that abstract idea, that name is annexed to? And I desire anyone but to reflect on his own thoughts, when he hears or speaks any of those or other names of substances, to know what sort of essences they stand for.

And that the species of things to us are nothing but the ranking them under distinct names, according to the complex ideas in *us,* and not according to precise, distinct real essences in *them,* is plain from hence:—That we find many of the individuals that are ranked into one sort, called by one common name, and so received as being of one species, have yet qualities, depending on their real constitutions, as far different one from another as from others from which they are accounted to differ specifically.

Nor indeed can we rank and sort things, and consequently (which is the end of sorting) denominate them, by their real essences; because we know them not. Our faculties carry us no further toward the knowledge and distinction of substances, than a collection of *those sensible ideas which we observe in them;* which, however made with the greatest diligence and exactness we are capable of, yet is more remote from the true internal constitution from which those qualities flow, than, as I said, a countryman's idea is from the inward contrivance of that famous clock at Strasburg, whereof he only sees the outward figure and motions. There is not so contemptible a plant or animal, that does not confound the most enlarged understanding. He that thinks he can distinguish sheep and goats by their real essences, that are unknown to him, may be pleased to try his skill in those species called *cassowary* and *querechinchio;* and by their internal real essences determine the boundaries of those species, without knowing the complex idea of sensible qualities that each of those names stand for, in the countries where those animals are to be found.

Those, therefore, who have been taught that the several species of substances had their distinct internal *substantial forms,* and that it was those *forms* which made the distinction of substances into their true species and genera, were led yet further out of the way by having their minds set upon fruitless inquiries after "substantial forms"; wholly unintelligible, and whereof we have scarce so much as any obscure or confused conception in general.

To distinguish substantial beings into species, according to the usual supposition, that there are certain precise essences or forms of things, whereby all the individuals existing are, by nature distinguished into species, these things are necessary:——

First, To be assured that nature, in the production of things, always designs them to partake of certain regulated established essences, which are to be the models of all things to be produced. This, in that crude sense it is usually proposed, would need some better explication, before it can fully be assented to.

Secondly, It would be necessary to know whether nature always attains that essence it designs in the production of things. The irregular and monstrous births, that in divers sorts of animals have been observed, will always give us reason to doubt of one or both of these.

Thirdly, It ought to be determined whether those we call monsters be really a distinct species, according to the scholastic notion of the word species; since it is certain that everything that exists has its particular constitution. And yet we find that some of these monstrous productions have few or none of those qualities which are supposed to result from, and accompany, the essence of that species from whence they derive their originals, and to which, by their descent, they seem to belong.

Fourthly, The real essences of those things which we distinguish into species, and as so distinguished we name, ought to be known; i.e. we ought to have ideas of them. But since we are ignorant in these four points, the supposed real essences of things stand *us* not in stead for the distinguishing substances into species.

Fifthly, The only imaginable help in this case would be,

that, having framed perfect complex ideas of the properties of things flowing from their different real essences, we should thereby distinguish them into species. But neither can this be done. For, being ignorant of the real essence itself, it is impossible to know all those properties that flow from it, and are so annexed to it, that any one of them being away, we may certainly conclude that that essence is not there, and so the thing is not of that species. We can never know what is the precise number of properties depending on the real essence of gold, any one of which failing, the real essence of gold, and consequently gold, would not be there, unless we knew the real essence of gold itself, and by that determined that species. By the word *gold* here, I must be understood to design a particular piece of matter; v.g. the last guinea that was coined. For, if it should stand here, in its ordinary signification, for that complex idea which I or anyone else calls gold, i.e. for the nominal essence of gold, it would be jargon. So hard is it to show the various meaning and imperfection of words, when we have nothing else but words to do it by.

By all which it is clear, that our distinguishing substances into species by names, is not at all founded on their real essences; nor can we pretend to range and determine them exactly into species, according to internal essential differences.

But since, as has been remarked, we have need of *general* words, though we know not the real essences of things; all we can do is, to collect such a number of simple ideas as, by examination, we find to be united together in things existing, and thereof to make one complex idea. Which, though it be not the real essence of any substance that exists, is yet the specific essence to which our name belongs, and is convertible with it; by which we may at least try the truth of these nominal essences. For example: there be that say that the essence of body is *extension;* if it be so, we can never mistake in putting the essence of anything for the thing itself. Let us then in discourse put extension for body, and when we would say that body moves, let us say that extension moves, and see how ill it will look. He that should say that one extension by impulse moves another extension, would, by the bare expression, sufficiently show the absurdity of such a notion. The essence of anything in respect of us, is the whole complex idea comprehended and marked by that name; and in substances, besides the several distinct simple ideas that make them up, the confused one of substance, or of an unknown support and cause of their union, is always a part: and therefore the essence of body is not bare extension, but an extended solid thing; and so to say, an extended solid thing moves, or impels another, is all one, and as intelligible, as to say, *body* moves or impels. Likewise, to say that a rational animal is capable of conversation, is all one as to say a man; but no one will say that rationality is capable of conversation, because it makes not the whole essence to which we give the name man.

Upon the whole matter, it is evident that it is their own collections of sensible qualities that men make the essences of *their* several sorts of substances; and that their real internal structures are not considered by the greatest part of men in the sorting them. Much less were any *substantial forms* ever thought on by any but those who have in this one part of the world learned the language of the schools: and yet those ignorant men, who pretend not any insight into the real essences, nor trouble themselves about substantial forms, but are content with knowing things one from another by their sensible qualities, are often better acquainted with their differences; can more nicely distinguish them from their uses; and better know what they expect from each, than those learned quick-sighted men, who look so deep into them, and talk so confidently of something more hidden and essential.

But supposing that the *real* essences of substances were discoverable by those that would severely apply themselves to that inquiry, yet we could not reasonably think that the ranking of things under general names was regulated by those internal real constitutions, or anything else but their *obvious* appearances; since languages, in all countries, have been established long before sciences. So that they have not been philosophers or logicians, or such who have troubled themselves about forms and essences, that have made the general names that are in use amongst the several nations of men: but those more or less comprehensive terms have, for the most part, in all languages, received their birth and signification from ignorant and illiterate people, who sorted and denominated things by those sensible qualities they found in them;

thereby to signify them, when absent, to others, whether they had an occasion to mention a sort or a particular thing.

Since then it is evident that we sort and name substances by their nominal and not by their real essences, the next thing to be considered is how, and by whom these essences come to be made. As to the latter, it is evident they are made by the mind, and not by nature: for were they Nature's workmanship, they could not be so various and different in several men as experience tells us they are. For if we will examine it, we shall not find the nominal essence of any one species of substances in all men the same: no, not of that which of all others we are the most intimately acquainted with. It could not possibly be that the abstract idea to which the name *man* is given should be different in several men, if it were of Nature's making; and that to one it should be *animal rationale,* and to another, *animal implume bipes latis unguibus*. He that annexes the name man to a complex idea, made up of sense and spontaneous motion, joined to a body of such a shape, has hereby one essence of the species man; and he that, upon further examination, adds rationality, has another essence of the species he calls man: by which means the same individual will be a true man to the one which is not so to the other. I think there is scarce anyone will allow this upright figure, so well known, to be the essential difference of the species man; and yet how far men determine of the sorts of animals rather by their shape than descent, is very visible; since it has been more than once debated, whether several human foetuses should be preserved or received to baptism or no, only because of the difference of their outward configuration from the ordinary make of children, without knowing whether they were not as capable of reason as infants cast in another mold: some whereof, though of an approved shape, are never capable of as much appearance of reason all their lives as is to be found in an ape, or an elephant, and never give any signs of being acted by a rational soul.

Wherein, then, would I gladly know, consist the precise and unmovable boundaries of that species? It is plain, if we examine, there is no such thing made by Nature, and established by her amongst men. The real essence of that or any other sort of substances, it is evident, we know not; and therefore are so undetermined in our nominal essences, which we make ourselves, that, if several men were to be asked concerning some oddly-shaped *foetus,* as soon as born, whether it were a *man* or no, it is past doubt one should meet with different answers. Which could not happen, if the nominal essences, whereby we limit and distinguish the species of substances, were not made by man with some liberty; but were exactly copied from precise boundaries set by nature, whereby it distinguished all substances into certain species. And I imagine none of the definitions of the word *man* which we yet have, nor descriptions of that sort of animal, are so perfect and exact as to satisfy a considerate inquisitive person; much less to obtain a general consent, and to be that which men would everywhere stick by, in the decision of cases, and determining of life and death, baptism or no baptism, in productions that might happen.

But though these nominal essences of substances are made by the mind, they are not yet made so arbitrarily as those of mixed modes. To the making of any nominal essence, it is necessary, First, that the ideas whereof it consists have such a union as to make but one idea, how compounded soever. Secondly, that the particular ideas so united be exactly the same, neither more nor less. For if two abstract complex ideas differ either in number or sorts of their component parts, they make two different, and not one and the same essence. In the first of these, the mind, in making its complex ideas of substances, only follows nature; and puts none together which are not supposed to have a union in nature. Nobody joins the voice of a sheep with the shape of a horse; nor the color of lead with the weight and fixedness of gold, to be the complex ideas of any real substances; unless he has a mind to fill his head with chimeras, and his discourse with unintelligible words. Men observing certain qualities always joined and existing together, therein copied nature; and of ideas so united made their complex ones of substances. For, though men may make what complex ideas they please, and give what names to them they will; yet, if they will be understood *when they speak of things really existing,* they must in some degree conform their ideas to the things they would speak of; or else men's language will be like that of Babel; and every man's words, being intelligible only to himself, would no longer serve to conversation and the ordinary affairs of life, if the ideas they stand for be not some way answering the common appearances and agreement of substances as they really exist.

Secondly, Though the mind of man, in making its complex ideas of substances, never puts any together that do not really, or are not supposed to, co-exist; and so it truly borrows that union from nature: yet the number it combines depends upon the various care, industry, or fancy of him that makes it. Men generally content themselves with some few sensible obvious qualities; and often, if not always, leave out others as material and as firmly united as those that they take.

But though this serves well enough for gross and confused conceptions, and inaccurate ways of talking and thinking; yet *men are far enough from having agreed on the precise number of simple ideas or qualities belonging to any sort of things, signified by its name.* Nor is it a wonder; since it requires much time, pains, and skill, strict inquiry, and long examination to find out what, and how many, those simple ideas are, which are constantly and inseparably united in nature, and are always to be found together in the same subject. Most men, wanting either time, inclination, or industry enough for this, even to some tolerable degree, content themselves with some few obvious and outward appearances of things, thereby readily to distinguish and sort them for the common affairs of life: and so, without further examination, give them names, or take up the names already in use. Which, though in common conversation they pass well enough for the signs of some few obvious qualities co-existing, are yet far enough from comprehending, in a settled signification, a precise number of simple ideas, much less all those which are united in nature.

But however these species of substances pass well enough in ordinary conversation, it is plain that this complex idea, wherein they observe several individuals to agree, is by different men made very differently; by some more, and others less accurately. In some, this complex idea contains a greater, and in others a smaller number of qualities; and so is apparently such as the mind makes it. The yellow shining color makes gold to children; others add weight, malleableness, and fusibility; and others yet other qualities, which they find joined with that yellow color, as constantly as its weight and fusibility. For in all these and the like qualities, one has as good a right to be put into the complex idea of that substance wherein they are all joined as another. And therefore different men, leaving out or putting in several simple ideas which others do not, according to their various examination, skill, or observation of that subject, have different essences of gold, which must therefore be of their own and not of nature's making.

If the number of simple ideas that make the nominal essence of the lowest species, or first sorting, of individuals, depends on the mind of man, variously collecting them, it is much more evident that they do so in the more comprehensive classes, which, by the masters of logic, are called *genera*. These are complex ideas designedly imperfect: and it is visible at first sight, that several of those qualities that are to be found in the things themselves are purposely left out of generical ideas. For, as the mind, to make general ideas comprehending several particulars, leaves out those of time and place, and such other, that make them incommunicable to more than one individual; so to make other yet more general ideas, that may comprehend different sorts, it leaves out those qualities that distinguish them, and puts into its new collection only such ideas as are common to several sorts. The same convenience that made men express several parcels of yellow matter coming from Guinea and Peru under one name, sets them also upon making of one name that may comprehend both gold and silver, and some other bodies of different sorts. This is done by leaving out those qualities, which are peculiar to each sort, and retaining a complex idea made up of those that are common to them all. To which the name *metal* being annexed, there is a genus constituted; the essence whereof being that abstract idea, containing only malleableness and fusibility, with certain degrees of weight and fixedness, wherein some bodies of several kinds agree, leaves out the color and other qualities peculiar to gold and silver, and the other sorts comprehended under the name metal. Whereby it is plain that men follow not exactly the patterns set them by nature, when they make their general ideas of substances; since there is no body to be found which has barely malleableness and fusibility in it, without other qualities as inseparable as those. But men, in making their general ideas, seeking more the convenience of language, and quick dispatch by short and comprehensive signs, than the true and precise nature of things as they exist, have, in the framing their abstract ideas, chiefly pursued that end; which was to be furnished with store of general and variously comprehensive names.

This is adjusted to the true end of speech, which is to be the easiest and shortest way of communicating our notions.

For thus he that would discourse of things, as they agreed in the complex idea of extension and solidity, needed but use the word *body* to denote all such. He that to these would join others, signified by the words life, sense, and spontaneous motion, needed but use the word *animal* to signify all which partook of those ideas, and he that had made a complex idea of a body, with life, sense, and motion, with the faculty of reasoning, and a certain shape joined to it, needed but use the short monosyllable *man,* to express all particulars that correspond to that complex idea. This is the proper business of genus and species: and this men do without any consideration of real essences, or substantial forms; which come not within the reach of our knowledge when we think of those things, nor within the signification of our words when we discourse with others.

From what has been said, it is evident that *men* make sorts of things. For, it being different essences alone that make different species, it is plain that they who make those abstract ideas which are the nominal essences do thereby make the species, or sort. Should there be a body found, having all the other qualities of gold except malleableness, it would no doubt be made a question whether it were gold or not, i.e. whether it were of that species. This could be determined only by that abstract idea to which every one annexed the name gold: so that it would be true gold to him, and belong to that species, who included not malleableness in his nominal essence, signified by the sound gold; and on the other side it would not be true gold, or of that species, to him who included malleableness in his specific idea. And who, I pray, is it that makes these diverse species, even under one and the same name, but men that make two different abstract ideas, consisting not exactly of the same collection of qualities?

This, then, in short, is the case: Nature makes many *particular things,* which do agree one with another in many sensible qualities, and probably too in their internal frame and constitution: but it is not this real essence that distinguishes them into species; it is men who, taking occasion from the qualities they find united in them, and wherein they observe often several individuals to agree, range them into sorts, in order to their naming, for the convenience of comprehensive signs; under which individuals, according to their conformity to this or that abstract idea, come to be ranked as under ensigns: so that this is of the blue, that the red regiment; this is a man, that a drill: and in this, I think, consists the whole business of genus and species.

I do not deny but nature, in the constant production of particular beings, makes them not always new and various, but very much alike and of kin one to another: but I think it nevertheless true, that the boundaries of the species, whereby men sort them, are made by men; since the essences of the species, distinguished by different names, are, as has been proved, of man's making, and seldom adequate to the internal nature of the things they are taken from. So that we may truly say, such a manner of sorting of things is the workmanship of men.

From what has been before said, we may see the reason why, in the species of artificial things, there is generally less confusion and uncertainty than in natural. Because an artificial thing being a production of man, which the artificer designed, and therefore well knows the idea of, the name of it is supposed to stand for no other idea, nor to import any other essence, than what is certainly to be known, and easy enough to be apprehended. For the idea or essence of the several sorts of artificial things, consisting for the most part in nothing but the determinate figure of sensible parts, and sometimes motion depending thereon, which the artificer fashions in matter, such as he finds for his turn; it is not beyond the reach of our faculties to attain a certain idea thereof; and so settle the signification of the names whereby the species of artificial things are distinguished, with less doubt, obscurity, and equivocation than we can in things natural, whose differences and operations depend upon contrivances beyond the reach of our discoveries.

I must be excused here if I think artificial things are of distinct species as well as natural: since I find they are as plainly and orderly ranked into sorts, by different abstract ideas, with general names annexed to them, as distinct one from another as those of natural substances. For why should we not think a watch and pistol as distinct species one from another, as a horse and a dog; they being expressed in our minds by distinct ideas, and to others by distinct appellations?

This is further to be observed concerning substances, that they alone of all our several sorts of ideas have particular or proper names, whereby one only particular thing is signified. Because in simple ideas, modes, and relations, it seldom happens that men have occasion to mention often this or that particular when it is absent. Besides, the greatest part of mixed modes, being actions which perish in their birth, are not capable of a lasting duration, as substances which are the actors; and wherein the simple ideas that make up the complex ideas designed by the name have a lasting union.

I must beg pardon of my reader for having dwelt so long upon this subject, and perhaps with some obscurity. But I desire it may be considered, how difficult it is to lead another by words into the thoughts of things, stripped of those specifical differences we give them: which things, if I name not, I say nothing; and if I do name them, I thereby rank them into some sort or other, and suggest to the mind the usual abstract idea of that species; and so cross my purpose. For, to talk of a man, and to lay by, at the same time, the ordinary signification of the name man, which is our complex idea usually annexed to it; and bid the reader consider man, as he is in himself, and as he is really distinguished from others in his internal constitution, or real essence, that is, by something he knows not what, looks like trifling: and yet thus one must do who would speak of the supposed real essences and species of things, as thought to be made by nature, if it be but only to make it understood, that there is no such thing signified by the general names which substances are called by. But because it is difficult by known familiar names to do this, give me leave to endeavor by an example to make the different consideration the mind has of specific names and ideas a little more clear; and to show how the complex ideas of modes are referred sometimes to archetypes in the minds of other intelligent beings, or, which is the same, to the signification annexed by others to their received names; and sometimes to no archetypes at all. Give me leave also to show how the mind always refers its ideas of substances, either to the substances themselves, or to the signification of their names, as to the archetypes; and also to make plain the nature of species or sorting of things, as apprehended and made use of by us; and of the essences belonging to those species: which is perhaps of more moment to discover the extent and certainty of our knowledge than we at first imagine.

But this is not all. It would also follow that the names of

substances would not only have, as in truth they have, but would also be supposed to have different significations, as used by different men, which would very much cumber the use of language. For if every distinct quality that were discovered in any matter by any one were supposed to make a necessary part of the complex idea signified by the common name given to it, it must follow, that men must suppose the same word to signify different things in different men: since they cannot doubt but different men may have discovered several qualities, in substances of the same denomination, which others know nothing of.

To avoid this therefore, they have supposed a real essence belonging to every species, from which these properties all flow, and would have their name of the species stand for that. But they, not having any idea of that real essence in substances, and their words signifying nothing but the ideas they have, that which is done by this attempt is only to put the name or sound in the place and stead of the thing having that real essence, without knowing what the real essence is, and this is that which men do when they speak of species of things, as supposing them made by nature, and distinguished by real essences.

For, let us consider, when we affirm that "all gold is fixed," either it means that fixedness is a part of the definition, i.e., part of the nominal essence the word gold stands for; and so this affirmation, "all gold is fixed," contains nothing but the signification of the term gold. Or else it means, that fixedness, not being a part of the definition of the gold, is a property of that substance itself: in which case it is plain that the word gold stands in the place of a substance, having the real essence of a species of things made by nature. In which way of substitution it has so confused and uncertain a signification, that, though this proposition—"gold is fixed"—be in that sense an affirmation of something real; yet it is a truth will always fail us in its particular application, and so is of no real use or certainty. For let it be ever so true, that all gold, i.e. all that has the real essence of gold, is fixed, what serves this for, whilst we know not, in this sense, *what is or is not gold?* For if we know not the real essence of gold, it is impossible we should know what parcel of matter has that essence, and so whether *it* be true gold or not.

To conclude: what liberty Adam had at first to make any

omplex ideas of *mixed modes* by no other pattern but by his wn thoughts, the same have all men ever since had. And the ame necessity of conforming his ideas of *substances* to things vithout him, as to archetypes made by nature, that Adam vas under, if he would not willfully impose upon himself, he same are all men ever since under too. The same liberty lso that Adam had of affixing any new name to any idea, he same has anyone still (especially the beginners of lanuages, if we can imagine any such); but only with this diference, that, in places where men in society have already stablished a language amongst them, the significations of vords are very warily and sparingly to be altered. Because nen being furnished already with names for their ideas, and ommon use having appropriated known names to certain leas, an affected misapplication of them cannot but be very idiculous. He that hath new notions will perhaps venture ometimes on the coining of new terms to express them: but nen think it a boldness, and it is uncertain whether common ise will ever make them pass for current. But in communicaion with others, it is necessary that we conform the ideas we nake the vulgar words of any language stand for to their nown proper significations (which I have explained at large lready), or else to make known that new signification we aply them to.

VII

Of Particles—Summary

[In the short Chapter VII Locke speaks—as he says, "lightly," of particles—the "is" and "is not," for example, by which the mind affirms and denies. The right use of particles is one of the secrets of good style. For this shows what relation the mind gives to its own thoughts. Hence their use is a matter for reflection.]

VIII

Of Abstract and Concrete Terms

THE ORDINARY WORDS OF LANGUAGE, and our common use of them, would have given us light into the nature of our ideas, if they had been but considered with attention. The mind, as has been shown, has a power to abstract its ideas, and so they become essences, general essences, whereby the sorts of things are distinguished. Now each abstract idea being distinct, so that of any two the one can never be the other, the mind will, by its intuitive knowledge, perceive their difference, and therefore in propositions no two whole ideas can ever be affirmed one of another. This we see in the common use of language, which permits not any two abstract words, or names of abstract ideas, to be affirmed one of another. For how near of kin soever they may seem to be, and how certain soever it is that man is an animal, or rational, or white, yet everyone at first hearing perceives the falsehood of these propositions: *humanity is animality*, or *rationality*, or *whiteness:* and this is as evident as any of the most allowed maxims. All our affirmations then are only in concrete, which is the affirming, not one abstract idea to be another, but one abstract idea to be joined to another; which abstract ideas, in substances, may be of any sort; in all the rest are little else but of relations; and in substances the most frequent are of powers: v.g. "a man is white," signifies that the thing that has the essence of a man has also in it the essence of whiteness, which is nothing but a power to produce the idea of whiteness in one whose eyes can discover ordinary objects: or, "a man is rational," signifies that the same thing that hath the essence of a man hath also in it the essence of rationality, i.e. a power of reasoning.

This distinction of names shows us also the difference of our ideas: for if we observe them, we shall find that *our simple ideas have all abstract as well as concrete names:* the one whereof is (to speak the language of grammarians) a substantive, the other an adjective; as whiteness, white; sweetness, sweet. The like also holds in our ideas of modes and relations; as justice, just; equality, equal: only with this difference, that some of the concrete names of relations amongst men chiefly are substantives; as, *paternitas, pater;* whereof it were easy to render a reason. But as to our ideas of substances, we have very few or no abstract names at all. For though the Schools have introduced *animalitas, humanitas, corporietas,* and some others; yet they hold no proportion with that infinite number of names of substances, to which they never were ridiculous enough to attempt the coining of abstract ones: and those few that the Schools forged, and put into the mouths of their scholars, could never yet get admittance into common use, or obtain the license of public approbation.

I X

Of the Imperfection of Words

FROM WHAT HAS BEEN SAID in the foregoing chapters, it is easy to perceive what imperfection there is in language, and how the very nature of words makes it almost unavoidable for many of them to be doubtful and uncertain in their significations. To examine the perfection or imperfection of words, it is necessary first to consider their use and end: for as they are more or less fitted to attain that, so they are more or less perfect. We have, in the former part of this discourse often, upon occasion, mentioned a double use of words.

First, One for the recording of our own thoughts.

Secondly, The other for the communicating of our thoughts to others.

As to the first of these, *for the recording our own thoughts for the help of our own memories,* whereby, as it were, we talk to ourselves, any words will serve the turn. For since sounds are voluntary and indifferent signs of any ideas, a man may use what words he pleases to signify his own ideas to himself: and there will be no imperfection in them, if he constantly use the same sign for the same idea: for then he cannot fail of having his meaning understood, wherein consists the right use and perfection of language.

Secondly, As to *communication by words,* that too has a double use.

I. *Civil.*

II. *Philosophical.*

First, By their *civil* use, I mean such a communication of thoughts and ideas by words, as may serve for the upholding common conversation and commerce, about the ordinary affairs and conveniences of civil life, in the societies of men, one amongst another.

Secondly, By the *philosophical* use of words, I mean such a use of them as may serve to convey the precise notions of things, and to express in general propositions certain and undoubted truths, which the mind may rest upon and be satisfied with in its search after true knowledge. These two uses are very distinct; and a great deal less exactness will serve in the one than in the other, as we shall see in what follows.

The chief end of language in communication being to be understood, words serve not well for that end, neither in civil nor philosophical discourse, when any word does not excite in the hearer the same idea which it stands for in the mind of the speaker. Now, since sounds have no natural connection with our ideas, but have all their signification from the arbitrary imposition of men, the doubtfulness and uncertainty of their signification, which is the imperfection we here are speaking of, has its cause more in the ideas they stand for than in any incapacity there is in one sound more than in another to signify any idea: for in that regard they are all equally perfect.

That then which makes doubtfulness and uncertainty in the signification of some more than other words, is the difference of ideas they stand for.

Words having naturally no signification, the idea which each stands for must be learned and retained, by those who would exchange thoughts, and hold intelligible discourse with others, in any language. But this is the hardest to be done where,

First, The ideas they stand for are very complex, and made up of a great number of ideas put together.

Secondly, Where the ideas they stand for have no certain connection in nature; and so no settled standard anywhere in nature existing, to rectify and adjust them by.

Thirdly, When the signification of the word is referred to a standard, which standard is not easy to be known.

Fourthly, Where the signification of the word and the real essence of the thing are not exactly the same.

These are difficulties that attend the signification of several words that are intelligible. Those which are not intelligible at all, such as names standing for any simple ideas which another has not organs or faculties to attain; as the names of colors to a blind man, or sounds to a deaf man, need not here be mentioned.

In all these cases we shall find an imperfection in words; which I shall more at large explain, in their particular application to our several sorts of ideas: for if we examine them, we shall find that the *names of Mixed Modes are most liable to doubtfulness and imperfection, for the two first of these reasons;* and the *names of Substances chiefly for the two latter.*

First, The names of *mixed modes* are, many of them, liable to great uncertainty and obscurity in their signification.

Because of that *great composition* these complex ideas are often made up of. To make words serviceable to the end of communication, it is necessary, as has been said, that they excite in the hearer exactly the same idea they stand for in the mind of the speaker. Without this, men fill one another's heads with noise and sounds; but convey not thereby their thoughts, and lay not before one another their ideas, which is the end of discourse and language. But when a word stands for a very complex idea that is compounded and decompounded, it is not easy for men to form and retain that idea so exactly, as to make the name in common use stand for the same precise idea, without any the least variation. Hence it comes to pass that men's names of very compound ideas, such as for the most part are moral words, have seldom in two different men the same precise signification; since one man's complex idea seldom agrees with another's, and often differs from his own—from that which he had yesterday, or will have tomorrow.

Because the names of mixed modes for the most part *want standards in nature,* whereby men may rectify and adjust their significations; therefore they are very various and doubtful. They are assemblages of ideas put together at the pleasure of the mind, pursuing its own ends of discourse, and suited to its own notions; whereby it designs not to copy anything really existing, but to denominate and rank things as they come to agree with those archetypes or forms it has made. He that first brought the word *sham,* or *wheedle,* or *banter,* in use, put together as he thought fit those ideas he made it stand for; and as it is with any new names of modes that are now brought into any language, so it was with the old ones when they were first made use of. Names, therefore, that stand for collections of ideas which the mind makes at pleasure must needs be of doubtful signification, when such collections are nowhere to be found constantly united in nature, nor any patterns to be shown whereby men may adjust them.

It is true, common use, that is, the rule of propriety may be supposed here to afford some aid, to settle the signification of language; and it cannot be denied but that in some measure it does. Common use regulates the meaning of words pretty well for common conversation; but nobody having an authority to establish the precise signification of words, nor determine to what ideas anyone shall annex them, common use is not sufficient to adjust them to Philosophical Discourses; there being scarce any name of any very complex idea (to say nothing of others) which, in common use, has not a great latitude, and which, keeping within the bounds of propriety, may not be made the sign of far different ideas. Besides, the rule and measure of propriety itself being nowhere established, it is often matter of dispute, whether this or that way of using a word be propriety of speech or no. From all which it is evident, that the names of such kind of very complex ideas are naturally liable to this imperfection, to be of doubtful and uncertain signification; and even in men that have a mind to understand one another, do not always stand for the same idea in speaker and hearer. Though the names *glory* and *gratitude* be the same in every man's mouth through a whole country, yet the complex collective idea which everyone thinks on or intends by that name, is apparently very different in men using the same language.

The way also wherein the names of mixed modes are ordinarily learned, does not a little contribute to the doubtfulness of their signification. For if we will observe how children learn languages, we shall find that, to make them understand what the names of simple ideas or substances stand for, people ordinarily show them the thing whereof they would have them have the idea; and then repeat to them the name that stands for it; as *white, sweet, milk, sugar, cat, dog.* But as for mixed modes, especially the most material of them, *moral words,* the sounds are usually learned first; and then, to know what complex ideas they stand for, they are either beholden to the explication of others, or (which happens for the most part) are left to their own observation and industry; which being little laid out in the search of the true and precise meaning of names, these moral words are in most men's mouths little more than bare sounds; or when they have any, it is for the most part but a very loose and undetermined, and, consequently, obscure and confused signification. And even those themselves who have with more attention settled their notions, do yet hardly avoid the inconvenience to have them stand for complex ideas different from those which other, even intelligent and studious men, make them the signs of. Where shall one find any, either controversial debate, or familiar discourse, concerning honor, faith, grace, religion, church, etc., wherein it is not easy to observe the different notions men have of them? Which is nothing but this, that they are not agreed in the signification of those words, nor have in their minds the same complex ideas which they make them stand for, and so all the contests that follow thereupon are only about the meaning of a sound. And hence we see that, in the interpretation of laws, whether divine or human, there is no end; comments beget comments, and explications make new matter for explications; and of limiting, distinguishing, varying the signification of these moral words there is no end.

If the signification of the names of mixed modes be uncertain, because there be no real standards existing in nature to which those ideas are referred, and by which they may be adjusted, the names of *substances* are of a doubtful signification, for a contrary reason, viz. because the ideas they stand for are supposed conformable to the reality of things, and are referred to as standards made by Nature. In our ideas of substances we have not the liberty, as in mixed modes, to frame what combinations we think fit, to be the characteristical notes to rank and denominate things by. In these we must follow Nature, suit our complex ideas to real existences, and regulate the signification of their names by the things themselves, if we will have our names to be signs of them, and stand for them. Here, it is true, we have patterns to follow; but patterns that will make the signification of their names very uncertain: for names must be of a very unsteady and various meaning, if the ideas they stand for be referred to standards without us, that either cannot be known at all, or can be known but imperfectly and uncertainly.

The names of substances have, as has been shown, a double reference in their ordinary use.

First, Sometimes they are made to stand for, and so their signification is supposed to agree to, *the real constitution of things,* from which all their properties flow, and in which they all center. But this real constitution, or (as it is apt to be called) essence, being utterly unknown to us, any sound that is put to stand for it must be very uncertain in its application; and it will be impossible to know what things are or ought to be called a *horse,* or *antimony,* when those words are put for real essences that we have no ideas of at all. And therefore in this supposition, the names of substances being referred to standards that cannot be known, their significations can never be adjusted and established by those standards.

Secondly, The simple ideas that are *found to co-exist in substances* being that which their names immediately signify, these, as united in the several sorts of things, are the proper standards to which their names are referred, and by which their significations may be best rectified. But neither will these archetypes so well serve to this purpose as to leave these names without very various and uncertain significations. Because these simple ideas that co-exist, and are united in the same subject, being very numerous, and having all an equal right to go into the complex specific idea which the specific name is to stand for, men, though they propose to themselves the very same subject to consider, yet frame very different ideas about it; and so the name they use for it unavoidably comes to have, in several men, very different significations. The simple qualities which make up the complex ideas, being most of them powers, in relation to changes which they are apt to make in, or receive from other bodies, are almost infinite.

It is true, as to civil and common conversation, the general names of substances, regulated in their ordinary signification by some obvious qualities (as by the shape and figure in things of known seminal propagation, and in other substances, for the most part by color, joined with some other sensible qualities), do well enough to design the things men would be understood to speak of: and so they usually conceive well enough the substances meant by the word gold or apple, to distinguish the one from the other. But in *philosophical* inquiries and debates, where general truths are to be established, and consequences drawn from positions laid down, there the precise signification of the names of substances will be found not only not to be well established, but also very hard to be so. For example: he that shall make malleability, or a certain degree of fixedness, a part of his complex idea of gold, may make propositions concerning gold, and draw consequences from them, that will truly and clearly follow from gold, taken in such a signification: but yet such as another man can never be forced to admit, nor be convinced of their truth, who makes not malleableness, or the same degree of fixedness, part of that complex idea that the name gold, in his use of it, stands for.

From what has been said, it is easy to observe what has been before remarked, viz. that the *names of simple ideas* are, of all others, the least liable to mistakes, and that for these reasons. *First,* Because the ideas they stand for, being each but one single perception, are much easier got, and more clearly retained, than the more complex ones, and therefore are not liable to the uncertainty which usually attends those compounded ones of substances and mixed modes, in which the precise number of simple ideas that make them up are not easily agreed, so readily kept in mind. And, *Secondly,* Because they are never referred to any other essence, but barely that perception they immediately signify: which reference is that which renders the signification of the names of substances naturally so perplexed, and gives occasion to so many disputes. Men that do not perversely use their words, or on purpose set themselves to cavil, seldom mistake, in any language which they are acquainted with, the use and signification of the name of simple ideas. *White* and *sweet, yellow* and *bitter,* carry a very obvious meaning with them, which everyone precisely comprehends, or easily perceives he is ignorant of, and seeks to be informed. But what precise collection of simple ideas *modesty* or *frugality* stand for, in another's use, is not so certainly known. And however we are apt to think we well enough know what is meant by *gold* or *iron;* yet the precise complex idea others make them the signs of is not so certain: and I believe it is very seldom that, in speaker and hearer, they stand for exactly the same collection. Which must needs produce mistakes and disputes, when they are made use of in discourses, wherein men have to do with universal propositions, and would settle in their minds universal truths, and consider the consequences that follow from them.

By the same rule, the names of *simple modes* are, next to those of simple ideas, least liable to doubt and uncertainty; especially those of figure and number of which men have so clear and distinct ideas. Whoever that had a mind to understand them mistook the ordinary meaning of *seven* or a *triangle?* And in general the least compounded ideas in every kind have the least dubious names.

Mixed modes, therefore, that are made up but of a few and obvious simple ideas, have usually names of no very uncertain signification. But the names of mixed modes which comprehend a great number of simple ideas, are commonly of a very doubtful and undetermined meaning, as has been shown. The names of substances, being annexed to ideas that are neither the real essences, nor exact representations of the patterns they are referred to, are liable to yet greater imperfection and uncertainty, especially when we come to a philosophical use of them.

The great disorder that happens in our names of substances, proceeding, for the most part, from our want of knowledge, and inability to penetrate into their real constitutions, it may probably be wondered why I charge this as an imperfection rather upon our words than understandings. This exception has so much appearance of justice, that I think myself obliged to give a reason why I have followed this method. I must confess, then, that, when I first began this Discourse of the Understanding, and a good while after, I had not the least thought that any consideration of words was at all necessary to it. But when, having passed over the original and composition of our ideas, I began to examine the extent and certainty of our knowledge, I found it had so near a connection with words, that, unless their force and manner of signification were first well observed, there could be very little said clearly and pertinently concerning knowledge: which being conversant about truth, had constantly to do with propositions. And though it terminated in things, yet it was for the most part so much by the intervention of words, that they seemed scarce separable from our general knowledge. At least they interpose themselves so much between our understandings, and the truth which it would contemplate and apprehend, that, like the medium through which visible objects pass, the obscurity and disorder do not seldom cast a mist before our eyes, and impose upon our understandings. If we consider, in the fallacies men put upon themselves, as well as others, and the mistakes in men's disputes and notions, how great a part is owing to words, and their uncertain or mistaken significations, we shall have reason to think this no small obstacle in the way to knowledge; which I conclude we are the more carefully to be warned of, because it has been so far from being taken notice of as an inconvenience, that the arts of improving it have been made the business of men's study, and obtained the reputation of learning and subtlety, as we shall see in the following chapter. But I am apt to imagine, that, were the imperfections of language, as the instrument of knowledge, more thoroughly weighed, a great many of the controversies that make such a noise in the world, would of themselves cease; and the way to knowledge, and perhaps peace too, lie a great deal opener than it does.

Sure I am that the signification of words in all languages, depending very much on the thoughts, notions, and ideas of him that uses them, must unavoidably be of great uncertainty to men of the same language and country. This is so evident in the Greek authors, that he that shall peruse their writings will find in almost every one of them, a distinct language, though the same words. But when to this natural difficulty in every country, there shall be added different countries and remote ages, wherein the speakers and writers had very different notions, tempers, customs, ornaments, and figures of speech, etc., every one of which influenced the signification of their words then, though to us now they are lost and unknown; it would become us to be charitable one to another in our interpretations or misunderstandings of those ancient writings; which, though of great concernment to be understood, are liable to the unavoidable difficulties of speech, which (if we except the names of simple ideas, and some very obvious things) is not capable, without a constant defining the terms, of conveying the sense and intention of the speaker, without any manner of doubt and uncertainty to the hearer. And in discourses of religion, law, and morality, as they are matters of the highest concernment, so there will be the greatest difficulty.

X

Of the Abuse of Words

Besides the imperfection that is naturally in language, and the obscurity and confusion that is so hard to be avoided in the use of words, there are several *willful* faults and neglects which men are guilty of in this way of communication, whereby they render these signs less clear and distinct in their signification than naturally they need to be.

First, In this kind the first and most palpable abuse is, the using of words without clear and distinct ideas; or, which is worse, signs without anything signified. Of these there are two sorts:—

I. One may observe, in all languages, certain words that, if they be examined, will be found in their first original, and their appropriated use, not to stand for any clear and distinct ideas. These, for the most part, the several sects of philosophy and religion have introduced. For their authors or promoters, either affecting something singular, and out of the way of common apprehensions, or to support some strange opinions, or cover some weakness of their hypothesis, seldom fail to coin new words, and such as, when they come to be examined, may justly be called *insignificant terms.* For, having either had no determinate collection of ideas annexed to them when they were first invented; or at least such as, if well examined, will be found inconsistent, it is no wonder, if, afterward, in the vulgar use of the same party, they remain empty sounds, with little or no signification, amongst those who think it enough to have them often in their mouths, as the distinguishing characters of their Church or School, without much troubling their heads to examine what are the precise ideas they stand for. I shall not need here to heap up instances; every man's reading and conversation will sufficiently furnish him. Or if he wants to be better stored, the great mintmasters of this kind of terms, I mean the Schoolmen and Metaphysicians (under which I think the disputing natural and moral philosophers of these latter ages may be comprehended) have wherewithal abundantly to content him.

II. Others there be who extend this abuse yet further, who take so little care to lay by words, which, in their primary notation have scarce any clear and distinct ideas which they are annexed to, that, by an unpardonable negligence, they familiarly use words which the propriety of language *has* affixed to very important ideas, without any distinct meaning at all. *Wisdom, glory, grace,* etc., are words frequent enough in every man's mouth; but if a great many of those who use them should be asked what they mean by them, they would be at a stand, and not know what to answer: a plain proof, that, though they have learned those sounds, and have them ready at their tongues' ends, yet there are no determined ideas laid up in their minds, which are to be expressed to others by them.

Men having been accustomed from their cradles to learn words which are easily got and retained, before they knew or had framed the complex ideas to which they were annexed, or which were to be found in the things they were thought to stand for, they usually continue to do so all their lives; and without taking the pains necessary to settle in their minds determined ideas, they use their words for such unsteady and confused notions as they have, contenting themselves with the same words other people use; as if their very sound necessarily carried with it constantly the same meaning. Thus, though men make a shift with in the ordinary occurrences of life, where they find it necessary to be understood, and therefore they make signs till they are so; yet this insignificancy in their words, when they come to reason concerning either their tenets or interest, manifestly fills their discourse with abundance of empty unintelligible noise and jargon, especially in moral matters, where the words for the most part standing for arbitrary and numerous collections of ideas, not regularly and permanently united in nature, their bare sounds are often only thought on, or at least very obscure and uncertain notions annexed to them. Men take the words they find in use amongst their neighbors; and that they may not seem ignorant what they stand for, use them confidently, without much troubling their heads about a certain fixed meaning; whereby, besides the ease of it, they obtain this advantage, That, as in such discourses they seldom are in the right, so they are as seldom to be convinced that they are in the wrong; it being all one to go about to draw those men out of their mistakes who have no settled notions, as to dispossess a vagrant of his habitation who has no settled abode. This I guess to be so;

and everyone may observe in himself and others whether it be so or not.

Secondly, Another great abuse of words is *inconstancy* in the use of them. It is hard to find a discourse written on any subject, especially of controversy, wherein one shall not observe, if he read with attention, the same words (and those commonly the most material in the discourse, and upon which the argument turns) used sometimes for one collection of simple ideas, and sometimes for another; which is a perfect abuse of language. Words being intended for signs of my ideas to make them known to others, not by any natural signification, but by a voluntary imposition, it is plain cheat and abuse, when I make them stand sometimes for one thing and sometimes for another; the willful doing whereof can be imputed to nothing but great folly, or greater dishonesty. And a man, in his accounts with another may, with as much fairness make the characters of numbers stand sometimes for one and sometimes for another collection of units: v.g. this character 3, stand sometimes for three, sometimes for four, and sometimes for eight, as in his discourse or reasoning make the same words stand for different collections of simple ideas. If men should do so in their reckonings, I wonder who would have to do with them? One who would speak thus in the affairs and business of the world, and call 8 sometimes seven, and sometimes nine, as best served his advantage, would presently have clapped upon him, one of the two names men are commonly disgusted with. And yet in arguings and learned contests, the same sort of proceedings passes commonly for wit and learning; but to me it appears a greater dishonesty than the misplacing of counters in the casting up a debt; and the cheat the greater, by how much truth is of greater concernment and value than money.

Thirdly, Another abuse of language is an *affected obscurity;* by either applying old words to new and unusual significations; or introducing new and ambiguous terms, without defining either; or else putting them so together, as may confound their ordinary meaning. Though the Peripatetic philosophy has been most eminent in this way, yet other sects have not been wholly clear of it. There are scarce any of them that are not cumbered with some difficulties (such is the imperfection of human knowledge), which they have been fain to cover with obscurity of terms, and to confound the ignification of words, which, like a mist before people's eyes, night hinder their weak parts from being discovered. That *ody* and *extension* in common use, stand for two distinct deas, is plain to anyone that will but reflect a little. For were heir signification precisely the same, it would be as proper, nd as intelligible to say, "the body of an extension," as the 'extension of a body"; and yet there are those who find it ecessary to confound their signification.

Fourthly, Another great abuse of words is, the *taking them or things.* This, though it in some degree concerns all names n general, yet more particularly affects those of substances. To this abuse those men are most subject who most confine heir thoughts to any one system, and give themselves up into firm belief of the perfection of any received hypothesis: whereby they come to be persuaded that the terms of that ect are so suited to the nature of things, that they perfectly orrespond with their real existence. Who is there that has een bred up in the Peripatetic philosophy, who does not hink the Ten Names, under which are ranked the Ten Predicments, to be exactly conformable to the nature of things? Who is there of that school that is not persuaded that *subtantial forms, vegetative souls, abhorrence of a vacuum, inentional species,* etc., are something real? These words men ave learned from their very entrance upon knowledge, and ave found their masters and systems lay great stress upon hem: and therefore they cannot quit the opinion, that they re conformable to nature, and are the representations of omething that really exists. The Platonists have their *soul of he world,* and the Epicureans their *endeavor toward motion* n their atoms when at rest. There is scarce any sect in philosophy has not a distinct set of terms that others understand ot. But yet this gibberish, which, in the weakness of human nderstanding, serves so well to palliate men's ignorance, and over their errors, comes, by familiar use amongst those of he same tribe, to seem the most important part of language, nd of all other the terms the most significant: and should *erial* and *etherial vehicles* come once, by the prevalency of hat doctrine, to be generally received anywhere, no doubt hose terms would make impressions on men's minds, so as o establish them in the persuasion of the reality of such hings, as much as Peripatetic *forms* and *intentional species* ave heretofore done.

Fifthly, Another abuse of words is, *the setting them in the place of things which they do or can by no means signify.* We may observe that, in the general names of substances, whereof the *nominal* essences are only known to us, when we put them into propositions, and affirm or deny anything about them, we do most commonly tacitly suppose or intend, they should stand for the *real* essence of a certain sort of substances. For, when a man says gold is malleable, he means and would insinuate something more than this, That what I call gold is malleable (though truly it amounts to no more), but would have this understood, viz. That gold, i.e. what has the real essence of gold, is malleable; which amounts to thus much, that malleableness depends on, and is inseparable from the real essence of gold. But a man, not knowing wherein that real essence consists, the connection in his mind of malleableness is not truly with an essence he knows not, but only with the sound gold he puts for it.

It is true the names of substances would be much more useful, and propositions made in them much more certain, were the real essences of substances the ideas in our minds which those words signified. And it is for want of those real essences that our words convey so little knowledge or certainty in our discourses about them; and therefore the mind, to remove that imperfection as much as it can, makes them, by a secret supposition, to stand for a thing having that real essence, as if thereby it made some nearer approaches to it. For, though the word *man* or *gold* signify nothing truly but a complex idea of properties united together in one sort of substances; yet there is scarce anybody, in the use of these words, but often supposes each of those names to stand for a thing having the real essence on which these properties depend. Which is so far from diminishing the imperfection of our words, that by a plain abuse it adds to it, when we would make them stand for something, which, not being in our complex idea, the name we use can no ways be the sign of.

This shows us the reason why in *mixed modes* any of the ideas that make the composition of the complex one being left out or changed, it is allowed to be another thing, i.e. to be of another species, as is plain in *chance-medley, manslaughter, murder, parricide,* etc. The reason whereof is, because the complex idea signified by that name is the real as well as nominal essence; and there is no secret reference of that name to any other essence but that. But in *substances,* it is not so. For though in that called *gold,* one puts into his complex idea what another leaves out, and vice versa: yet men do not usually think that therefore the species is changed: because they secretly in their minds refer that name, and suppose it annexed to a real immutable essence of a thing existing, on which those properties depend. He that adds to his complex idea of gold that of fixedness and solubility in *aqua regia,* which he put not in it before, is not thought to have changed the species; but only to have a more perfect idea, by adding another simple idea, which is always in fact joined with those other, of which his former complex idea consisted. But this reference of the name to a thing, whereof we have not the idea, is so far from helping at all, that it only serves the more to involve us in difficulties. For by this tacit reference to the real essence of that species of bodies, the word *gold* (which, by standing for a more or less perfect collection of simple ideas, serves to design that sort of body well enough in civil discourse) comes to have no signification at all, being put for somewhat whereof we have no idea at all, and so can signify nothing at all, when the body itself is away. For however it may be thought all one, yet, if well considered, it will be found a quite different thing, to argue about gold in name, and about a parcel in the body itself, v.g. a piece of leaf-gold laid before us; though in discourse we are fain to substitute the name for the thing.

Sixthly, there remains yet another more general, though perhaps less observed, abuse of words; and that is, that men having by a long and familiar use annexed to them certain ideas, they are apt to imagine *so near and necessary a connection between the names and the signification they use them in,* that they forwardly suppose one cannot but understand what their meaning is; and therefore one ought to acquiesce in the words delivered, as if it were past doubt that, in the use of those common received sounds, the speaker and hearer had necessarily the same precise ideas.

To conclude this consideration of the imperfection and abuse of language. The ends of language in our discourse with others being chiefly these three: First, to make known one man's thoughts or ideas to another; Secondly, to do it with as much ease and quickness as possible; and, Thirdly, thereby to convey the knowledge of things: language is either abused or deficient, when it fails of any of these three.

First, Words fail in the first of these ends, and lay not open one man's ideas to another's view: 1. When men have names in their mouths without any determinate ideas in their minds, whereof they are the signs: or, 2. When they apply the common received names of any language to ideas, to which the common use of that language does not apply them: or, 3. When they apply them very unsteadily, making them stand, now for one, and by and by for another idea.

Secondly, Men fail of conveying their thoughts with all the quickness and ease that may be, when they have complex ideas without having any distinct names for them. This is sometimes the fault of the language itself, which has not in it a sound yet applied to such a signification; and sometimes the fault of the man, who has not yet learned the name for that idea he would show another.

Thirdly, There is no knowledge of things conveyed by men's words, when their ideas agree not to the reality of things. Though it be a defect that has its original in our ideas, which are not so conformable to the nature of things as attention, study, and application might make them, yet it fails not to extend itself to our words too, when we use them as signs of real beings, which yet never had any reality or existence.

First, He that hath words of any language, without distinct ideas in his mind to which he applies them, does, so far as he uses them in discourse, only make a noise without any sense or signification; and how learned soever he may seem, by the use of hard words or learned terms, is not much more advanced thereby in knowledge, than he would be in learning, who had nothing in his study but the bare titles of books, without possessing the contents of them. For all such words, however put into discourse, according to the right construction of grammatical rules, or the harmony of well-turned periods, do yet amount to nothing but bare sounds, and nothing else.

Secondly, He that has complex ideas, without particular names for them, would be in no better case than a bookseller, who had in his warehouse volumes that lay there unbound, and without titles, which he could therefore make known to others only by showing the loose sheets, and communicate them only by tale. This man is hindered in his discourse, for want of words to communicate his complex ideas, which he is therefore forced to make known by an enumeration of the simple ones that compose them; and so is fain often to use twenty words, to express what another man signifies in one.

Thirdly, He that puts not constantly the same sign for the same idea, but uses the same words sometimes in one and sometimes in another signification, ought to pass in the schools and conversation for as fair a man, as he does in the market and exchange, who sells several things under the same name.

Fourthly, He that applies the words of any language to ideas different from those to which the common use of that country applies them, however his own understanding may be filled with truth and light, will not by such words be able to convey much of it to others, without defining his terms. For however the sounds are such as are familiarly known, and easily enter the ears of those who are accustomed to them; yet standing for other ideas than those they usually are annexed to, and are wont to excite in the mind of the hearers, they cannot make known the thoughts of him who thus uses them.

Fifthly, He that imagined to himself substances such as never have been, and filled his head with ideas which have not any correspondence with the real nature of things, to which yet he gives settled and defined names, may fill his discourse, and perhaps another man's head, with the fantastical imaginations of his own brain, but will be very far from advancing thereby one jot in real and true knowledge.

He that hath names without ideas, wants meaning in his words, and speaks only empty sounds. He that hath complex ideas without names for them, wants liberty and dispatch in his expressions, and is necessitated to use periphrases. He that uses his words loosely and unsteadily will either be not minded or not understood. He that applies his names to ideas different from their common use, wants propriety in his language, and speaks gibberish. And he that hath the ideas of substances disagreeing with the real existence of things, so far wants the materials of true knowledge in his understanding, and hath instead thereof chimeras.

In our notions concerning Substances, we are liable to all

the former inconveniences: v.g. he that uses the word *tarantula,* without having any imagination or idea of what it stands for, pronounces a good word; but so long means nothing at all by it. 2. He that, in a newly-discovered country, shall see several sorts of animals and vegetables, unknown to him before, may have as true ideas of them, as of a horse or a stag; but can speak of them only by a description, till he shall either take the names the natives call them by, or give them names himself. 3. He that uses the word *body* sometimes for pure extension, and sometimes for extension and solidity together, will talk very fallaciously. 4. He that gives the name *horse* to that idea which common usage calls *mule,* talks improperly, and will not be understood. 5. He that thinks the name *centaur* stands for some real being, imposes on himself, and mistakes words for things.

In Modes and Relations generally, we are liable only to the four first of these inconveniences; viz. 1. I may have in my memory the names of modes, as *gratitude* or *charity,* and yet not have any precise ideas annexed in my thoughts to those names. 2. I may have ideas, and not know the names that belong to them: v.g. I may have the idea of a man's drinking till his color and humor be altered, till his tongue trips, and his eyes look red, and his feet fail him; and yet not know that it is to be called *drunkenness.* 3. I may have the ideas of virtues or vices, and names also, but apply them amiss: v.g. when I apply the name *frugality* to that idea which others call and signify by this sound, *covetousness.* 4. I may use any of those names with inconstancy. 5. But, in modes and relations, I cannot have ideas disagreeing to the existence of things: for modes being complex ideas, made by the mind at pleasure, and relation being but by way of considering or comparing two things together, and so also an idea of my own making, these ideas can scarce be found to disagree with anything existing; since they are not in the mind as the copies of things regularly made by nature, nor as properties inseparably flowing from the internal constitution or essence of any substance; but, as it were, patterns lodged in my memory, with names annexed to them, to denominate actions and relations by, as they come to exist. But the mistake is commonly in my giving a wrong name to my conceptions; and so using words in a different sense from other people: I am not understood, but am thought to have wrong ideas of them, when I give wrong names to them. Only if I put in my ideas of mixed modes or relations any inconsistent ideas together, I fill my head also with chimeras; since such ideas, if well examined, cannot so much as exist in the mind, much less any real being ever be denominated from them.

Since wit and fancy find easier entertainment in the world than dry truth and real knowledge, figurative speeches and allusion in language will hardly be admitted as an imperfection or abuse of it. I confess, in discourses where we seek rather pleasure and delight than information and improvement, such ornaments as are borrowed from them can scarce pass for faults. But yet if we would speak of things as they are, we must allow that all the art of rhetoric, besides order and clearness; all the artificial and figurative application of words eloquence hath invented, are for nothing else but to insinuate wrong ideas, move the passions, and thereby mislead the judgment; and so indeed are perfect cheats: and therefore, however laudable or allowable oratory may render them in harangues and popular addresses, they are certainly, in all discourses that pretend to inform or instruct, wholly to be avoided; and where truth and knowledge are concerned, cannot but be thought a great fault, either of the language or person that makes use of them. What and how various they are, will be superfluous here to take notice; the books of rhetoric which abound in the world, will instruct those who want to be informed: only I cannot but observe how little the preservation and improvement of truth and knowledge is the care and concern of mankind; since the arts of fallacy are endowed and preferred. It is evident how much men love to deceive and be deceived, since rhetoric, that powerful instrument of error and deceit, has its established professors, is publicly taught, and has always been had in great reputation: and I doubt not but it will be thought great boldness, if not brutality, in me to have said thus much against it. Eloquence, like the fair sex, has too prevailing beauties in it to suffer itself ever to be spoken against. And it is in vain to find fault with those arts of deceiving, wherein men find pleasure to be deceived.

X I

Of the Remedies of the Foregoing Imperfections and Abuses of Words

THE NATURAL AND IMPROVED IMPERFECTIONS of languages we have seen above at large: and speech being the great bond that holds society together, and the common conduit, whereby the improvements of knowledge are conveyed from one man and one generation to another, it would well deserve our most serious thoughts to consider, what remedies are to be found for the inconveniences above mentioned.

I am not so vain as to think that anyone can pretend to attempt the perfect reforming the languages of the world, no not so much as of his own country, without rendering himself ridiculous. To require that men should use their words constantly in the same sense, and for none but determined and uniform ideas, would be to think that all men should have the same notions, and should talk of nothing but what they have clear and distinct ideas of: which is not to be expected by anyone who hath not vanity enough to imagine he can prevail with men to be very knowing or very silent. And he must be very little skilled in the world, who thinks that a voluble tongue shall accompany only a good understanding; or that men's talking much or little should hold proportion only to their knowledge.

But though the market and exchange must be left to their own ways of talking, and gossipings not be robbed of their ancient privilege: though the schools, and men of argument would perhaps take it amiss to have anything offered, to abate the length or lessen the number of their disputes; yet methinks those who pretend seriously to search after or maintain truth, should think themselves obliged to study how they might deliver themselves without obscurity, doubtfulness, or equivocation, to which men's words are naturally liable, if care be not taken.

For he that shall well consider the errors and obscurity, the mistakes and confusion, that are spread in the world by an ill use of words, will find some reason to doubt whether language, as it has been employed, has contributed more to the improvement or hindrance of knowledge amongst mankind. How many are there, that, when they would think on things, fix their thoughts only on words, especially when they would apply their minds to moral matters? And who then can wonder if the result of such contemplations and reasonings, about little more than sounds, whilst the ideas they annex to them are very confused and very unsteady, or perhaps none at all; who can wonder, I say, that such thoughts and reasonings end in nothing but obscurity and mistake, without any clear judgment or knowledge?

This inconvenience, in an ill use of words, men suffer in their own private meditations: but much more manifest are the disorders which follow from it, in conversation, discourse, and arguings with others. For language being the great conduit, whereby men convey their discoveries, reasonings, and knowledge, from one to another, he that makes an ill use of it, though he does not corrupt the fountains of knowledge, which are in things themselves, yet he does, as much as in him lies, break or stop the pipes whereby it is distributed to the public use and advantage of mankind. He that uses words without any clear and steady meaning, what does he but lead himself and others into errors?

To remedy the defects of speech before mentioned to some degree, and to prevent the inconveniences that follow from them, I imagine the observation of these following rules may be of use, till somebody better able shall judge it worth his while to think more maturely on this matter, and oblige the world with his thoughts on it.

First, A man shall take care to use no word without a signification, no name without an idea for which he makes it stand. This rule will not seem altogether needless to anyone who shall take the pains to recollect how often he has met with such words as *instinct, sympathy,* and *antipathy,* etc., in the discourse of others, so made use of as he might easily conclude that those that used them had no ideas in their minds to which they applied them, but spoke them only as sounds, which usually served instead of reasons on the like occasions. Not but that these words, and the like, have very proper significations in which they may be used; but there being no natural connection between any words and any ideas, these, and any other, may be learned by rote, and pronounced or writ by men who have no ideas in their minds to which they have annexed them, and for which they make them stand; which is necessary they should, if men would speak intelligibly even to themselves alone.

Secondly, It is not enough a man uses his words as signs of some ideas: those he annexes them to, if they be simple, must be clear and distinct; if complex, must be determinate, i.e. the precise collection of simple ideas settled in the mind, with that sound annexed to it, as the sign of that precise determined collection, and no other. This is very necessary in names of modes, and especially moral words; which, having no settled objects in nature, from whence their ideas are taken, as from their original, are apt to be very confused. *Justice* is a word in every man's mouth, but most commonly with a very undetermined, loose signification; which will always be so, unless a man has in his mind a distinct comprehension of the component parts that complex idea consists of: and if it be decompounded, must be able to resolve it still on, till he at last comes to the simple ideas that make it up: and unless this be done, a man makes an ill use of the word, let it be justice, for example, or any other. I do not say, a man needs stand to recollect, and make this analysis at large, every time the word justice comes in his way: but this at least is necessary, that he have so examined the signification of that name, and settled the idea of all its parts in his mind, that he can do it when he pleases. If anyone who makes his complex idea of justice to be, such a treatment of the person or goods of another as is according to law, hath not a clear and distinct idea what *law* is, which makes a part of his complex idea of justice, it is plain his idea of justice itself will be confused and imperfect. This exactness will, perhaps, be judged very troublesome; and therefore most men will think they may be excused from settling the complex ideas of mixed modes so precisely in their minds. But yet I must say, till this be done, it must not be wondered, that they have a great deal of obscurity and confusion in their own minds, and a great deal of wrangling in their discourse with others.

In the names of substances, for a right use of them, something more is required than barely *determined ideas*. In these the names must also be *conformable to things as they exist;* but of this I shall have occasion to speak more at large by and by. This exactness is absolutely necessary in inquiries after philosophical knowledge, and in controversies about truth.

ınd though it would be well, too, if it extended itself to comıon conversation and the ordinary affairs of life; yet I think ıat is scarce to be expected. Vulgar notions suit vulgar disɔurses: and both, though confused enough, yet serve pretty ’ell the market and the wake. Merchants and lovers, cooks nd tailors, have words wherewithal to dispatch their ordinary ffairs: and so, I think, might philosophers and disputants too, they had a mind to understand, and to be clearly underood.

Thirdly, It is not enough that men have ideas, determined leas, for which they make these signs stand; but they must lso take care to apply their words as near as may be to such leas as common use has annexed them to. For words, esecially of languages already framed, being no man's private ossession, but the common measure of commerce and comıunication, it is not for anyone at pleasure to change the tamp they are current in, nor alter the ideas they are affixed ›; or at least, when there is a necessity to do so, he is bound › give notice of it. Men's intentions in speaking are, or at east should be, to be understood; which cannot be without requent explanations, demands, and other the like incomıodious interruptions, where men do not follow common use. ropriety of speech is that which gives our thoughts entrance ıto other men's minds with the greatest ease and advantage: nd therefore deserves some part of our care and study, esecially in the names of moral words. The proper significaon and use of terms is best to be learned from those who in ıeir writings and discourses appear to have had the clearest otions, and applied to them their terms with the exactest hoice and fitness. This way of using a man's words, accordıg to the propriety of the language, though it have not al’ays the good fortune to be understood; yet most commonly eaves the blame of it on him who is so unskillful in the lanuage he speaks, as not to understand it when made use of s it ought to be.

Fourthly, But, because common use has not so visibly anexed any signification to words, as to make men know al’ays certainly what they precisely stand for: and because men, ı the improvement of their knowledge, come to have ideas ifferent from the vulgar and ordinary received ones, for ’hich they must either make new words (which men seldom enture to do, for fear of being thought guilty of affectation or novelty), or else must use old ones in a new signification therefore, after the observation of the foregoing rules, it i sometimes necessary, for the ascertaining the signification o words, to *declare their meaning;* where either common us has left it uncertain and loose (as it has in most names of ver complex ideas); or where the term, being very material i the discourse, and that upon which it chiefly turns, is liabl to any doubtfulness or mistake.

As the ideas men's words stand for are of different sort so the way of making known the ideas they stand for, whe there is occasion, is also different. For though *defining* b thought the proper way to make known the proper significa tion of words; yet there are some words that will not be de fined, as there are others whose precise meaning cannot b made known but by definition: and perhaps a third, whic partake somewhat of both the other, as we shall see in th names of simple ideas, modes, and substances.

First, When a man makes use of the name of any simpl idea, which he perceives is not understood, or is in danger t be mistaken, he is obliged, by the laws of ingenuity and th end of speech, to declare his meaning, and make known wha idea he makes it stand for. This, as has been shown, cannc be done by definition: and therefore, when a synonymou word fails to do it, there is but one of these ways left. First Sometimes the *naming* the subject wherein that simple ide is to be found, will make its name to be understood by thos who are acquainted with that subject, and know it by tha name. So to make a countryman understand what *feuillemort* color signifies, it may suffice to tell him, it is the color o withered leaves falling in autumn. Secondly, but the only sur way of making known the signification of the name of an simple idea, is *by presenting to his senses that subject whic may produce it in his mind,* and make him actually have th idea that word stands for.

Secondly, Mixed modes, especially those belonging t morality, being most of them such combinations of ideas a the mind puts together of its own choice, and whereof ther are not always standing patterns to be found existing, the sig nification of their names cannot be made known, as those o simple ideas, by any showing: but, in recompense thereo may be perfectly and exactly defined. For they being combi nations of several ideas that the mind of man has arbitraril put together, without reference to any archetypes, men may, i they please, exactly know the ideas that go to each composition, and so both use these words in a certain and undoubted signification, and perfectly declare, when there is occasion, what they stand for. This, if well considered, would lay great blame on those who make not their discourses about *moral* things very clear and distinct. For since the precise signification of the names of mixed modes, or, which is all one, the real essence of each species is to be known, they being not of nature's, but man's making, it is a great negligence and perverseness to discourse of moral things with uncertainty and obscurity; which is more pardonable in treating of natural substances, where doubtful terms are hardly to be avoided, for a quite contrary reason, as we shall see by and by.

Upon this ground it is that I am bold to think that morality is capable of demonstration, as well as mathematics: since the precise real essence of the things moral words stand for may be perfectly known, and so the congruity and incongruity of the things themselves be certainly discovered; in which consists perfect knowledge. Nor let anyone object, that the names of substances are often to be made use of in morality, as well as those of modes, from which will arise obscurity. For, as to substances, when concerned in moral discourses, their divers natures are not so much inquired into as supposed: v.g. when we say that man is subject to law, we mean nothing by man but a corporeal rational creature: what the real essence or other qualities of that creature are in this case is no way considered. And, therefore, whether a child or changeling be a man, in a physical sense, may amongst the naturalists be as disputable as it will, it concerns not at all the moral man, as I may call him, which is this immovable, unchangeable idea, a corporeal rational being. For, were there a monkey, or any other creature, to be found that had the use of reason to such a degree, as to be able to understand general signs, and to deduce consequences about general ideas, he would no doubt be subject to law, and in that sense be a *man*, how much soever he differed in shape from others of that name. The names of substances, if they be used in them as they should, can no more disturb moral than they do mathematical discourses; where, if the mathematician speaks of a cube or globe of gold, or of any other body, he has his clear, settled idea, which varies not, though it may by mistake be applied to a particular body to which it belongs not.

This I have here mentioned, by the by, to show of what

consequence it is for men, in their names of mixed modes and consequently in all their moral discourses, to define thei words when there is occasion: since thereby moral knowledg may be brought to so great clearness and certainty. And i must be great want of ingenuousness (to say no worse of it to refuse to do it: since a definition is the only way whereb the precise meaning of moral words can be known; and ye a way whereby their meaning may be known certainly, an without leaving any room for any contest about it. And therefore the negligence or perverseness of mankind cannot b excused, if their discourses in morality be not much mor clear than those in natural philosophy: since they are abou ideas in the mind, which are none of them false or disproportionate; they having no external beings for the archetype which they are referred to and must correspond with. It i far easier for men to frame in their minds an idea, whic shall be the standard to which they will give the name justice with which pattern so made, all actions that agree shall pas under that denomination, than, having seen Aristides, t frame an idea that shall in all things be exactly like him; wh is as he is, let men make what idea they please of him. Fo the one, they need but know the combination of ideas tha are put together in their own minds; for the other, they mus inquire into the whole nature, and abstruse hidden constitution, and various qualities of a thing existing without them.

Another reason that makes the defining of mixed modes s necessary, especially of moral words, is what I mentioned little before, viz. that it is the only way whereby the signification of the most of them can be known with certainty. Fo the ideas they stand for, being for the most part such whos component parts nowhere exist together, but scattered an mingled with others, it is the mind alone that collects them and gives them the union of one idea: and it is only by word enumerating the several simple ideas which the mind ha united, that we can make known to others what their name stand for; the assistance of the senses in this case not helpin us, by the proposal of sensible objects, to show the idea which our names of this kind stand for, as it does often i the names of sensible simple ideas, and also to some degre in those of substances.

Thirdly, For the explaining the signification of the names of substances, as they stand for the ideas we have of thei distinct species, both the forementioned ways, viz. of showing and defining, are requisite, in many cases, to be made use of. For, there being ordinarily in each sort some leading qualities, to which we suppose the other ideas which make up our complex idea of that species annexed, we forwardly give the specific name to that thing wherein that characteristical mark is found, which we take to be the most distinguishing idea of that species. These leading or characteristical (as I may call them) ideas, in the sorts of animals and vegetables, are (as has been before remarked, Chapter 6 and Chapter 9) mostly figure; and in inanimate bodies, color; and in some, both together. Now,

These leading sensible qualities are those which make the chief ingredients of our specific ideas, and consequently the most observable and invariable part in the definitions of our specific names, as attributed to sorts of substances coming under our knowledge. For though the sound *man,* in its own nature, be as apt to signify a complex idea made up of animality and rationality, united in the same subject, as to signify any other combination; yet, used as a mark to stand for a sort of creatures we count of our own kind, perhaps the outward shape is as necessary to be taken into our complex idea, signified by the word man, as any other we find in it: and therefore, why Plato's *animal implume bipes latis unguibus* should not be a good definition of the name man, standing for that sort of creatures, will not be easy to show: for it is the shape, as the leading quality, that seems more to determine that species, than a faculty of reasoning, which appears not at first, and in some never.

Now these leading qualities are best made known by showing, and can hardly be made known otherwise. For the shape of a horse or cassowary will be but rudely and imperfectly imprinted on the mind by words; the sight of the animals doth it a thousand times better. And the idea of the particular color of gold is not to be got by any description of it, but only by the frequent exercise of the eyes about it; as is evident in those who are used to this metal, who will frequently distinguish true from counterfeit, pure from adulterate, by the sight, where others (who have as good eyes, but yet by use have not got the precise nice idea of that peculiar yellow) shall not perceive any difference. The like may be said of those other simple ideas, peculiar in their kind to any substance; for which precise ideas there are no peculiar name: The particular ringing sound there is in gold, distinct fron the sound of other bodies, has no particular name annexe to it, no more than the particular yellow that belongs to tha metal.

But because many of the simple ideas that make up ou specific ideas of substances are powers which lie not obviou to our senses in the things as they ordinarily appear; there fore, in the signification of our names of substances, som part of the signification will be better made known by enumer ating those simple ideas, than by showing the substance itsel For, he that to the yellow shining color of gold, got by sigh shall, from my enumerating them, have the ideas of grea ductility, fusibility, fixedness, and solubility, in *aqua regia* will have a perfecter idea of gold than he can have by seein a piece of gold, and thereby imprinting in his mind only it obvious qualities. But if the formal constitution of this shining heavy, ductile thing (from whence all these its propertie flow), lay open to our senses, as the formal constitution o essence of a triangle does, the signification of the word gol might as easily be ascertained as that of triangle.

Fourthly, But, though definitions will serve to explai the names of substances as they stand for our ideas, yet the leave them not without great imperfection as they stand fo things. For our names of substances being not put barely fo our ideas, but being made use of ultimately to represent things and so are put in their place, their signification must agre with the truth of things as well as with men's ideas. An therefore, in substances, we are not always to rest in th ordinary complex idea commonly received as the significatio of that word, but must go a little further, and inquire into th nature and properties of the things themselves, and thereb perfect, as much as we can, our ideas of their distinct species or else learn them from such as are used to that sort of things and are experienced in them. For, since it is intended thei names should stand for such collections of simple ideas as d really exist in things themselves, as well as for the comple idea in other men's minds, which in their ordinary accepta tion they stand for, therefore, to define their names right natural history is to be inquired into, and their properties are with care and examination, to be found out. For it is nc enough, for the avoiding inconveniences in discourse an arguings about natural bodies and substantial things, to have learned, from the propriety of the language, the common, but confused, or very imperfect, idea to which each word is applied, and to keep them to that idea in our use of them; but we must, by acquainting ourselves with the history of that sort of things, rectify and settle our complex idea belonging to each specific name; and in discourse with others (if we find they mistake us), we ought to tell what the complex idea is that we make such a name stand for.

Fifthly, If men will not be at the pains to declare the meaning of their words, and definitions of their terms are not to be had, yet this is the least that can be expected, that, in all discourses wherein one man pretends to instruct or convince another, he should use the same word constantly in the same sense. If this were done (which nobody can refuse without great disingenuity), many of the books extant might be spared; many of the controversies in dispute would be at an end; several of those great volumes, swollen with ambiguous words, now used in one sense, and by and by in another, would shrink into a very narrow compass; and many of the philosophers' (to mention no other) as well as poets' works, might be contained in a nutshell.

But after all, the provision of words is so scanty in respect to that infinite variety of thoughts, that men, wanting terms to suit their precise notions, will, notwithstanding their utmost caution, be forced often to use the same word in somewhat different senses. And though in the continuation of a discourse, or the pursuit of an argument, there can be hardly room to digress into a particular definition, as often as a man varies the signification of any term; yet the import of the discourse will, for the most part, if there be no designed fallacy, sufficiently lead candid and intelligent readers into the true meaning of it; but where there is not sufficient to guide the reader, there it concerns the writer to explain his meaning, and show in what sense he there uses that term.

BOOK FOUR

OF KNOWLEDGE AND OPINION

I

Of Knowledge in General

SINCE THE MIND, in all its thoughts and reasonings, hath no other immediate object but its own ideas, which it alone does or can contemplate, it is evident that our knowledge is only conversant about them.

Knowledge that seems to me to be nothing but *the perception of the connection of and agreement, or disagreement and repugnancy, of any of our ideas.* In this alone it consists. Where this perception is, there is knowledge, and where it is not, there, though we may fancy, guess, or believe, yet we always come short of knowledge. For when we know that white is not black, what do we else but perceive, that these two ideas do not agree? When we possess ourselves with the utmost security of the demonstration, that the three angles of a triangle are equal to two right ones, what do we more but perceive, that equality to two right ones does necessarily agree to, and is inseparable from, the three angles of a triangle?

But to understand a little more distinctly wherein this agreement or disagreement consists, I think we may reduce it all to these four sorts:

I. *Identity,* or *diversity.*

II. *Relation.*

III. *Co-existence,* or *necessary connection.*

IV. *Real existence.*

First, As to the first sort of agreement or disagreement, viz. *identity* or *diversity.* It is the first act of the mind, when it has any sentiments or ideas at all, to perceive its ideas; and so far as it perceives them, to know each what it is, and thereby also to perceive their difference, and that one is not another. This is so absolutely necessary, that without it there could be no knowledge, no reasoning, no imagination, no distinct thoughts at all. By this the mind clearly and infallibly perceives each idea to agree with itself, and to be what it is; and all distinct ideas to disagree, i.e. the one not to be the other: and this it does without pains, labor, or deduction; but at first view, by its natural power of perception and distinction. And though men of art have reduced this into those general rules, *What is, is,* and *It is impossible for the same thing to be and not to be,* for ready application in all cases, wherein there may be occasion to reflect on it: yet it is certain that the first exercise of this faculty is about particular ideas. A man infallibly knows, as soon as ever he has them in his mind, that the ideas he calls *white* and *round* are the very ideas they are; and that they are not other ideas which he calls *red* or *square.* Nor can any maxim or proposition in the world make him know it clearer or surer than he did before, and without any such general rule. This then is the first agreement or disagreement which the mind perceives in its ideas; which it always perceives at first sight: and if there ever happen any doubt about it, it will always be found to be about the names, and not the ideas themselves, whose identity and diversity will always be perceived, as soon and clearly as the ideas themselves are; nor can it possibly be otherwise.

Secondly, The next sort of agreement or disagreement the mind perceives in any of its ideas may, I think, be called *relative,* and is nothing but the perception of the *relation* between any two ideas, of what kind soever, whether substances, modes, or any other. For, since all distinct ideas must eternally be known not to be the same, and so be universally and constantly denied one of another, there could be no room for any positive knowledge at all, if we could not perceive any relation between our ideas, and find out the agreement or disagreement they have one with another, in several ways the mind takes of comparing them.

Thirdly, The third sort of agreement or disagreement to be found in our ideas, which the perception of the mind is employed about, is *co-existence* or *non-co-existence* in the *same subject;* and this belongs particularly to substances. Thus when we pronounce concerning gold, that it is fixed, our knowledge of this truth amounts to no more but this, that fixedness, or a power to remain in the fire unconsumed, is an idea that always accompanies and is joined with that particular sort of yellowness, weight, fusibility, malleableness, and solubility in *aqua regia,* which make our complex idea signified by the word gold.

Fourthly, The fourth and last sort is that of *actual real existence* agreeing to any idea.

Within these four sorts of agreement or disagreement is, I suppose, contained all the knowledge we have, or are capable of. For all the inquiries we can make concerning any of our ideas, all that we know or can affirm concerning any of them, is, That it is, or is not, the same with some other; that it does or does not always co-exist with some other idea in the same subject; that it has this or that relation with some other idea; or that it has a real existence without the mind. Thus, "blue is not yellow," is of identity. "Two triangles upon equal bases between two parallels are equal," is of relation. "Iron is susceptible of magnetical impressions," is of co-existence. "God is," is of real existence. Though identity and co-existence are truly nothing but relations, yet they are such peculiar ways of agreement or disagreement of our ideas, that they deserve well to be considered as distinct heads, and not under relation in general; since they are so different grounds of affirmation and negation, as will easily appear to anyone, who will but reflect on what is said in several places of this *Essay*.

I should now proceed to examine the several degrees of our knowledge, but that it is necessary first, to consider the different acceptations of the word *knowledge*.

There are several ways wherein the mind is possessed of truth; each of which is called knowledge.

I. There is *actual knowledge,* which is the present view the mind has of the agreement or disagreement of any of its ideas, or of the relation they have one to another.

II. A man is said to know any proposition, which having been once laid before his thoughts, he evidently perceived the agreement or disagreement of the ideas whereof it consists; and so lodged it in his memory, that whenever that proposition comes again to be reflected on, he, without doubt or hesitation, embraces the right side, assents to, and is certain of the truth of it. This, I think, one may call *habitual knowledge*. And thus a man may be said to know all those truths which are lodged in his memory, by a foregoing clear and full perception, whereof the mind is assured past doubt as often as it has occasion to reflect on them. For our finite understandings being able to think clearly and distinctly but on one thing at once, if men had no knowledge of any more than what they actually thought on, they would all be very ignorant: and he that knew most, would know but one truth, that being all he was able to think on at one time.

Of habitual knowledge there are, also, vulgarly speaking, two degrees:

First, The one is of such truths laid up in the memory as, whenever they occur to the mind, it *actually perceives the relation* between those ideas. And this is in all those truths whereof we have an intuitive knowledge; where the ideas themselves, by an immediate view, discover their agreement or disagreement one with another.

Secondly, The other is of such truths whereof the mind having been convinced, it *retains the memory of the conviction, without the proofs.* Thus, a man that remembers certainly that he once perceived the demonstration, that the three angles of a triangle are equal to two right ones, is certain that he knows it, because he cannot doubt the truth of it. In his adherence to a truth, where the demonstration by which it was at first known is forgot, though a man may be thought rather to believe his memory than really to know, and this way of entertaining a truth seemed formerly to me like something between opinion and knowledge; a sort of assurance which exceeds bare belief, for that relies on the testimony of another;—yet upon a due examination I find it comes not short of perfect certainty, and is in effect true knowledge. That which is apt to mislead our first thoughts into a mistake in this matter is, that the agreement or disagreement of the ideas in this case is not perceived, as it was at first, by an actual view of all the intermediate ideas whereby the agreement or disagreement of those in the proposition was at first perceived; but by other intermediate ideas, that show the agreement or disagreement of the ideas contained in the proposition whose certainty we remember. For example: in this proposition, that "the three angles of a triangle are equal to two right ones," one who has seen and clearly perceived the demonstration of this truth knows it to be true, when that demonstration is gone out of his mind; so that at present it is not actually in view, and possibly cannot be recollected: but he knows it in a different way from what he did before. The agreement of the two ideas joined in that proposition is perceived; but it is by the intervention of other ideas than those which at first produced that perception. He remembers, i.e. he knows (for remembrance is but the reviving of some past knowledge) that he was once certain of the truth of this proposition, that the three angles of a triangle are equal to two right ones. The immutability of the same relations between the same immutable things is now the idea that shows him, that if the three angles of a triangle were once equal to two right ones, they will always be equal to two right ones. And hence he comes to be certain, that what was once true in the case, is always true; what ideas once agreed will always agree; and consequently what he once knew to be true, he will always know to be true; as long as he can remember that he once knew it. Upon this ground it is, that particular demonstrations in mathematics afford general knowledge. If then the perception, that the same ideas will *eternally* have the same habitudes and relations, be not a sufficient ground of knowledge, there could be no knowledge of general propositions in mathematics; for no mathematical demonstration would be any other than particular: and when a man had demonstrated any proposition concerning one triangle or circle, his knowledge would not reach beyond that particular diagram. If he would extend it further, he must renew his demonstration in another instance, before he could know it to be true in another like triangle, and so on: by which means one could never come to the knowledge of any general propositions. Nobody, I think, can deny, that Mr. Newton certainly knows any proposition that he now at any time reads in his book to be true; though he has not in actual view that admirable chain of intermediate ideas whereby he at first discovered it to be true. Such a memory as that, able to retain such a train of particulars, may be well thought beyond the reach of human faculties, when the very discovery, perception, and laying together that wonderful connection of ideas, is found to surpass most readers' comprehension. But yet it is evident the author himself knows the proposition to be true, remembering he once saw the connection of those ideas; as certainly as he knows such a man wounded another, remembering that he saw him run him through. But because the memory is not always so clear as actual perception, and does in all men more or less decay in length of time, this, amongst other differences, is one which shows that *demonstrative* knowledge is much more imperfect than *intuitive*, as we shall see in the following chapter.

II

Of the Degrees of Our Knowledge

ALL OUR KNOWLEDGE CONSISTING, as I have said, in the view the mind has of its own ideas, which is the utmost light and greatest certainty we, with our faculties, and in our way of knowledge, are capable of, it may not be amiss to consider a little the degrees of its evidence. The different clearness of our knowledge seems to me to lie in the different way of perception the mind has of the agreement or disagreement of any of its ideas. For if we will reflect on our own ways of thinking, we will find, that sometimes the mind perceives the agreement or disagreement of two ideas *immediately by themselves*, without the intervention of any other: and this I think we may call *intuitive knowledge*. For in this the mind is at no pains of proving or examining, but perceives the truth as the eye doth light, only by being directed towards it. Thus the mind perceives that *white* is not *black*, that a *circle* is not a *triangle*, that *three* are more than *two* and equal to *one and two*. Such kinds of truths the mind perceives at the first sight of the ideas together, by bare intuition; without the intervention of any other idea: and this kind of knowledge is the clearest and most certain that human frailty is capable of. This part of knowledge is irresistible, and, like bright sunshine, forces itself immediately to be perceived, as soon as ever the mind turns its view that way; and leaves no room for hesitation, doubt, or examination, but the mind is presently filled with the clear light of it. *It is on this intuition that depends all the certainty and evidence of all our knowledge;* which certainty everyone finds to be so great, that he cannot imagine, and therefore not require a greater: for a man cannot conceive himself capable of a greater certainty than to know that any idea in his mind is such as he perceives it to be; and that two ideas, wherein he perceives a difference, are different and not precisely the same. He that demands a greater certainty than this, demands he knows not what, and shows only that he has a mind to be a skeptic, without being able to be so. Certainty depends so wholly on this intuition, that, in the next degree of knowledge which I call demonstrative, this intuition is necessary in all the connections of the intermediate ideas, without which we cannot attain knowledge and certainty.

The next degree of knowledge is, where the mind perceives the agreement or disagreement of any ideas, but not immediately. Though wherever the mind perceives the agreement or disagreement of any of its ideas, there be certain knowledge; yet it does not always happen, that the mind sees that agreement or disagreement, which there is between them, even where it is discoverable; and in that case remains in ignorance, and at most gets no further than a probable conjecture. The reason why the mind cannot always perceive presently the agreement or disagreement of two ideas, is, because those ideas, concerning whose agreement or disagreement the inquiry is made, cannot by the mind be so put together as to show it. In this case then, when the mind cannot so bring its ideas together as by their immediate comparison, and as it were juxtaposition or application one to another, to perceive their agreement or disagreement, it is fain, *by the intervention of other ideas* (one or more, as it happens) to discover the agreement or disagreement which it searches; and this is that which we call reasoning. Thus, the mind being willing to know the agreement or disagreement in bigness between the three angles of a triangle and two right ones, cannot by an immediate view and comparing them do it: because the three angles of a triangle cannot be brought at once, and be compared with any other one, or two, angles; and so of this the mind has no immediate, no intuitive knowledge. In this case the mind is fain to find out some other angles, to which the three angles of a triangle have an equality; and, finding those equal to two right ones, comes to know their equality to two right ones.

Those intervening ideas, which serve to show the agreement of any two others, are called *proofs;* and where the agreement and disagreement is by this means plainly and clearly perceived, it is called *demonstration;* it being *shown* to the understanding, and the mind made to see that it is so. A quickness in the mind to find out these intermediate ideas (that shall discover the agreement or disagreement of any other), and to apply them right, is, I suppose, that which is called *sagacity.*

This knowledge, by intervening proofs, though it be certain, yet the evidence of it is not altogether so clear and bright, nor the assent so ready, as in intuitive knowledge. For, though in demonstration the mind does at last perceive the agreement or disagreement of the ideas it considers; yet it is not without pains and attention: there must be more than one transient view to find it. A steady application and pursuit are required to this discovery: and there must be a progression by steps and degrees, before the mind can in this way arrive at certainty, and come to perceive the agreement or repugnancy between two ideas that need proofs and the use of reason to show it.

Another difference between intuitive and demonstrative knowledge is, that, though in the latter all doubt be removed when, by the intervention of the intermediate ideas, the agreement or disagreement is perceived, yet before the demonstration there was a doubt; which in intuitive knowledge cannot happen to the mind that has its faculty of perception left to a degree capable of distinct ideas; no more than it can be a doubt to the eye (that can distinctly see white and black), Whether this ink and this paper be all of a color.

It is true, the perception produced by demonstration is also very clear; yet it is often with a great abatement of that evident lustre and full assurance that always accompany that which I call intuitive: like a face reflected by several mirrors one to another, where, as long as it retains the similitude and agreement with the object, it produces a knowledge; but it is still, in every successive reflection, with a lessening of that perfect clearness and distinctness which is in the first; till at last, after many removes, it has a great mixture of dimness, and is not at first sight so knowable, especially to weak eyes. Thus it is with knowledge made out by a long train of proof.

Now, in every step reason makes in demonstrative knowledge, there is an intuitive knowledge of that agreement or disagreement it seeks with the next intermediate idea which it uses as a proof: for if it were not so, that yet would need a proof; since without the perception of such agreement or disagreement, there is no knowledge produced: if it be perceived by itself, it is intuitive knowledge: if it cannot be perceived by itself, there is need of some intervening idea, as a common measure, to show their agreement or disagreement. By which it is plain, that every step in reasoning that produces knowledge, has intuitive certainty; which when the mind perceives, there is no more required but to remember it, to make the agreement or disagreement of the ideas concerning which we inquire visible and certain. So that to make anything a demonstration, it is necessary to perceive the immediate agreement of the intervening ideas, whereby the agreement or disagreement of the two ideas under examination (whereof the one is always the first, and the other the last in the account) is found. This intuitive perception of the agreement or disagreement of the intermediate ideas, in each step and progression of the demonstration, must also be carried exactly in the mind, and a man must be sure that no part is left out: which, because in long deductions, and the use of many proofs, the memory does not always so readily and exactly retain; therefore it comes to pass, that this is more imperfect than intuitive knowledge, and men embrace often falsehood for demonstrations.

These two, viz. intuition and demonstration, are the degrees of our *knowledge;* whatever comes short of one of these, with what assurance soever embraced, is but *faith* or *opinion,* but not knowledge, at least in all general truths. There is, indeed, another perception of the mind, employed about *the particular existence of finite beings without us,* which, going beyond bare probability, and yet not reaching perfectly to either of the foregoing degrees of certainty, passes under the name of *knowledge.* There can be nothing more certain than that the idea we receive from an external object is in our minds: this is intuitive knowledge. But whether there be anything more than barely that idea in our minds; whether we can thence certainly infer the existence of anything without us, which corresponds to that idea, is that whereof some men think there may be a question made; because men may have such ideas in their minds, when no such thing exists, no such object affects their senses. But yet here I think we are provided with an evidence that puts us past doubting. For I ask anyone, Whether he be not invincibly conscious to himself of a different perception, when he looks on the sun by day, and thinks on it by night; when he actually tastes wormwood, or smells a rose, or only thinks on that savor or odor? We as plainly find the difference there is between any idea revived in our minds by our own memory, and actually coming into our minds by our senses, as we do between any two distinct ideas. If anyone say, a dream may do the same thing, and all these ideas may be produced in us without any external objects; he may please to dream that I make him this answer:—1. That it is no great matter, whether I remove his scruple or no: where all is but dream, reasoning and arguments are of no use, truth and knowledge nothing. 2. That I believe he will allow a very manifest difference between dreaming of being in the fire, and being actually in it. But yet if he be resolved to appear so skeptical as to maintain, that what I call being actually in the fire is nothing but a dream; and that we cannot thereby certainly know, that any such thing as fire actually exists without us: I answer, That we certainly finding that pleasure or pain follows upon the application of certain objects to us, whose existence we perceive, or dream that we perceive, by our senses; this certainty is as great as our happiness or misery, beyond which we have no concernment to know or to be. So that, I think, we may add to the two former sorts of knowledge this also, of the existence of particular external objects, by that perception and consciousness we have of the actual entrance of ideas from them, and allow these three degrees of knowledge, viz. *intuitive*, *demonstrative*, and *sensitive:* in each of which there are different degrees and ways of evidence and certainty.

But since our knowledge is founded on and employed about our ideas only, will it not follow from thence that it is conformable to our ideas; and that where our ideas are clear and distinct, or obscure and confused, our knowledge will be so too? To which I answer, No: for our knowledge consisting in the perception of the agreement or disagreement of any two ideas, its clearness or obscurity consists in the clearness or obscurity of that perception, and not in the clearness or obscurity of the ideas themselves: v.g. a man that has as clear ideas of the angles of a triangle, and of equality to two right ones, as any mathematician in the world, may yet have but a very obscure perception of their *agreement*, and so have but a very obscure knowledge of it.

III

Of the Extent of Human Knowledge

KNOWLEDGE, AS HAS BEEN SAID, lying in the perception of the agreement or disagreement of any of our ideas, it follows from hence, That,

First, We can have knowledge no further than we have *ideas*.

Secondly, That we can have no knowledge further than we can have *perception* of that agreement or disagreement. Which perception being: 1. Either by *intuition*, or the immediate comparing any two ideas; or, 2. By *reason*, examining the agreement or disagreement of two ideas, by the intervention of some others; or, 3. By *sensation*, perceiving the existence of particular things: hence it also follows:

Thirdly, That we cannot have an *intuitive knowledge* that shall extend itself to all our ideas, and all that we would know about them; because we cannot examine and perceive all the relations they have one to another, by juxtaposition, or an immediate comparison one with another. Thus, having the ideas of an obtuse and an acute angled triangle, both drawn from equal bases, and between parallels, I can, by intuitive knowledge, perceive the one not to be the other, but cannot that way know whether they be equal or no; because their agreement or disagreement in equality can never be perceived by an immediate comparing them: the difference of figure makes their parts incapable of an exact immediate application; and therefore there is need of some intervening qualities to measure them by, which is demonstration, or rational knowledge.

Fourthly, It follows, also, from what is above observed, that our *rational knowledge* cannot reach to the whole extent of our ideas: because between two different ideas we would examine, we cannot always find such mediums as we can connect one to another with an intuitive knowledge in all the parts of the deduction; and wherever that fails, we come short of knowledge and demonstration.

Fifthly, Sensitive knowledge reaching no further than the existence of things actually present to our senses, is yet much narrower than either of the former.

Sixthly, From all which it is evident, that the *extent of our knowledge* comes not only short of the reality of things, but even of the extent of our own ideas. Though our knowledge be limited to our ideas, and cannot exceed them either in extent or perfection; and though these be very narrow bounds in respect of the extent of All-being, and far short of what we may justly imagine to be in some even created understandings, not tied down to the dull and narrow information that is to be received from some few, and not very acute, ways of perception, such as are our senses; yet it would be well with us if our knowledge were but as large as our ideas, and there were not many doubts and inquiries *concerning the ideas we have,* whereof we are not, nor I believe ever shall be in this world resolved. Nevertheless, I do not question but that human knowledge, under the present circumstances of our beings and constitutions, may be carried much further than it has hitherto been, if men would sincerely, and with freedom of mind, employ all that industry and labor of thought in improving the means of discovering truth, which they do for the coloring or support of falsehood, to maintain a system, interest, or party they are once engaged in. But yet after all, I think I may, without injury to human perfection, be confident, that our knowledge would never reach to all we might desire to know concerning those ideas we have; nor be able to surmount all the difficulties, and resolve all the questions that might arise concerning any of them.

The affirmations or negations we make concerning the ideas we have, may, as I have before intimated in general, be reduced to these four sorts, viz. identity, co-existence, relation, and real existence. I shall examine how far our knowledge extends in each of these:

First, As to *identity* and *diversity*. In this way of agreement or disagreement of our ideas, our intuitive knowledge is as far extended as our ideas themselves: and there can be no idea in the mind, which it does not, presently, by an intuitive knowledge, perceive to be what it is, and to be different from any other.

Secondly, As to the second sort, which is the agreement or disagreement of our ideas in *co-existence,* in this our knowledge is very short; though in this consists the greatest and most material part of our knowledge concerning substances. For our ideas of the species of substances being, as I have showed, nothing but certain collections of simple ideas united in one subject, and so co-existing together; v.g. our idea of flame is a body hot, luminous, and moving upward; of gold, a body heavy to a certain degree, yellow, malleable, and fusible: for these, or some such complex ideas as these, in men's minds, do these two names of the different substances, flame and gold, stand for. When we would know anything further concerning these, or any other sort of substances, what do we inquire, but what *other* qualities or powers these substances have or have not? Which is nothing else but to know what *other* simple ideas do, or do not co-exist with those that make up that complex idea?

This, how weighty and considerable a part soever of human science, is yet very narrow, and scarce any at all. The reason whereof is, that the simple ideas whereof our complex ideas of substances are made up are, for the most part, such as carry with them, in their own nature, no *visible necessary* connection or inconsistency with any other simple ideas, whose co-existence with them we would inform ourselves about.

The ideas that our complex ones of substances are made up of, and about which our knowledge concerning substances is most employed, are those of their secondary qualities; which depending all (as has been shown) upon the primary qualities of their minute and insensible parts; or, if not upon them, upon something yet more remote from our comprehension; it is impossible we should know which have a *necessary* union or inconsistency one with another. For, not knowing the root they spring from, not knowing what size, figure, and texture of parts they are, on which depend, and from which result those qualities which make our complex idea of gold, it is impossible we should know what *other* qualities result from, or are incompatible with, the same constitution of the insensible parts of gold; and so consequently must always co-exist with that complex idea we have of it, or else are inconsistent with it.

Besides this ignorance of the primary qualities of the insensible parts of bodies, on which depend all their secondary qualities, there is yet another and more incurable part of ignorance, which sets us more remote from a certain knowledge of the co-existence or *inco-existence* (if I may so say) of different ideas in the same subject; and that is, that there is no discoverable connection between any secondary qualit and those primary qualities which it depends on.

That the size, figure, and motion of one body should caus a change in the size, figure, and motion of another body, i not beyond our conception; the separation of the parts of on body upon the intrusion of another; and the change from res to motion upon impulse; these and the like seem to hav *some connection* one with another. And if we knew these pri mary qualities of bodies, we might have reason to hope w might be able to know a great deal more of these operation of them one upon another: but our minds not being able t discover any connection betwixt these primary qualities c bodies and the sensations that are produced in us by then we can never be able to establish certain and undoubted rule of the *consequence* or *co-existence* of any secondary qualitie though we could discover the size, figure, or motion of thos invisible parts which immediately produce them. We are s far from knowing *what* figure, size, or motion of parts prc duce a yellow color, a sweet taste, or a sharp sound, that w can by no means conceive how *any* size, figure, or motion c any particles, can possibly produce in us the idea of an color, taste, or sound whatsoever: there is no conceivabl connection between the one and the other.

In vain, therefore, shall we endeavor to discover by ou ideas (the only true way of certain and universal knowledge what other ideas are to be found constantly joined with tha of *our* complex idea of any substance: since we neither kno the real constitution of the minute parts on which their qual ties do depend; nor, did we know them, could we discove any necessary connection between them and any of the se ondary qualities: which is necessary to be done before we ca certainly know their necessary co-existence. So, that, let ou complex idea of any species of substances be what it will, w can hardly, from the simple ideas contained in it, certainl determine the necessary co-existence of any other qualit whatsoever. Our knowledge in all these inquiries reaches ver little further than our experience. Indeed some few of th primary qualities have a necessary dependence and visib connection one with another, as figure necessarily suppos extension; receiving or communicating motion by impuls supposes solidity. But though these, and perhaps some othe of our ideas have: yet there are so few of them that have visible connection one with another, that we can by intuition or demonstration discover the co-existence of very few of the qualities that are to be found united in substances: and we are left only to the assistance of our senses to make known to us what qualities they contain. For of all the qualities that are co-existent in any subject, without this dependence and evident connection of their ideas one with another, we cannot know certainly any two to co-exist, any further than experience, by our senses, informs us. Thus, though we see the yellow color, and, upon trial, find the weight, malleableness, fusibility, and fixedness that are united in a piece of gold; yet, because no one of these ideas has any evident dependence or necessary connection with the other, we cannot certainly know that where any four of these are, the fifth will be there also, how highly probable soever it may be; because the highest probability amounts not to certainty, without which there can be no true knowledge. For this co-existence can be no further known than it is perceived; and it cannot be perceived but either in particular subjects, by the observation of our senses, or, in general, by the necessary connection of the ideas themselves.

But as to the powers of substances to change the sensible qualities of other bodies, which make a great part of our inquiries about them, and is no inconsiderable branch of our knowledge; I doubt as to these, whether our knowledge reaches much further than our experience; or whether we can come to the discovery of most of these powers, and be certain that they are in any subject, by the connection with any of those ideas which to us make its essence. Because the active and passive powers of bodies, and their ways of operating, consisting in a texture and motion of parts which we cannot by any means come to discover; it is but in very few cases we can be able to perceive their dependence on, or repugnance to, any of those ideas which make our complex one of that sort of things.

Thirdly, As to the third sort of our knowledge, viz. the agreement or disagreement of any of our ideas in any other relation: this, as it is the largest field of our knowledge, so it is hard to determine how far it may extend: because the advances that are made in this part of knowledge, depending on our sagacity in finding intermediate ideas, that may show the relations and habitudes of ideas whose co-existence is not considered, it is a hard matter to tell when we are at an end of such discoveries; and when reason has all the helps it is capable of, for the finding of proofs, or examining the agreement or disagreement of remote ideas. They that are ignorant of Algebra cannot imagine the wonders in this kind are to be done by it: and what further improvements and helps advantageous to other parts of knowledge the sagacious mind of man may yet find out, it is not easy to determine. This at least I believe, that the *ideas of quantity* are not those alone that are capable of demonstration and knowledge; and that other, and perhaps more useful, parts of contemplation, would afford us certainty, if vices, passions, and domineering interest did not oppose or menace such endeavors.

The idea of a supreme Being, infinite in power, goodness, and wisdom, whose workmanship we are, and on whom we depend; and the idea of ourselves, as understanding, rational creatures, being such as are clear in us, would, I suppose, if duly considered and pursued, afford such foundations of our duty and rules of action as might place *morality* amongst the *sciences capable of demonstration:* wherein I doubt not but from self-evident propositions, by necessary consequences, as incontestible as those in mathematics, the measures of right and wrong might be made out, to anyone that will apply himself with the same indifferency and attention to the one as he does to the other of these sciences. The *relation* of other *modes* may certainly be perceived, as well as those of number and extension: and I cannot see why they should not also be capable of demonstration, if due methods were thought on to examine or pursue their agreement or disagreement. "Where there is no property there is no injustice," is a proposition as certain as any demonstration in Euclid: for the idea of property being a right to anything, and the idea to which the name "injustice" is given being the invasion or violation of that right, it is evident that these ideas, being thus established, and these names annexed to them, I can as certainly know this proposition to be true, as that a triangle has three angles equal to two right ones. Again: "No government allows absolute liberty." The idea of government being the establishment of society upon certain rules or laws which require conformity to them; and the idea of absolute liberty being for anyone to do whatever he pleases; I am as capable of being certain of the truth of this proposition as of any in the mathematics.

That which in this respect has given the advantage to the ideas of quantity, and made them thought more capable of certainty and demonstration, is,

First, That they can be set down and represented by sensible marks, which have a greater and nearer correspondence with them than any words or sound whatsoever. Diagrams drawn on paper are copies of the ideas in the mind, and not liable to the uncertainty that words carry in their signification. An angle, circle, or square, drawn in lines, lies open to the view, and cannot be mistaken: it remains unchangeable, and may at leisure be considered and examined, and the demonstration be revised, and all the parts of it may be gone over more than once, without any danger of the least change in the ideas. This cannot be thus done in moral ideas: we have no sensible marks that resemble them, whereby we can set them down; we have nothing but words to express them by; which, though when written they remain the same, yet the ideas they stand for may change in the same man; and it is very seldom that they are not different in different persons.

Secondly, Another thing that makes the greater difficulty in ethics is, That moral ideas are commonly more complex than those of the figures ordinarily considered in mathematics. From whence these two inconveniences follow:—First, that their names are of more uncertain signification, the precise collection of simple ideas they stand for not being so easily agreed on; and so the sign that is used for them in communication always, and in thinking often, does not steadily carry with it the same idea. Upon which the same disorder, confusion, and error follow, as would if a man, going to demonstrate something of an heptagon, should, in the diagram he took to do it, leave out one of the angles, or by oversight make the figure with one angle more than the name ordinarily imported, or he intended it should when at first he thought of his demonstration. This often happens, and is hardly avoidable in very complex moral ideas, where the same name being retained, one angle, i.e. one simple idea, is left out, or put in the complex one (still called by the same name) more at one time than another. Secondly, From the complexedness of these moral ideas there follows another inconvenience, viz. that the mind cannot easily retain those precise combinations so exactly and perfectly as is necessary in the examination of the habitudes and correspondences, agreements or disagreements, of several of them one with another; especially where it is to be judged of by long deductions, and the intervention of several other complex ideas to show the agreement or disagreement of two remote ones.

The great help against this which mathematicians find in diagrams and figures, which remain unalterable in their draughts, is very apparent, and the memory would often have great difficulty otherwise to retain them so exactly, whilst the mind went over the parts of them step by step to examine their several correspondences. And though in casting up a long sum either in addition, multiplication, or division, every part be only a progression of the mind taking a view of its own ideas, and considering their agreement or disagreement, and the resolution of the question be nothing but the result of the whole, made up of such particulars, whereof the mind has a clear perception: yet, without setting down the several parts by marks, whose precise significations are known, and by marks that last, and remain in view when the memory had let them go, it would be almost impossible to carry so many different ideas in the mind, without confounding or letting slip some parts of the reckoning, and thereby making all our reasonings about it useless. In which case the ciphers or marks help not the mind at all to perceive the agreement of any two or more numbers, their equalities or proportions; that the mind has only by intuition of its own ideas of the numbers themselves. But the numerical characters are helps to the memory, to record and retain the several ideas about which the demonstration is made, whereby a man may know how far his intuitive knowledge in surveying several of the particulars has proceeded; that so he may without confusion go on to what is yet unknown; and at last have in one view before him the result of all his perceptions and reasonings.

One part of these disadvantages in moral ideas which has made them be thought not capable of demonstration, may in a good measure be remedied by definitions, setting down that collection of simple ideas, which every term shall stand for; and then using the terms steadily and constantly for that precise collection. And what methods algebra, or something of that kind, may hereafter suggest, to remove the other difficulties, it is not easy to foretell. Confident I am, that, if men would in the same method, and with the same indifferency, search after moral as they do mathematical truths, they would find them have a stronger connection one with another, and a more necessary consequence from our clear and distinct ideas, and to come nearer perfect demonstration than is commonly imagined. But much of this is not to be expected, whilst the desire of esteem, riches, or power makes men espouse the well-endowed opinions in fashion, and then seek arguments either to make good their beauty, or varnish over and cover their deformity. Nothing being so beautiful to the eye as truth is to the mind; nothing so deformed and irreconcilable to the understanding as a lie. For though many a man can with satisfaction enough own a not very handsome wife in his bosom; yet who is bold enough openly to avow that he has espoused a falsehood, and received into his breast so ugly a thing as a lie? Whilst the parties of men cram their tenets down all men's throats whom they can get into their power, without permitting them to examine their truth or falsehood; and will not let truth have fair play in the world, nor men the liberty to search after it; what improvements can be expected of this kind? What greater light can be hoped for in the moral sciences? The subject part of mankind in most places might, instead thereof, with Egyptian bondage, expect Egyptian darkness, were not the candle of the Lord set up by Himself in men's minds, which it is impossible for the breath or power of man wholly to extinguish.

Fourthly, As to the fourth sort of our knowledge, viz. of the *real actual existence of things,* we have an intuitive knowledge of *our own existence,* and a demonstrative knowledge of the existence of a *God:* of the existence of *anything else,* we have no other but a sensitive knowledge; which extends not beyond the objects present to our senses.

Our knowledge being so narrow, as I have shown, it will perhaps give us some light into the present state of our minds if we look a little into the dark side, and take a view of *our ignorance;* which, being infinitely larger than our knowledge, may serve much to the quieting of disputes, and improvement of useful knowledge; if, discovering how far we have clear and distinct ideas, we confine our thoughts within the contemplation of those things that are within the reach of our understandings, and launch not out into that abyss of darkness (where we have not eyes to see, nor faculties to perceive anything), out of a presumption that nothing is beyond our comprehension. But to be satisfied of the folly of such a conceit, we need not go far. He that knows anything, knows this, in the first place, that he need not seek long for instances of his ignorance. The meanest and most obvious things that come in our way have dark sides, that the quickest sight cannot penetrate into. The clearest and most enlarged understandings of thinking men find themselves puzzled and at a loss in every particle of matter.

[Locke goes on to consider the *causes* of our ignorance, which are 1. want of ideas; 2. want of a discoverable connection between the ideas we have; 3. want of tracing and examining our ideas.]

Hitherto we have examined the extent of our knowledge, in respect of the several sorts of beings that are. There is another extent of it, in respect of *universality*, which will also deserve to be considered; and in this regard, our knowledge follows the nature of our ideas. If the ideas are abstract, whose agreement or disagreement we perceive, our knowledge is universal. For what is known of such general ideas, will be true of every particular thing in whom that essence, i.e. that abstract idea, is to be found: and what is once known of such ideas, will be perpetually and forever true. So that as to all *general knowledge* we must search and find it only in our minds; and it is only the examining of our own ideas that furnisheth us with that. Truths belonging to essences of things (that is, to abstract ideas) are eternal; and are to be found out by the contemplation only of those essences: as the existence of things is to be known only from experience. But having more to say of this in the chapters where I shall speak of general and real knowledge, this may here suffice as to the universality of our knowledge in general.

I V

Of the Reality of Knowledge

I DOUBT NOT BUT MY READER, by this time, may be apt to think that I have been all this while only building a castle in the air; and be ready to say to me:——

"To what purpose all this stir? Knowledge, say you, is only the perception of the agreement or disagreement of our own ideas: but who knows what those ideas may be? Is there anything so extravagant as the imaginations of men's brains? Where is the head that has no chimeras in it? Or if there be a sober and a wise man, what difference will there be, by your rules, between his knowledge and that of the most extravagant fancy in the world? They both have their ideas, and perceive their agreement and disagreement one with another. If there be any difference between them, the advantage will be on the warm-headed man's side, as having the more ideas, and the more lively. And so, by your rules, he will be the more knowing. If it be true, that all knowledge lies only in the perception of the agreement or disagreement of our own ideas, the visions of an enthusiast and the reasonings of a sober man will be equally certain. It is no matter how things are: so a man observe but the agreement of his own imaginations, and talk conformably, it is all truth, all certainty. Such castles in the air will be as strongholds of truth, as the demonstrations of Euclid. That a harpy is not a centaur is by this way as certain knowledge, and as much a truth, as that a square is not a circle.

"But of what use is all this fine knowledge of *men's own imaginations,* to a man that inquires after the reality of things? It matters not what men's fancies are, it is the knowledge of things that is only to be prized: it is this alone gives a value to our reasonings, and preference to one man's knowledge over another's, that it is of things as they really are, and not of dreams and fancies."

To which I answer, That if our knowledge of our ideas terminate in them, and reach no further, where there is something further intended, our most serious thoughts will be of little more use than the reveries of a crazy brain; and the truths built thereon of no more weight than the discourses of a man who sees things clearly in a dream, and with great assurance utters them. But I hope, before I have done, to make it evident, that this way of certainty, by the knowledge of our own ideas, goes a little further than bare imagination: and I believe it will appear that all the certainty of general truths a man has lies in nothing else.

It is evident the mind knows not things immediately, but only by the intervention of the ideas it has of them. Our knowledge, therefore, is real only so far as there is a *conformity* between our ideas and the reality of things. But what shall be here the criterion? How shall the mind, when it perceives nothing but its own ideas, know that they agree with things themselves? This, though it seems not to want difficulty, yet, I think, there be two sorts of ideas that we may be assured agree with things.

First, The first are simple ideas, which since the mind, as has been showed, can by no means make to itself, must necessarily be the product of things operating on the mind, in a natural way, and producing therein those perceptions which by the Wisdom and Will of our Maker they are ordained and adapted to. From whence it follows, that simple ideas are not fictions of our fancies, but the natural and regular productions of things without us, really operating upon us; and so carry with them all the conformity which is intended; or which our state requires: for they represent to us things under those appearances which they are fitted to produce in us: whereby we are enabled to distinguish the sorts of particular substances, to discern the states they are in, and so to take them for our necessities, and apply them to our uses. Thus the idea of whiteness, or bitterness, as it is in the mind, exactly answering that power which is in any body to produce it there, has all the real conformity it can or ought to have, with things without us. And this conformity between our simple ideas and the existence of things, is sufficient for real knowledge.

Secondly, All our complex ideas, *except those of substances,* being archetypes of the mind's own making, not intended to be the copies of anything, nor referred to the existence of anything, as to their originals, cannot want any conformity necessary to real knowledge. For that which is not designed to represent anything but itself, can never be capable of a wrong representation, nor mislead us from the true apprehension of anything, by its dislikeness to it: and such, excepting those of substances, are all our complex ideas. Which, as I have showed in another place, are combinations of ideas, which the mind, by its free choice, puts together, without considering any connection they have in nature. And hence it is, that in all these sorts the ideas themselves are considered as the archetypes, and things no otherwise regarded, but as they are conformable to them. So that we cannot but be infallibly certain, that all the knowledge we attain concerning these ideas is real, and reaches things themselves. Because in all our thoughts, reasonings, and discourses of this kind, we intend things no further than as they are conformable to our ideas. So that in these we cannot miss of a certain and undoubted reality.

I doubt not but it will be easily granted, that the knowledge we have of mathematical truths is not only certain, but real knowledge; and not the bare empty vision of vain, insignificant chimeras of the brain: and yet, if we will consider, we shall find that it is only of our own ideas. The mathematician considers the truth and properties belonging to a rectangle or circle only as they are in idea in his own mind. For it is possible he never found either of them existing mathematically, i.e. precisely true, in his life. But yet the knowledge he has of any truths or properties belonging to a circle, or any other mathematical figure, are nevertheless true and certain, even of real things existing: because real things are no further concerned, nor intended to be meant by any such propositions, than as things really agree to those archetypes in his mind. Is it true of the *idea* of a triangle, that its three angles are equal to two right ones? It is true also of a triangle, wherever it *really exists*. Whatever other figure exists, that it is not exactly answerable to that idea of a triangle in his mind, is not at all concerned in that proposition. And therefore he is certain all his knowledge concerning such ideas is real knowledge: because, intending things no further than they agree with those his ideas, he is sure what he knows concerning those figures, when they have *barely an ideal existence* in his mind, will hold true of them also when they have *a real existence* in matter: his consideration being barely of those figures, which are the same wherever or however they exist.

And hence it follows that moral knowledge is as capable of

real certainty as mathematics. For certainty being but the perception of the agreement or disagreement of our ideas, and demonstration nothing but the perception of such agreement, by the intervention of other ideas or mediums; our moral ideas, as well as mathematical, being archetypes themselves, and so adequate and complete ideas; all the agreement or disagreement which we shall find in them will produce real knowledge, as well as in mathematical figures.

For the attaining of knowledge and certainty, it is requisite that we have determined ideas: and, to make our knowledge real, it is requisite that the ideas answer their archetypes. Nor let it be wondered, that I place the certainty of our knowledge in the consideration of our ideas, with so little care and regard (as it may seem) to the real existence of things: since most of those discourses which take up the thoughts and engage the disputes of those who pretend to make it their business to inquire after truth and certainty, will, I presume, upon examination, be found to be general propositions, and notions in which existence is not at all concerned. All the discourses of the mathematicians about the squaring of a circle, conic sections, or any other part of mathematics, concern not the existence of any of those figures: but their demonstrations, which depend on their ideas, are the same, whether there be any square or circle existing in the world or no. In the same manner, the truth and certainty of moral discourses abstracts from the lives of men, and the existence of those virtues in the world whereof they treat: nor are Tully's Offices less true, because there is nobody in the world that exactly practices his rules, and lives up to that pattern of a virtuous man which he has given us, and which existed nowhere when he writ but in idea. If it be true in speculation, i.e. in idea, that murder deserves death, it will also be true in reality of any action that exists conformable to that idea of murder. As for other actions, the truth of that proposition concerns them not. And thus it is of all other species of things, which have no other essences but those ideas which are in the minds of men.

But it will here be said, that if moral knowledge be placed in the contemplation of our own moral ideas, and those, as other modes, be of our own making, What strange notions will there be of justice and temperance? What confusion of virtues and vices, if everyone may make what ideas of them he pleases? No confusion or disorder in the things themselves, nor the reasonings about them; no more than (in mathematics) there would be a disturbance in the demonstration, or a change in the properties of figures, and their relations one to another, if a man should make a triangle with four corners, or a trapezium with four right angles: that is, in plain English, change the names of the figures, and call that by one name, which mathematicians call ordinarily by another. For, let a man make to himself the idea of a figure with three angles, whereof one is a right one, and call it, if he please, *equilaterum* or *trapezium,* or anything else; the properties of, and demonstrations about that idea will be the same as if he called it a rectangular triangle. I confess the change of the name, by the impropriety of speech, will at first disturb him who knows not what idea it stands for: but as soon as the figure is drawn, the consequences and demonstrations are plain and clear. Just the same is it in moral knowledge; let a man have the idea of taking from others, without their consent, what their honest industry has possessed them of, and call this *justice* if he please. He that takes the name here without the idea put to it will be mistaken, by joining another idea of his own to that name: but strip the idea of that name, or take it such as it is in the speaker's mind, and the same things will agree to it, as if you called it *injustice.* Indeed, wrong names in moral discourses breed usually more disorder, because they are not so easily rectified as in mathematics, where the figure, once drawn and seen, makes the name useless and of no force. For what need of a sign, when the thing signified is present and in view? But in moral names, that cannot be so easily and shortly done, because of the many decompositions that go to the making up the complex ideas of those modes. But yet for all this, the miscalling of any of those ideas, contrary to the usual signification of the words of that language, hinders not but that we may have certain and demonstrative knowledge of their several agreements and disagreements, if we will carefully, as in mathematics, keep to the same precise ideas, and trace *them* in their several relations one to another, without being led away by their names. If we but separate the idea under consideration from the sign that stands for it, our knowledge goes equally on in the discovery of real truth and certainty, whatever sounds we make use of.

One thing more we are to take notice of, That where God or any other lawmaker, hath defined any moral names, there they have made the essence of that species to which that name belongs; and there it is not safe to apply or use them otherwise: but in other cases it is bare impropriety of speech to apply them contrary to the common usage of the country. But yet even this too disturbs not the certainty of that knowledge, which is still to be had by a due contemplation and comparing of those even nicknamed ideas.

Thirdly, There is another sort of complex ideas, which, being referred to archetypes without us, may differ from them, and so our knowledge about them may come short of being real. Such are our ideas of substances, which, consisting of a collection of simple ideas, supposed taken from the works of nature, may yet vary from them; by having more or different ideas united in them than are to be found united in the things themselves. From whence it comes to pass, that they may, and often do, fail of being exactly conformable to things themselves.

I say, then, that to have ideas of *substances* which, by being conformable to things, may afford us real knowledge, it is not enough, as in *modes,* to put together such ideas as have no inconsistence, though they did never before so exist: v.g. the ideas of sacrilege or perjury, etc., were as real and true ideas before, as after the existence of any such fact. But our ideas of substances, being supposed copies, and referred to archetypes without us, must still be taken from something that does or has existed: they must not consist of ideas put together at the pleasure of our thoughts, without any real pattern they were taken from, though we can perceive no inconsistence in such a combination. The reason whereof is, because we, knowing not what real constitution it is of substances whereon our simple ideas depend, and which really is the cause of the strict union of some of them one with another, and the exclusion of others; there are very few of them that we can be sure are or are not inconsistent in nature, any further than experience and sensible observation reach. Herein, therefore, is founded the reality of our knowledge concerning substances—That all our complex ideas of them must be such, and such only, as are made up of such simple ones as have been discovered to co-exist in nature. And our ideas being thus true, though not perhaps very exact copies, are yet the subjects of real (as far as we have any) knowledge of them. Which (as has been already shown) will not be found to reach very far: but so far as it does, it will still be real knowledge. Whatever ideas we have, the agreement we find they have with others will still be knowledge. If those ideas be abstract, it will be general knowledge. But to make it real concerning substances, the ideas must be taken from the real existence of things. Whatever simple ideas have been found to co-exist in any substance, these we may with confidence join together again, and so make abstract ideas of substances. For whatever have once had a union in nature, may be united again.

This, if we rightly consider, and confine not our thoughts and abstract ideas to names, as if there were, or could be no other *sorts* of things than what known names had already determined, and, as it were, set out, we should think of things with greater freedom and less confusion than perhaps we do.

Would we accustom ourselves to separate our contemplations and reasonings from words, we might in a great measure remedy this inconvenience within our own thoughts: but yet it would still disturb us in our discourse with others, as long as we retained the opinion, that *species* and their *essences* were anything else but our abstract ideas (such as they are) with names annexed to them, to be the signs of them.

Wherever we perceive the agreement or disagreement of any of our ideas, there is certain knowledge: and wherever we are sure those ideas agree with the reality of things, there is certain real knowledge. Of which agreement of our ideas with the reality of things, having here given the marks, I think, I have shown *wherein it is that certainty, real certainty, consists*. Which, whatever it was to others, was, I confess, to me heretofore, one of those desiderata which I found great want of.

V

Of Truth in General

WHAT IS TRUTH? was an inquiry many ages since; and it being that which all mankind either do, or pretend to search after, it cannot but be worth our while carefully to examine wherein it consists; and so acquaint ourselves with the nature of it, as to observe how the mind distinguishes it from falsehood.

Truth, then, seems to me, in the proper import of the word, to signify nothing but *the joining or separating of Signs, as the Things signified by them do agree or disagree one with another.* The joining or separating of signs here meant, is what by another name we call *proposition.* So that truth properly belongs only to propositions: whereof there are two sorts, viz. mental and verbal; as there are two sorts of signs commonly made use of, viz. ideas and words.

To form a clear notion of truth, it is very necessary to consider truth of thought, and truth of words, distinctly one from another: but yet it is very difficult to treat of them asunder. Because it is unavoidable, in treating of mental propositions, to make use of words: and then the instances given of mental propositions cease immediately to be barely mental, and become verbal. For a *mental proposition* being nothing but a bare consideration of the ideas, as they are in our minds, stripped of names, they lose the nature of purely mental propositions as soon as they are put into words.

And that which makes it yet harder to treat of mental and verbal propositions separately is, that most men, if not all, in their thinking and reasonings within themselves, make use of words instead of ideas; at least when the subject of their meditation contains in it complex ideas. Which is a great evidence of the imperfection and uncertainty of our ideas of that kind, and may, if attentively made use of, serve for a mark to show us what are those things we have clear and perfect established ideas of, and what not. For if we will curiously observe the way our mind takes in thinking and reasoning, we shall find, I suppose, that when we make any propositions within our own thoughts about *white* or *black, sweet* or *bitter,* a *triangle* or a *circle,* we can and often do frame in our minds the ideas themselves, without reflecting on the names. But when we would consider, or make propositions about the more complex ideas, as of a *man, vitriol, fortitude, glory,* we usually put the name for the idea: because the ideas these names stand for, being for the most part imperfect, confused, and undetermined, we reflect on the names themselves, because they are more clear, certain, and distinct, and readier occur to our thoughts than the pure ideas: and so we make use of these words instead of the ideas themselves, even when we would meditate and reason within ourselves, and make tacit mental propositions.

But to return to the consideration of truth: we must, I say, observe two sorts of propositions that we are capable of making:——

First, *Mental,* wherein the ideas in our understandings are without the use of words put together, or separated, by the mind perceiving or judging of their agreement or disagreement.

Secondly, *Verbal* propositions, which are words, the signs of our ideas, put together or separated in affirmative or negative sentences. By which way of affirming or denying, these signs, made by sounds, are, as it were, put together or separated one from another. So that proposition consists in joining or separating signs; and truth consists in the putting together or separating those signs, according as the things which they stand for agree or disagree.

Everyone's experience will satisfy him, that the mind, either by perceiving, or supposing, the agreement or disagreement of any of its ideas, does tacitly within itself put them into a kind of proposition affirmative or negative; which I have endeavored to express by the terms putting together and separating. But this action of the mind, which is so familiar to every thinking and reasoning man, is easier to be conceived by reflecting on what passes in us when we affirm or deny, than to be explained by words. When a man has in his head the idea of two lines, viz. the side and diagonal of a square, whereof the diagonal is an inch long, he may have the idea also of the division of that line into a certain number of equal parts; v.g. into five, ten, a hundred, a thousand, or any other number, and may have the idea of that inch line being divisible, or not divisible, into such equal parts, as a certain number of them will be equal to the sideline. Now, whenever he perceives, believes, or supposes such a kind of divisibility to agree or disagree to his idea of that line, he, as it were, joins or separates those two ideas, viz. the idea of that line, and the idea of that kind of divisibility; and so makes a mental proposition, which is true or false, according as such a kind of divisibility, a divisibility into such *aliquot* parts, does really agree to that line or no. When ideas are so put together, or separated in the mind, as they or the things they stand for do agree or not, that is, as I may call it, *mental truth*. But *truth of words* is something more; and that is the affirming or denying of words one of another, as the ideas they stand for agree or disagree: and this again is two-fold; either purely verbal and trifling, which I shall speak of (Chapter 8), or real and instructive; which is the object of that real knowledge which we have spoken of already.

But here again will be apt to occur the same doubt about truth, that did about knowledge: and it will be objected, that if truth be nothing but the joining and separating of words in propositions, as the ideas they stand for agree or disagree in men's minds, the knowledge of truth is not so valuable a thing as it is taken to be, nor worth the pains and time men employ in the search of it: since by this account it amounts to no more than the conformity of words to the chimeras of men's brains. Who knows not what odd notions many men's heads are filled with, and what strange ideas all men's brains are capable of? But if we rest here, we know the truth of nothing by this rule, but of the visionary words in our own imaginations; nor have other truth, but what as much concerns harpies and centaurs, as men and horses. For those, and the like, may be ideas in our heads, and have their agreement or disagreement there, as well as the ideas of real beings, and so have as true propositions made about them. And it will be altogether as true a proposition to say *all centaurs are animals*, as that *all men are animals;* and the certainty of one as great as the other. For in both the propositions, the words are put together according to the agreement of the ideas in our minds: and the agreement of the idea of animal with that of centaur is as clear and visible to the mind, as the agreement of the idea of animal with that of man; and so these two propositions are equally true, equally certain. But of what use is all such truth to us?

Though what has been said in the foregoing chapter to distinguish real from imaginary knowledge might suffice here, in answer to this doubt, to distinguish real truth from chimerical, or (if you please) barely nominal, they depending both on the same foundation; yet it may not be amiss here again to consider, that though our words signify nothing but our ideas, yet being designed by them to signify things, the truth they contain when put into propositions will be only verbal, when they stand for ideas in the mind that have not an agreement with the reality of things. And therefore truth as well as knowledge may well come under the distinction of verbal and real; that being only verbal truth, wherein terms are joined according to the agreement or disagreement of the ideas they stand for; without regarding whether our ideas are such as really have, or are capable of having, an existence in nature. But then it is they contain *real truth,* when these signs are joined, as our ideas agree; and when our ideas are such as we know are capable of having an existence in nature: which in substances we cannot know, but by knowing that such have existed.

Truth is the marking down in words the agreement or disagreement of ideas as it is. Falsehood is the marking down in words the agreement or disagreement of ideas otherwise than it is. And so far as these ideas, thus marked by sounds, agree to their archetypes, so far only is the truth real. The knowledge of this truth consists in knowing what ideas the words stand for, and the perception of the agreement or disagreement of those ideas, according as it is marked by those words.

But because words are looked on as the great conduits of truth and knowledge, and that in conveying and receiving of truth, and commonly in reasoning about it, we make use of words and propositions, I shall more at large inquire wherein the certainty of real truths contained in propositions consists, and where it is to be had; and endeavor to show in what sort of universal propositions we are capable of being certain of their real truth or falsehood.

I shall begin with *general* propositions, as those which most employ our thoughts, and exercise our contemplation. General truths are most looked after by the mind as those that most enlarge our knowledge; and by their comprehensiveness satisfying us at once of many particulars, enlarge our view, and shorten our way to knowledge.

Besides truth taken in the strict sense before mentioned, there are other sorts of truths: As, 1. Moral truth, which is speaking of things according to the persuasion of our own minds, though the proposition we speak agree not to the reality of things; 2. Metaphysical truth, which is nothing but the real existence of things, conformable to the ideas to which we have annexed their names. This, though it seems to consist in the very beings of things, yet, when considered a little nearly, will appear to include a tacit proposition, whereby the mind joins that particular thing to the idea it had before settled with the name to it. But these considerations of truth, either having been before taken notice of, or not being much to our present purpose, it may suffice here only to have mentioned them.

V I

Of Universal Propositions: Their Truth and Certainty

THOUGH THE EXAMINING AND JUDGING of ideas by themselves, their names being quite laid aside, be the best and surest way to clear and distinct knowledge: yet, through the prevailing custom of using sounds for ideas, I think it is very seldom practiced. Everyone may observe how common it is for names to be made use of, instead of the ideas themselves, even when men think and reason within their own breasts; especially if the ideas be very complex, and made up of a great collection of simple ones. This makes the consideration of *words* and *propositions* so necessary a part of the Treatise of Knowledge, that it is very hard to speak intelligibly of the one, without explaining the other.

All the knowledge we have, being only of particular or general truths, it is evident that whatever may be done in the former of these, the latter, which is that which with reason is most sought after, can never be well made known, and is very seldom apprehended, but as conceived and expressed in words. It is not, therefore, out of our way, in the examination of our knowledge, to inquire into the truth and certainty of universal propositions.

But that we may not be misled in this case by that which is the danger everywhere, I mean by the doubtfulness of terms, it is fit to observe that certainty is twofold: *certainty of truth* and *certainty of knowledge*. Certainty of truth is, when words are so put together in propositions as exactly to express the agreement or disagreement of the ideas they stand for, as really it is. Certainty of knowledge is to perceive the agreement or disagreement of ideas, as expressed in any proposition. This we usually call knowing, or being certain of the truth of any proposition.

Now, because we cannot be certain of the truth of any general proposition, unless we know the precise bounds and extent of the species its terms stand for, it is necessary we should know the essence of each species, which is that which constitutes and bounds it.

This, in all simple ideas and modes, is not hard to do. For in these the real and nominal essence being the same, or, which is all one, the abstract idea which the general term stands for being the sole essence and boundary that is or can be supposed of the species, there can be no doubt how far the species extends, or what things are comprehended under each term; which, it is evident, are all that have an exact conformity with the idea it stands for, and no other.

But in substances, wherein a real essence, distinct from the nominal, is supposed to constitute, determine, and bound the species, the extent of the general word is very uncertain; because, not knowing this real essence, we cannot know what is, or what is not of that species; and, consequently, what may or may not with certainty be affirmed of it. And thus, speaking of a *man,* or *gold,* or any other species of natural substances, as supposed constituted by a precise and real essence which nature regularly imparts to every individual of that kind, whereby it is made to be of that species, we cannot be certain of the truth of any affirmation or negation made of it. For man or gold, taken in this sense, and used for species of things constituted by real essences, different from the complex idea in the mind of the speaker, stand for we know not what; and the extent of these species, with such boundaries, are so unknown and undetermined, that it is impossible with any certainty to affirm, that all men are rational, or that all gold is yellow. But where the nominal essence is kept to, as the boundary of each species, and men extend the application of any general term no further than to the particular things in which the complex idea it stands for is to be found, there they are in no danger to mistake the bounds of each species, nor can be in doubt, on this account, whether any proposition be true or not. I have chosen to explain this uncertainty of propositions in this scholastic way, and have made use of the terms of *essences,* and *species,* on purpose to show the absurdity and inconvenience there is to think of them as of any other sort of realities, than barely abstract ideas with names to them. To suppose that the species of things are anything but the sorting of them under general names, according as they agree to several abstract ideas of which we make those names the signs, is to confound truth, and introduce uncertainty into all general propositions that can be made about them. Though therefore these things might, to people not possessed with scholastic learning, be treated of in a better and clearer way; yet those wrong notions of essences or species having got root in most people's minds who have received any tincture from the learning which has prevailed in this part of the world, are to be discovered and removed, to make way for that use of words which should convey certainty with it.

The names of substances, then, whenever made to stand for species which are supposed to be constituted by real essences which we know not, are not capable to convey certainty to the understanding. Of the truth of general propositions made up of such terms we cannot be sure. The reason whereof is plain: for how can we be sure that this or that quality is in gold, when we know not what is or is not gold? Since in this way of speaking, nothing is gold but what partakes of an essence, which we, not knowing, cannot know where it is or is not, and so cannot be sure that any parcel of matter in the world is or is not in this sense gold; being incurably ignorant whether *it* has or has not that which makes anything to be called gold; i.e. that real essence of gold whereof we have no idea at all. This being as impossible for us to know as it is for a blind man to tell in what flower the color of a pansy is or is not to be found, whilst he has no idea of the color of a pansy at all. Or if we could (which is impossible) certainly know where a real essence, which we know not, is, v.g. in what parcels of matter the real essence of gold is, yet could we not be sure that this or that quality could with truth be affirmed of gold; since it is impossible for us to know that this or that quality or idea has a necessary connection with a real essence of which we have no idea at all, whatever species that supposed real essence may be imagined to constitute.

On the other side, the names of substances, when made use of as they should be, for the ideas men have in their minds, though they carry a clear and determinate signification with them, will not yet serve us to make many universal propositions of whose truth we can be certain. Not because in this use of them we are uncertain what things are signified by them, but because the complex ideas they stand for are such combinations of simple ones as carry not with them any discoverable connection or repugnancy, but with a very few other ideas.

The complex ideas that our names of the species of substances properly stand for, are collections of such qualities as have been observed to co-exist in an unknown substratum, which we call substance; but what other qualities necessarily co-exist with such combinations, we cannot certainly know, unless we can discover their natural dependence; which, in their primary qualities, we can go but a very little way in; and in all their secondary qualities we can discover no connection at all: for the reasons mentioned, Chapter 3. Viz. 1. Because we know not the real constitutions of substances, on which each secondary quality particularly depends. 2. Did we know that, it would serve us only for experimental (not universal) knowledge; and reach with certainty no further than that bare instance: because our understandings can discover no conceivable connection between any secondary quality and any modification whatsoever of any of the primary ones. And therefore there are very few general propositions to be made concerning substances, which can carry with them undoubted certainty.

"All gold is fixed," is a proposition whose truth we cannot be certain of, how universally soever it be believed. For if, according to the useless imagination of the Schools, anyone supposes the term gold to stand for a species of things set out by nature, by a real essence belonging to it, it is evident he knows not what particular substances are of that species; and so cannot with certainty affirm anything universally of gold. But if he makes gold stand for a species determined by its nominal essence, let the nominal essence, for example, be the complex idea of a body of a certain yellow color, malleable, fusible, and heavier than any other known;—in this proper use of the word gold, there is no difficulty to know what is or is not gold. But yet no other quality can with certainty be universally affirmed or denied of gold, but what hath a *discoverable* connection or inconsistency with that nominal essence. Fixedness, for example, having no necessary connection that we can discover, with the color, weight, or any other simple idea of our complex one, or with the whole combination together; it is impossible that we should certainly know the truth of this proposition, that all gold is fixed.

As there is no discoverable connection between fixedness and the color, weight, and other simple ideas of that nominal essence of gold; so, if we make our complex idea of gold, a body yellow, fusible, ductile, weighty, and fixed, we shall be at the same uncertainty concerning solubility in *aqua regia,* and for the same reason. Since we can never, from consideration of the ideas themselves, with certainty affirm or deny of a body whose complex idea is made up of yellow, very weighty, ductile, fusible, and fixed, that it is soluble in *aqua regia:* and so on of the rest of its qualities. I would gladly meet with one general affirmation concerning any quality of gold, that anyone can certainly know is true. It will, no doubt, be presently objected, Is not this a universal proposition, *All gold is malleable?* To which I answer, It is a very certain proposition, if malleableness be a part of the complex idea the word gold stands for. But then here is nothing affirmed of gold, but that that sound stands for an idea in which malleableness is contained: and such a sort of truth and certainty as this it is, to say a centaur is four-footed. But if malleableness make not a part of the specific essence the name of gold stands for, it is plain, *all gold is malleable,* is not a certain proposition. Because, let the complex idea of gold be made up of whichsoever of its other qualities you please, malleableness will not appear to depend on that complex idea, nor follow from any simple one contained in it: the connection that malleableness has (if it has any) with those other qualities being only by the intervention of the real constitution of its insensible parts; which, since we know not, it is impossible we should perceive that connection, unless we could discover that which ties them together.

The more, indeed, of these co-existing qualities we unite into one complex idea, under one name, the more precise and determinate we make the signification of that word; but never yet make it thereby more capable of universal certainty, *in respect of other qualities not contained in our complex idea:* since we perceive not their connection or dependence on one another; being ignorant both of that real constitution in which they are all founded, and also how they flow from it. For the chief part of our knowledge concerning substances is not, as in other things, barely of the relation of two ideas that may exist separately; but is of the necessary connection and co-existence of several distinct ideas in the same subject, or of their repugnancy so to co-exist. Could we begin at the other end, and discover what it was wherein that color consisted, what made a body lighter or heavier, what texture of parts made it malleable, fusible, and fixed, and fit to be dissolved in this sort of liquor, and not in another;—if, I say, we had such an idea as this of bodies, and could perceive wherein all sensible qualities originally consist, and how they are produced; we might frame such abstract ideas of them as would furnish us with matter of more general knowledge, and enable us to make universal propositions, that should carry general truth and certainty with them. But whilst our complex ideas of the sorts of substances are so remote from that internal real constitution on which their sensible qualities depend, and are made up of nothing but an imperfect collection of those apparent qualities our senses can discover, there can be few general propositions concerning substances of whose real truth we can be certainly assured; since there are but few simple ideas of whose connection and necessary coexistence we can have certain and undoubted knowledge. I imagine, amongst all the secondary qualities of substances, and the powers relating to them, there cannot any two be named, whose necessary co-existence, or repugnance to coexist, can certainly be known; unless in those of the same sense, which necessarily exclude one another, as I have elsewhere showed. No one, I think, by the color that is in any body, can certainly know what smell, taste, sound, or tangible qualities it has, nor what alterations it is capable to make or receive on or from other bodies. The same may be said of the sound or taste, etc. Our specific names of substances standing for any collections of such ideas, it is not to be wondered that we can with them make very few general propositions of undoubted real certainty. But yet so far as any complex idea of any sort of substances contains in it any simple idea, whose *necessary* co-existence with any other *may* be discovered, so far universal propositions may with certainty be made concerning it: v.g. could anyone discover a necessary connection between malleableness and the color or weight of gold, or any other part of the complex idea signified by that name, he might make a certain universal proposition concerning gold in this respect; and the real truth of this proposition, that *all gold is malleable,* would be as certain as of this, *the three angles of all right-lined triangles are all equal to two right ones.*

Had we such ideas of substances as to know what real constitutions produce those sensible qualities we find in them, and how those qualities flowed from thence, we could, by the specific ideas of their real essences in our own minds, more certainly find out their properties, and discover what qualities they had or had not, than we can now by our senses: and to know the properties of gold, it would be no more necessary that gold should exist, and that we should make experiments upon it, than it is necessary for the knowing the properties of a triangle, that a triangle should exist in any matter, the idea in our minds would serve for the one as well as the other. But we are so far from being admitted into the secrets of nature, that we scarce so much as ever approach the first entrance toward them. For we are wont to consider the substances we meet with, each of them, as an entire thing by itself, having all its qualities in itself, and independent of other things; overlooking, for the most part, the operations of those invisible fluids they are encompassed with, and upon whose motions and operations depend the greatest part of those qualities which are taken notice of in them, and are made by us the inherent marks of distinction whereby we know and denominate them. Put a piece of gold anywhere by itself, separate from the reach and influence of all other bodies, it will immediately lose all its color and weight, and perhaps malleableness too; which, for aught I know, would be changed into a perfect friability. Water, in which to us fluidity is an essential quality, left to itself, would cease to be fluid. But if inanimate bodies owe so much of their present state to other bodies without them, that they would not be what they appear to us were those bodies that environ them removed; it is yet more so in vegetables, which are nourished, grow, and produce leaves, flowers, and seeds, in a constant succession. And if we look a little nearer into the state of animals, we shall find that their dependence, as to life, motion, and the most considerable qualities to be observed in them, is so wholly on extrinsical causes and qualities of other bodies that make no part of them, that they cannot subsist a moment without them: though yet those bodies on which they depend are little taken notice of, and make no part of the complex ideas we frame of those animals. Take the air but for a minute from the greatest part of living creatures, and they presently lose sense, life, and motion. This the necessity of breathing has forced into our knowledge. But how many other extrinsical and possibly very remote bodies do the springs of these admirable machines depend on, which are not vulgarly observed, or so much as thought on; and how many are there which the severest inquiry can never discover? The inhabitants of this spot of the universe, though removed so many millions of miles from the sun, yet depend so much on the duly tempered motion of particles coming from or agitated by it, that were this earth removed but a small part of the distance out of its present situation, and placed a little further or nearer that source of heat, it is more than probable that the greatest part of the animals in it would immediately perish: since we find them so often destroyed by an excess or defect of the sun's warmth, which an accidental position in some parts of this our little globe exposes them to. The qualities observed in a loadstone must needs have their source far beyond the confines of that body; and the ravage made often on several sorts of animals by invisible causes, the certain death (as we are told) of some of them, by barely passing the line, or, as it is certain of other, by being removed into a neighboring country; evidently show that the concurrence and operations of several bodies, with which they are seldom thought to have anything to do, is absolutely necessary to make them be what they appear to us, and to preserve those qualities by which we know and distinguish them. We are then quite out of the way, when we think that things contain *within themselves* the qualities that appear to us in them; and we in vain search for that constitution within the body of a fly or an elephant, upon which depend those qualities and powers we observe in them. For which, perhaps, to understand them aright, we ought to look not only beyond this our earth and atmosphere, but even beyond the sun or remotest star our eyes have yet discovered. For how much the being and operation of particular substances in this our globe depends on causes utterly beyond our view, is impossible for us to determine. We see and perceive some of the motions and grosser operations of things here about us; but whence the streams come that keep all these curious machines in motion and repair, how conveyed and modified, is beyond our notice and apprehension: and the great parts and wheels, as I may so say, of this stupendous structure of the universe, may, for aught we know, have such a connection and dependence in their influences and operations one upon another, that perhaps things in this our mansion would put on quite another face, and cease to be what they are, if some one of the stars or great bodies incomprehensibly remote from us, should cease to be or move as it does. This is certain: things, however absolute and entire they seem in themselves, are but retainers to other parts of nature, for that which they are most taken notice of by us. Their observable qualities, actions, and powers are owing to something without them; and there is not so complete and perfect a part that we know of nature, which does not owe the being it has, and the excellences of it, to its neighbors; and we must not confine our thoughts within the surface of any body, but look a great deal further, to comprehend perfectly those qualities that are in it.

If this be so, it is not to be wondered that we have very imperfect ideas of substances, and that the real essences, on which depend their properties and operations, are unknown to us. We cannot discover so much as that size, figure, and texture of their minute and active parts, which is really in them; much less the different motions and impulses made in and upon them by bodies from without, upon which depends, and by which is formed the greatest and most remarkable part of those qualities we observe in them, and of which our complex ideas of them are made up. This consideration alone is enough to put an end to all our hopes of ever having the ideas of their real essences; which whilst we want, the nominal essences we make use of instead of them will be able to furnish us but very sparingly with any general knowledge, or universal propositions capable of real certainty.

We are not therefore to wonder, if certainty be to be found in very few general propositions made concerning substances: our knowledge of their qualities and properties goes very seldom further than our senses reach and inform us. Possibly inquisitive and observing men may, by strength of judgment, penetrate further, and, on probabilities taken from wary observation, and hints well laid together, often guess right at what experience has not yet discovered to them. But this is but guessing still; it amounts only to opinion, and has not that certainty which is requisite to knowledge. For all general knowledge lies only in our own thoughts, and consists barely in the contemplation of our own abstract ideas. Wherever we perceive any agreement or disagreement amongst them, there we have general knowledge; and by putting the names of those ideas together accordingly in propositions, can with certainty pronounce general truths. But because the abstract ideas of substances, for which their specific names stand, whenever they have any distinct and determinate signification, have a discoverable connection or inconsistency with but a very few other ideas, the certainty of universal propositions concerning substances is very narrow and scanty, in that part which is our principal inquiry concerning them; and there are scarce any of the names of substances, let the idea it is applied to be what it will, of which we can generally, and with certainty, pronounce, that it has or has not this or that other quality belonging to it, and constantly co-existing or inconsistent with that idea, wherever it is to be found.

Before we can have any tolerable knowledge of this kind, we must First know what changes the primary qualities of one body do regularly produce in the primary qualities of another, and how. Secondly, We must know what primary qualities of any body produce certain sensations or ideas in us. This is in truth no less than to know *all* the effects of matter, under its divers modifications of bulk, figure, cohesion of parts, motion and rest. Which, I think everybody will allow, is utterly impossible to be known by us without revelation. Nor if it were revealed to us what sort of figure, bulk, and motion of corpuscles would produce in us the sensation of a yellow color, and what sort of figure, bulk, and texture of parts in the superficies of any body were fit to give such corpuscles their due motion to produce that color; would that be enough to make universal propositions with certainty, concerning the several sorts of them; unless we had faculties acute enough to perceive the precise bulk, figure, texture, and motion of bodies, in those minute parts, by which they operate on our senses, so that we might by those frame our abstract ideas of them. I have mentioned here only corporeal substances, whose operations seem to lie more level to our understandings. For as to the operations of spirits, both their thinking and moving of bodies, we at first sight find ourselves at a loss; though perhaps, when we have applied our thoughts a little nearer to the consideration of bodies and their operations, and examined how far our notions, even in these reach with any clearness beyond sensible matter of fact, we shall be bound to confess that, even in these too, our discoveries amount to very little beyond perfect ignorance and incapacity.

This is evident, the abstract complex ideas of substances, for which their general names stand, not comprehending their real constitutions, can afford us very little universal certainty. Because our ideas of them are not made up of that on which those qualities we observe in them, and would inform ourselves about, do depend, or with which they have any certain connection: v.g. let the ideas to which we give the name *man* be, as it commonly is, a body of the ordinary shape, with sense, voluntary motion, and reason joined to it. This being the abstract idea, and consequently the essence of *our* species, man, we can make but very few general certain propositions concerning man, standing for such an idea. Because, not knowing the real constitution on which sensation, power of motion, and reasoning, with that peculiar shape, depend, and whereby they are united together in the same subject, there are very few other qualities with which we can perceive them to have a necessary connection: and therefore we cannot with certainty affirm: That all men sleep by intervals; That no man can be nourished by wood or stones; That all men will be poisoned by hemlock: because these ideas have no connection nor repugnancy with this our nominal essence of man, with this abstract idea that name stands for. We must, in these and the like, appeal to trial in particular subjects, which can reach but a little way. We must content ourselves with probability in the rest: but can have no general certainty, whilst our specific idea of man contains not that real constitution which is the root wherein all his inseparable qualities are united, and from whence they flow. Whilst our idea the word *man* stands for is only an imperfect collection of some sensible qualities and powers in him, there is no discernible connection or repugnance between our specific idea, and the operation of either the parts of hemlock or stones upon his constitution. There are animals that safely eat hemlock, and others that are nourished by wood and stones: but as long as we want ideas of those real constitutions of different sorts of animals whereon these and the like qualities and powers depend, we must not hope to reach certainty in universal propositions concerning them. Those few ideas only which have a discernible connection with our nominal essence, or any part of it, can afford us such propositions. But these are so few, and of so little moment, that we may justly look on our certain general knowledge of substances as almost none at all.

To conclude: general propositions, of what kind soever, are then only capable of certainty, when the terms used in them stand for such ideas, whose agreement or disagreement, as there expressed, is capable to be discovered by us. And we are then certain of their truth or falsehood, when we perceive the ideas the terms stand for to agree or not agree, according as they are affirmed or denied one of another. Whence we may take notice, that general certainty is never to be found but in our ideas. Whenever we go to seek it elsewhere, in experiment or observations without us, our knowledge goes not beyond particulars. It is the contemplation of our own abstract ideas that alone is able to afford us general knowledge.

VII

Of Maxims—Summary

[In Chapter VII, Locke deals with the traditional maxims or axioms of knowledge, "which have passed for first principles of science." He does not deny their self-evidence, as he has denied their innateness, but he argues that these exalted maxims are in no way distinguished by their self-evidence from millions of other self-evident propositions. He denies that these maxims are the first principles the mind learns, or that our perception of other parts of knowledge depend on them, and that they could not serve as foundations for any science. They are of no use in the discovery of new knowledge: and, indeed their utility is confined—1. to teach known science to pupils; 2. to silence "obstinate wranglers" in philosophical disputations.]

VIII

Of Trifling Propositions

BEFORE A MAN MAKES ANY PROPOSITION, he is supposed to understand the terms he uses in it, or else he talks like a parrot, only making a noise by imitation, and framing certain sounds, which he has learnt of others; but not as a rational creature, using them for signs of ideas which he has in his mind. The hearer also is supposed to understand the terms as the speaker uses them, or else he talks jargon, and makes an unintelligible noise. And therefore, he trifles with words who makes such a proposition, which, when it is made, contains no more than one of the terms does, and which a man was supposed to know before: v.g. a triangle has three sides, or saffron is yellow. And this is no further tolerable than where a man goes to explain his terms to one who is supposed or declares himself not to understand him; and then it teaches only the signification of that word, and the use of that sign.

We can know then the truth of two sorts of propositions with perfect certainty. The one is, of those trifling propositions which have a certainty in them, but it is only a verbal certainty, but not instructive. And, secondly, we can know the truth, and so may be certain in propositions, which affirm something of another, which is a necessary consequence of its precise complex idea, but not contained in it: as that the external angle of all triangles is bigger than either of the opposite internal angles. Which relation of the outward angle to either of the opposite internal angles, making no part of the complex idea signified by the name triangle, this is a real truth, and conveys with it instructive real knowledge.

We having little or no knowledge of what combinations there be of simple ideas existing together in substances, but by our senses, we cannot make any universal certain propositions concerning them, any further than our nominal essences lead us. Which being to a very few and inconsiderable truths, in respect of those which depend on their real constitutions, the general propositions that are made about substances, if they are certain, are for the most part but trifling; and if they are instructive, are uncertain, and such as we can have no knowledge of their real truth, how much soever constant observation and analogy may assist our judgment in guessing. Hence it comes to pass, that one may often meet with very clear and coherent discourses, that amount yet to nothing. For it is plain that names of substantial beings, as well as others, as far as they have relative significations affixed to them, may, with great truth, be joined negatively and affirmatively in propositions, as their relative definitions make them fit to be so joined; and propositions consisting of such terms, may, with the same clearness, be deduced one from another, as those that convey the most real truths: and all this without any knowledge of the nature or reality of things existing without us. By this method one may make demonstrations and undoubted propositions in words, and yet thereby advance not one jot in the knowledge of the truth of things: v.g. he that having learnt these following words, with their ordinary mutual relative acceptations annexed to them; v.g. *substance, man, animal, form, soul, vegetative, sensitive, rational,* may make several undoubted propositions about the soul, without knowing at all what the soul really is: and of this sort, a man may find an infinite number of propositions, reasonings, and conclusions, in books of metaphysics, school-divinity, and some sort of natural philosophy; and, after all, know as little of God, spirits, or bodies, as he did before he set out.

He that hath liberty to define, i.e. to determine the signification of his names of substances (as certainly everyone does in effect, who makes them stand for his own ideas), and makes their significations at a venture, taking them from his own or other men's fancies, and not from an examination or inquiry into the nature of things themselves; may with little trouble demonstrate them one of another, according to those several respects and mutual relations he has given them one to another; wherein, however things agree or disagree in their own nature, he needs mind nothing but his own notions, with the names he hath bestowed upon them: but thereby no more increases his own knowledge than he does his riches, who, taking a bag of counters, calls one in a certain place a pound, another in another place a shilling, and a third in a third place a penny; and so proceeding, may undoubtedly reckon right, and cast up a great sum, according to his counters so placed, and standing for more or less as he pleases, without being one jot the richer, or without even knowing how much a pound, shilling, or penny is, but only that one is contained in the other twenty times, and contains the other twelve: which a man may also do in the signification of words, by making them, in respect of one another, more or less, or equally comprehensive.

Though yet concerning most words used in discourses, equally argumentative and controversial, there is this more to be complained of, which is the worst sort of trifling, and which sets us yet further from the certainty of knowledge we hope to attain by them, or find in them; viz. that most writers are so far from instructing us in the nature and knowledge of things, that they use their words loosely and uncertainly, and do not, by using them constantly and steadily in the same significations, make plain and clear deductions of words one from another, and make their discourses coherent and clear (how little soever they were instructive); which were not difficult to do, did they not find it convenient to shelter their ignorance or obstinacy under the obscurity and perplexedness of their terms: to which, perhaps, inadvertency and ill custom do in many men much contribute.

To conclude. Barely verbal propositions may be known by these following marks:

First, All propositions wherein two abstract terms are affirmed one of another, are barely about the signification of sounds. For since no abstract idea can be the same with any other but itself, when its abstract name is affirmed of any other term, it can signify no more but this, that it may, or ought to be called by that name; or that these two names signify the same idea. Thus, should anyone say that parsimony is frugality, that gratitude is justice, that this or that action is or is not temperate: however specious these and the like propositions may at first sight seem, yet when we come to press them, and examine nicely what they contain, we shall find that it all amounts to nothing but the signification of those terms.

Secondly, All propositions wherein a part of the complex idea which any term stands for is predicated of that term, are only verbal: v.g. to say that gold is a metal, or heavy. And thus all propositions wherein more comprehensive words, called *genera,* are affirmed of subordinate or less comprehensive, called *species,* or individuals, are barely verbal.

When by these two rules we have examined the propositions that make up the discourses we ordinarily meet with, both in and out of books, we shall perhaps find that a greater part of them than is usually suspected are purely about the signification of words, and contain nothing in them but the use and application of these signs.

This I think I may lay down for an infallible rule, That, wherever the distinct idea any word stands for is not known and considered, and something not contained in the idea is not affirmed or denied of it, there our thoughts stick wholly in sounds, and are able to attain no real truth or falsehood. This, perhaps, if well heeded, might save us a great deal of useless amusement and dispute; and very much shorten our trouble and wandering in the search of real and true knowledge.

IX

Of Our Threefold Knowledge of Existence

HITHERTO WE HAVE ONLY CONSIDERED the essences of things; which being only abstract ideas, and thereby removed in our thoughts from particular existence (that being the proper operation of the mind, in abstraction, to consider an idea under no other existence but what it has in the understanding), gives us no knowledge of real existence at all. Where, by the way, we may take notice, that universal propositions of whose truth or falsehood we can have certain knowledge concern not existence: and further, that all particular affirmations or negations that would not be certain if they were made general, are only concerning existence; they declaring only the accidental union or separation of ideas in things existing, which, in their abstract natures, have no known necessary union or repugnancy.

But, leaving the nature of propositions, and different ways of predication to be considered more at large in another place, let us proceed now to inquire concerning our knowledge of the *existence of things,* and how we come by it. I say, then, that we have the knowledge of *our own* existence by intuition; of the existence of *God* by demonstration; and of *other things* by sensation.

As for *our own existence,* we perceive it so plainly and so certainly, that it neither needs nor is capable of any proof. For nothing can be more evident to us than our own existence. I think, I reason, I feel pleasure and pain: can any of these be more evident to me than my own existence? If I doubt of all other things, that very doubt makes me perceive my own existence, and will not suffer me to doubt of that. For if I know I feel pain, it is evident I have as certain perception of my own existence, as of the existence of the pain I feel: or if I know I doubt, I have as certain perception of the existence of the thing doubting, as of that thought which I *call doubt.* Experience then convinces us, that we have an *intuitive knowledge* of our own existence, and an internal infallible perception that we are. In every act of sensation, reasoning, or thinking, we are conscious to ourselves of our own being; and, in this matter, come not short of the highest degree of certainty.

X

Of Our Knowledge of the Existence of a God

THOUGH GOD HAS GIVEN US no innate ideas of Himself; though He has stamped no original characters on our minds, wherein we may read His being; yet having furnished us with those faculties our minds are endowed with, He hath not left Himself without witness: since we have sense, perception, and reason, and cannot want a clear proof of Him, as long as we carry *ourselves* about us. Nor can we justly complain of our ignorance in this great point; since He has so plentifully provided us with the means to discover and know Him; so far as is necessary to the end of our being, and the great concernment of our happiness. But, though this be the most obvious truth that reason discovers, and though its evidence be (if I mistake not) equal to mathematical certainty: yet it requires thought and attention; and the mind must apply itself to a regular deduction of it from some part of our intuitive knowledge, or else we shall be as uncertain and ignorant of this as of other propositions, which are in themselves capable of clear demonstration. To show, therefore, that we are capable of *knowing*, i.e. *being certain* that there is a God, and *how we may come by* this certainty, I think we need go no further than *ourselves*, and that undoubted knowledge we have of our own existence.

I think it is beyond question, that man has a clear idea of his own being; he knows certainly he exists, and that he is something. He that can doubt whether he be anything or no, I speak not to; no more than I would argue with pure nothing, or endeavor to convince nonentity that it were something. If anyone pretends to be so skeptical as to deny his own existence (for really to doubt of it is manifestly impossible), let him for me enjoy his beloved happiness of being nothing, until hunger or some other pain convince him of the contrary. This, then, I think I may take for a truth, which everyone's certain knowledge assures him of, beyond the liberty of doubting, viz. that he is *something that actually exists*.

In the next place, man knows, by an intuitive certainty, that bare *nothing can no more produce any real being, than it can be equal to two right angles.* If a man knows not that nonentity, or the absence of all being, cannot be equal to two right angles, it is impossible he should know any demonstration in Euclid. If, therefore, we know there is some real being, and that nonentity cannot produce any real being, it is an evident demonstration, that *from eternity there has been something;* since what was not from eternity had a beginning; and what had a beginning must be produced by something else.

Next, it is evident, that what had its being and beginning from another, must also have all that which is in and belongs to its being from another too. All the powers it has must be owing to and received from the same source. This eternal source, then, of all being must also be the source and original of all power; and so *this eternal Being must be also the most powerful.*

Again, a man finds in *himself* perception and knowledge. We have then got one step further; and we are certain now that there is not only some being, but some knowing, intelligent being in the world. There was a time, then, when there was no knowing being, and when knowledge began to be; or else there has been also *a knowing being from eternity.* If it be said, there was a time when no being had any knowledge, when that eternal being was void of all understanding; I reply, that then it was impossible there should ever have been any knowledge: it being as impossible that things wholly void of knowledge, and operating blindly, and without any perception, should produce a knowing being, as it is impossible that a triangle should make itself three angles bigger than two right ones. For it is as repugnant to the idea of senseless matter, that it should put into itself sense, perception, and knowledge, as it is repugnant to the idea of a triangle, that it should put into itself greater angles than two right ones.

Thus, from the consideration of ourselves, and what we infallibly find in our own constitutions, our reason leads us to the knowledge of this certain and evident truth,—*That there is an eternal, most powerful, and most knowing Being;* which whether any one will please to call God, it matters not. The thing is evident; and from this idea duly considered, will easily be deduced all those other attributes, which we ought to ascribe to this eternal Being.

From what has been said, it is plain to me we have a more

certain knowledge of the existence of a God, than of anything our senses have not immediately discovered to us. Nay, I presume I may say, that we more certainly know that there is a God, than that there is anything else without us. When I say we *know*, I mean there is such a knowledge within our reach which we cannot miss, if we will but apply our minds to that, as we do to several other inquiries.

[Locke goes on to argue that there is no truth more evident than that there must be *something* existing from eternity. This eternal being must be a cognitative being, because an incognitative being could not produce cognitative beings. This eternal being cannot be material, because each particle of matter is not cognitative, and a system of incognitative matter could not be cognitative.]

X I

Of Our Knowledge of the Existence of Other Things

THE KNOWLEDGE OF OUR OWN BEING we have by intuition. The existence of a God, reason clearly makes known to us, as has been shown.

The knowledge of the existence of *any other thing* we can have only by *sensation:* for there being no necessary connection of real existence with any *idea* a man has in his memory; nor of any other existence but that of God with the existence of any particular man: no particular man can know the existence of any other being, but only when, by actual operating upon him, it makes itself perceived by him. For, the having the idea of anything in our mind, no more proves the existence of that thing, than the picture of a man evidences his being in the world, or the visions of a dream make thereby a true history.

It is therefore the *actual receiving* of ideas from without that gives us notice of the existence of other things, and makes us know, that something doth exist at that time without us, which causes that idea in us; though perhaps we neither know nor consider how it does it. For it takes not from the certainty of our senses, and the ideas we receive by them, that we know not the manner wherein they are produced: v.g. whilst I write this, I have, by the paper affecting my eyes, that idea produced in my mind, which, whatever object causes, I call *white;* by which I know that that quality or accident (i.e. whose appearance before my eyes always causes that idea) doth really exist, and hath a being without me. And of this, the greatest assurance I can possibly have, and to which my faculties can attain, is the testimony of my eyes, which are the proper and sole judges of this thing; whose testimony I have reason to rely on as so certain, that I can no more doubt, whilst I write this, that I see white and black, and that something really exists that causes that sensation in me, than that I write or move my hand; which is a certainty as great as human nature is capable of, concerning the existence of anything, but a man's self alone, and of God.

The notice we have by our senses of the existing of things without us, though it be not altogether so certain as our intuitive knowledge, or the deductions of our reason employed about the clear abstract ideas of our own minds; yet it is an assurance that deserves the name of *knowledge*. If we persuade ourselves that our faculties act and inform us right concerning the existence of those objects that affect them, it cannot pass for an ill-grounded confidence: for I think nobody can, in earnest, be so skeptical as to be uncertain of the existence of those things which he sees and feels. At least, he that can doubt so far (whatever he may have with his own thoughts), will never have any controversy with me; since he can never be sure I say anything contrary to his own opinion. As to myself, I think God has given me assurance enough of the existence of things without me: since, by their different application, I can produce in myself both pleasure and pain, which is one great concernment of my present state. This is certain: the confidence that our faculties do not herein deceive us, is the greatest assurance we are capable of concerning the existence of material beings. For we cannot act anything but by our faculties; nor talk of knowledge itself, but by the help of those faculties which are fitted to apprehend even what knowledge is.

But besides the assurance we have from our senses themselves, that they do not err in the information they give us of the existence of things without us, when they are affected by them, we are further confirmed in this assurance by other concurrent reasons:——

I. It is plain those perceptions are produced in us by exterior causes affecting our senses: because those that want the *organs* of any sense, never can have the ideas belonging to that sense produced in their minds. This is too evident to be doubted: and therefore we cannot but be assured that they come in by the organs of that sense, and no other way. The organs themselves, it is plain, do not produce them: for then the eyes of a man in the dark would produce colors, and his nose smell roses in the winter: but we see nobody gets the relish of a pineapple, till he goes to the Indies, where it is, and tastes it.

II. Because sometimes I find that *I cannot avoid the having those ideas produced in my mind*. For though, when my eyes are shut, or windows fast, I can at pleasure recall to my mind the ideas of light, or the sun, which former sensations had lodged in my memory; so I can at pleasure lay by *that* idea, and take into my view that of the smell of a rose, or taste of sugar. But, if I turn my eyes at noon toward the sun, I cannot avoid the ideas which the light or sun then produces in me. So that there is a manifest difference between the ideas laid up in my memory (over which, if they were there only, I should have constantly the same power to dispose of them, and lay them by at pleasure), and those which force themselves upon me, and I cannot avoid having. And therefore it must needs be some exterior cause, and the brisk acting of some objects without me, whose efficacy I cannot resist, that produces those ideas in my mind, whether I will or no. Besides, there is nobody who doth not perceive the difference in himself between contemplating the sun, as he hath the idea of it in his memory, and actually looking upon it: of which two, his perception is so distinct, that few of his ideas are more distinguishable one from another. And therefore he hath certain knowledge that they are not *both* memory, or the actions of his mind, and fancies only within him; but that actual seeing hath a cause without.

III. Add to this, that many of those ideas are *produced in us with pain,* which afterwards we remember without the least offense. Thus, the pain of heat or cold, when the idea of it is revived in our minds, gives us no disturbance; which, when felt, was very troublesome; and is again, when actually repeated: which is occasioned by the disorder the external object causes in our bodies when applied to them: and we remember the pains of hunger, thirst, or the headache, without any pain at all; which would either never disturb us, or else constantly do it, as often as we thought of it, were there nothing more but ideas floating in our minds, and appearances entertaining our fancies, without the real existence of things affecting us from abroad. The same may be said of *pleasure,* accompanying several actual sensations. And though mathematical demonstration depends not upon sense, yet the examining them by diagrams gives great credit to the evidence of our sight, and seems to give it a certainty approaching to that of demonstration itself. For, it would be very strange that a man should allow it for an undeniable truth, that two angles of a figure, which he measures by lines and angles of a diagram, should be bigger one than the other, and yet doubt of the existence of those lines and angles, which by looking on he makes use of to measure that by.

IV. Our *senses* in many cases *bear witness to the truth of each other's report,* concerning the existence of sensible things without us. He that *sees* a fire, may, if he doubt whether it be anything more than a bare fancy, *feel* it too; and be convinced, by putting his hand in it. Which certainly could never be put into such exquisite pain by a bare idea or phantom, unless that the pain be a fancy too: which yet he cannot, when the burn is well, by raising the idea of it, bring upon himself again.

Thus I see, whilst I write this, I can change the appearance of the paper; and by designing the letters, tell *beforehand* what new idea it shall exhibit the very next moment, by barely drawing my pen over it: which will neither appear (let me fancy as much as I will) if my hands stand still; or though I move my pen, if my eyes be shut: nor, when those characters are once made on the paper, can I choose afterward but see them as they are; that is, have the ideas of such letters as I have made. Whence it is manifest, that they are not barely the sport and play of my own imagination, when I find that the characters that were made at the pleasure of my own thoughts, do not obey them; nor yet cease to be, whenever I shall fancy it, but continue to affect my senses constantly and regularly, according to the figures I made them. To which if we will add, that the sight of those shall, from another man, draw such sounds as I beforehand design they shall stand for, there will be little reason left to doubt that those words I write do really exist without me, when they cause a long series of regular sounds to affect my ears, which could not be the effect of my imagination, nor could my memory retain them in that order.

But yet, if after all this anyone will be so sceptical as to distrust his senses, and to affirm that all we see and hear, feel and taste, think and do, during our whole being, is but the series and deluding appearances of a long dream, whereof there is no reality; and therefore will question the existence of all things, or our knowledge of anything: I must desire him to consider, that, if all be a dream, then he doth but dream that he makes the question, and so it is not much matter that a waking man should answer him. But yet, if he pleases, he may dream that I make him this answer, That the certainty of things existing in *rerum natura* when we have the testimony of our senses for it is not only as great as our frame can attain to, but as our condition needs. For, our faculties being suited not to the full extent of being, nor to a perfect, clear, comprehensive knowledge of things free from all doubt and scruple; but to the preservation of us, in whom they are; and accommodated to the use of life: they serve to our purpose well enough, if they will but give us certain notice of those things, which are convenient or inconvenient to us. For he that sees a candle burning, and hath experimented the force of its flame by putting his finger in it, will little doubt that this is something existing without him, which does him harm, and puts him to great pain: which is assurance enough, when no man requires greater certainty to govern his actions by than what is as certain as his actions themselves. And if our dreamer pleases to try whether the glowing heat of a glass furnace be barely a wandering imagination in a drowsy man's fancy, by putting his hand into it, he may perhaps be wakened into a certainty greater than he could wish, that it is something more than bare imagination. So that this evidence is as great as we can desire, being as certain to us as our pleasure or pain, i.e. happiness or misery; beyond which we have no concernment, either of knowing or being. Such an assurance of the existence of things without us is sufficient to direct us in the attaining the good and avoiding the evil which is caused by them, which is the important concernment we have of being made acquainted with them.

In fine, then, when our senses do actually convey into our understandings, any idea, we cannot but be satisfied that there doth something *at that time* really exist without us, which doth affect our senses, and by them give notice of itself to our apprehensive faculties, and actually produce that idea which we then perceive: and we cannot so far distrust their testimony, as to doubt that such *collections* of simple ideas as we have observed by our senses to be united together, do really exist together. But this knowledge extends as far as the present testimony of our senses, employed about particular objects that do then affect them, and no further. For if I saw such a collection of simple ideas as is wont to be called *man* existing together one minute since, and am now alone, I cannot be certain that the same man exists now, since there is no *necessary connection* of his existence a minute since with his existence now: by a thousand ways he may cease to be, since I had the testimony of my senses for his existence. And if I cannot be certain that the man I saw last today is now in being, I can less be certain that he is so who hath been longer removed from my senses, and I have not seen since yesterday, or since the last year: and much less can I be certain of the existence of men that I never saw. And, therefore, though it be highly probable that millions of men do now exist, yet, whilst I am alone, writing this, I have not that certainty of it which we strictly call knowledge; though the great likelihood of it puts me past doubt, and it be reasonable for me to do several things upon the confidence that there are men (and men also of my acquaintance, with whom I have to do) now in the world: but this is but probability, not knowledge.

Whereby yet we may observe how foolish and vain a thing it is for a man of a narrow knowledge, who having reason given him to judge of the different evidence and probability of things, and to be swayed accordingly; how vain, I say, it is to expect demonstration and certainty in things not capable of it; and refuse assent to very rational propositions, and act contrary to very plain and clear truths, because they cannot be made out so evident, as to surmount every the least (I will not say reason, but) pretense of doubting. He that, in the ordinary affairs of life, would admit of nothing but direct plain demonstration, would be sure of nothing in this world, but of perishing quickly. The wholesomeness of his meat or drink would not give him reason to venture on it: and I would fain know what it is he could do upon such grounds as are capable of no doubt, no objection.

As *when our senses are actually employed about any object,* we do know that it does exist; so *by our memory* we may be assured, that heretofore things that affected our senses have existed. And thus we have knowledge of the past existence of several things, whereof our senses having informed us, our memories still retain the ideas; and of this we are past all doubt, so long as we remember well. But this knowledge also reaches no further than our senses have formerly assured us. Thus, seeing water at this instant, it is an unquestionable truth to me that water doth exist: and remembering that I saw it yesterday, it will also be always true, and as long as my memory retains it always an undoubted proposition to me, that water did exist the 10th of July, 1688; as it will also be equally true that a certain number of very fine colors did exist, which at the same time I saw upon a bubble of that water: but, being now quite out of sight both of the water and bubbles too, it is no more certainly known to me that the water doth now exist, than that the bubbles or colors therein do so: it being no more necessary that water should exist today, because it existed yesterday, than that the colors or bubbles exist today, because they existed yesterday, though it be exceedingly much more probable; because water hath been observed to continue long in existence, but bubbles, and the colors on them, quickly cease to be.

What ideas we have of spirits, and how we come by them, I have already shown. But though we have those ideas in our minds, and know we have them there, the having the ideas of spirits does not make us know that any such things do exist without us, or that there are any finite spirits, or any other spiritual beings, but the Eternal God. We have ground from revelation, and several other reasons, to believe with assurance that there are such creatures: but our senses not being able to discover them, we want the means of knowing their particular existences. For we can no more know that there are finite spirits really existing, by the idea we have of such beings in our minds, than by the ideas any one has of fairies or centaurs, he can come to know that things answering those ideas do really exist.

And therefore concerning the existence of finite spirits, as well as several other things, we must content ourselves with the evidence of faith; but universal, certain propositions concerning this matter are beyond our reach. For however true it may be, v.g. that all the intelligent spirits that God ever created do still exist, yet it can never make a part of our certain knowledge. These and the like propositions we may assent to, as highly probable, but are not, I fear, in this state capable of knowing. We are not, then, to put others upon demonstrating, nor ourselves upon search of universal certainty in all those matters; wherein we are not capable of any other knowledge, but what our senses give us in this or that particular.

By which it appears that there are two sorts of propositions:—(1) There is one sort of propositions concerning the *existence* of anything answerable to such an idea: as having the idea of an elephant, phoenix, motion, or an angel, in my mind, the first and natural inquiry is, Whether such a thing does anywhere exist? And this knowledge is only of particulars. No existence of anything without us, but only of God, can certainly be known further than our senses inform us. (2) There is another sort of propositions, wherein is expressed the agreement or disagreement of *our abstract ideas,* and their dependence on one another. Such propositions may be universal and certain. So, having the idea of God and myself, of fear and obedience, I cannot but be sure that God is to be feared and obeyed by me: and this proposition will be certain, concerning man in general, if I have made an abstract idea of such a species, whereof I am one particular. But yet this proposition, how certain soever, that "men ought to fear and obey God" proves not to me the *existence* of *men* in the world; but will be true of all such creatures, whenever they do exist: which certainty of such general propositions depends on the agreement or disagreement to be discovered in those abstract ideas.

In the former case, our knowledge is the consequence of the existence of things, producing ideas in our minds by our senses: in the latter, knowledge is the consequence of the ideas (be they what they will) that are in our minds, producing there general certain propositions. Many of these are called *aeternae veritates,* and all of them indeed are so; not from being written, all or any of them, in the minds of all men; or that they were any of them propositions in any one's mind, till he, having got the abstract ideas, joined or separated them by affirmation or negation. But wheresoever we can suppose such a creature as man is, endowed with such faculties, and thereby furnished with such ideas as we have, we must conclude, he must needs, when he applies his thoughts to the consideration of his ideas, know the truth of certain propositions that will arise from the agreement or disagreement which he will perceive in his own ideas. Such propositions are therefore called *eternal truths,* not because they are eternal propositions actually formed, and antecedent to the understanding that at any time makes them; nor because they are imprinted on the mind from any patterns that are anywhere out of the mind, and existed before: but because, being once made about abstract ideas, so as to be true, they will, whenever they can be supposed to be made again at any time, past or to come, by a mind having those ideas, always actually be true. For names being supposed to stand perpetually for the same ideas, and the same ideas having immutably the same habitudes one to another, propositions concerning any abstract ideas that are once true must needs be *eternal verities.*

XII

Of the Improvement of Our Knowledge

IT HAVING BEEN THE COMMON RECEIVED OPINION amongst men of letters, that *maxims* were the foundation of all knowledge; and that the sciences were each of them built upon certain *praecognita,* from whence the understanding was to take its rise, and by which it was to conduct itself in its inquiries into the matters belonging to that science, the beaten road of the Schools has been, to lay down in the beginning one or more *general propositions,* as foundations whereon to build the knowledge that was to be had of that subject.

But if anyone will consider, he will (I guess) find, that the great advancement and certainty of real knowledge which men arrived to in these sciences, was not owing to the influence of these principles, nor derived from any peculiar advantage they received from two or three general maxims, laid down in the beginning; but from the clear, distinct, complete ideas their thoughts were employed about, and the relation of equality and excess so clear between some of them, that they had an intuitive knowledge, and by *that* a way to discover it in others; and this without the help of those maxims. For I ask, Is it not possible for a young lad to know that his whole body is bigger than his little finger, but by virtue of this axiom, that *the whole is bigger than a part;* nor be assured of it, till he has learned that maxim? Or cannot a country wench know that, having received a shilling from one that owes her three, and a shilling also from another that owes her three, the remaining debts in each of their hands are equal? Cannot she know this, I say, unless she fetch the certainty of it from this maxim, that *if you take equals from equals, the remainder will be equals,* a maxim which possibly she never heard or thought of? I desire anyone to consider, from what has been elsewhere said, which is known first and clearest by most people, the particular instance, or the general rule; and which it is that gives life and birth to the other. These general rules are but the comparing our more general and abstract ideas, which are the workmanship of the mind, made, and names given to them for the easier dispatch in its reasonings, and drawing into comprehensive terms and short rules its various and multiplied observations. But knowledge began in the mind, and was founded on particulars; though afterward, perhaps, no notice was taken thereof: it being natural for the mind (forward still to enlarge its knowledge) most attentively to lay up those general notions, and make the proper use of them, which is to disburden the memory of the cumbersome load of particulars. For I desire it may be considered, what more certainty there is to a child, or anyone, that his body, little finger, and all, is bigger than his little finger alone, after you have given to his body the name *whole,* and to his little finger the name *part,* than he could have had before; or what new knowledge concerning his body can these two relative terms give him, which he could not have without them? Could he not know that his body was bigger than his little finger, if his language were yet so imperfect that he had no such relative terms as whole and part? I ask, further, when he has got these names, how is he more certain that his body is a whole, and his little finger a part, than he was or might be certain before he learnt those terms, that his body was bigger than his little finger? Anyone may as reasonably doubt or deny that his little finger is a part of his body, as that it is less than his body. And he that can doubt whether it be less, will as certainly doubt whether it be a part. So that the maxim, the whole is bigger than a part, can never be made use of to prove the little finger less than the body, but when it is useless, by being brought to convince one of a truth which he knows already. For he that does not certainly know that any parcel of matter, with another parcel of matter joined to it, is bigger than either of them alone, will never be able to know it by the help of these two relative terms, whole and part, make of them what maxim you please.

But be it in the mathematics as it will, whether it be clearer, that, taking an inch from a black line of two inches, and an inch from a red line of two inches, the remaining parts of the two lines will be equal, or that *if you take equals from equals, the remainder will be equals:* which, I say, of these two is the clearer and first known, I leave to anyone to determine, as not being material to my present occasion. That which I have here to do, is to inquire, whether, if it be the readiest way to knowledge to begin with general maxims, and build upon them, it be yet a safe way to take the *principles* which are laid down in any other science as unquestionable truths; and so receive them without examination, and adhere to them, without suffering them to be doubted of, because mathematicians have been so happy, or so fair, to use none but self-evident and undeniable. If this be so, I know not what may not pass for truth in morality, what may not be introduced and proved in natural philosophy.

If, therefore, those that pass for *principles* are *not certain* (which we must have some way to know, that we may be able to distinguish them from those that are doubtful), but are only made so to us by our blind assent, we are liable to be misled by them; and instead of being guided into truth, we shall, by principles, be only confirmed in mistake and error.

But since the knowledge of the certainty of principles, as well as of all other truths, depends only upon the perception we have of the agreement or disagreement of our ideas, the way to improve our knowledge is not, I am sure, blindly, and with an implicit faith, to receive and swallow principles; but is, I think, to get and fix in our minds clear, distinct, and complete ideas, as far as they are to be had, and annex to them proper and constant names. And thus, perhaps, without any other principles, but *barely considering those perfect ideas,* and by *comparing them one with another,* finding their agreement and disagreement, and their several relations and habitudes; we shall get more true and clear knowledge by the conduct of this one rule, than by taking up principles, and thereby putting our minds into the disposal of others.

We must, therefore, if we will proceed as reason advises, adapt our methods of inquiry to *the nature of the ideas we examine,* and the truth we search after. General and certain truths are only founded in the habitudes and relations of *abstract ideas.* A sagacious and methodical application of our thoughts, for the finding out these relations, is the only way to discover all that can be put with truth and certainty concerning them into general propositions. By what steps we are to proceed in these, is to be learned in the schools of the mathematicians, who, from very plain and easy beginnings, by gentle degrees, and a continued chain of reasonings, proceed to the discovery and demonstration of truths that appear at first sight beyond human capacity. The art of finding proofs, and the admirable methods they have invented for the singling out and laying in order those intermediate ideas that demonstratively show the equality or inequality of unapplicable quantities, is that which has carried them so far, and produced such wonderful and unexpected discoveries: but whether something like this, in respect of other ideas, as well as those of magnitude, may not in time be found out, I will not determine. This, I think, I may say, that if other ideas that are the real as well as nominal essences of their species, were pursued in the way familiar to mathematicians, they would carry our thoughts further, and with greater evidence and clearness than possibly we are apt to imagine.

This gave me the confidence to advance that conjecture, which I suggest (Chapter 3) viz. that *morality* is capable of demonstration as well as mathematics. For the ideas that ethics are conversant about, being all real essences, and such as I imagine have a discoverable connection and agreement one with another; so far as we can find their habitudes and relations, so far we shall be possessed of certain, real, and general truths; and I doubt not but, if a right method were taken, a great part of morality might be made out with that clearness, that could leave, to a considering man, no more reason to doubt, than he could have to doubt of the truth of propositions in mathematics, which have been demonstrated to him.

In our search after the knowledge of *substances,* our want of ideas that are suitable to such a way of proceeding obliges us to a quite different method. We advance not here, as in the other (where our abstract ideas are real as well as nominal essences), by contemplating our ideas, and considering their relations and correspondences; that helps us very little, for the reasons, that in another place we have at large set down. By which I think it is evident, that substances afford matter of very little *general* knowledge: and the bare contemplation of their abstract ideas will carry us but a very little way in the search of truth and certainty. What, then, are we to do for the improvement of our knowledge in substantial beings? Here we are to take a quite contrary course: the want of ideas of their real essences sends us from our own thoughts to the things themselves as they exist. *Experience here must teach me what reason cannot:* and it is by *trying* alone, that I can *certainly know,* what other qualities co-exist with those of my complex idea, v.g. whether that yellow, heavy, fusible body I call *gold,* be malleable, or no; which experience (which way ever it prove in that particular body I examine) makes me not certain, that it is so in all, or any other yellow, heavy, fusible bodies, but that which I have tried. Because it is no consequence one way or the other from my complex idea: the necessity or inconsistence of malleability hath no visible connection with the combination of that color, weight, and fusibility in any body. What I have said here of the nominal essence of gold, supposed to consist of a body of such a determinate color, weight, and fusibility, will hold true, if malleableness, fixedness, and solubility in *aqua regia* be added to it. Our reasonings from these ideas will carry us but a little way in the certain discovery of the other properties in those masses of matter wherein all these are to be found. Because the *other* properties of such bodies, depending not on these, but on that unknown real essence on which these also depend, we cannot by them discover the rest; we can go no further than the simple ideas of our nominal essence will carry us, which is very little beyond themselves; and so afford us but very sparingly any certain, universal, and useful truths. For, upon trial, having found that particular piece (and all others of that color, weight, and fusibility, that I ever tried) malleable, that also makes now, perhaps, a part of my complex idea, part of my nominal essence of gold: whereby though I make my complex idea to which I affix the name gold, to consist of more simple ideas than before; yet still, it not containing the real essence of any species of bodies, it helps me not certainly to know (I say to know, perhaps it may be to conjecture) the other remaining properties of that body, further than they have a visible connection with some or all of the simple ideas that make up my nominal essence. For example, I cannot be certain, from this complex idea, whether gold be fixed or no; because, as before, there is no *necessary* connection or inconsistence to be discovered betwixt *a complex idea of a body yellow, heavy, fusible, malleable;* betwixt these, I say, and *fixedness;* so that I may certainly know, that in whatsoever body these are found, there fixedness is sure to be. Here, again, for assurance, I must apply myself to experience; as far as that reaches, I may have certain knowledge, but no further.

I deny not but a man, accustomed to rational and regular experiments, shall be able to see further into the nature of bodies, and guess righter at their yet unknown properties, than one that is a stranger to them: but yet, as I have said, this is but judgment and opinion, not knowledge and certainty. This way of *getting and improving our knowledge in substances only by experience and history,* which is all that the weakness of our faculties in this state of mediocrity which we are in in this world can attain to, makes me suspect that *natural philosophy is not capable of being made a science.* We are able, I imagine, to reach very little general knowledge concerning the species of bodies, and their several properties. Experiments and historical observations we may have, from which we may draw advantages of ease and health, and thereby increase our stock of conveniences for this life; but beyond this I fear our talents reach not, nor are our faculties, as I guess, able to advance.

From whence it is obvious to conclude, that, since our faculties are not fitted to penetrate into the internal fabric and real essences of bodies; but yet plainly discover to us the being of a God, and the knowledge of ourselves, enough to lead us into a full and clear discovery of our duty and great concernment; it will become us, as rational creatures, to employ those faculties we have about what they are most adapted to, and follow the direction of nature, where it seems to point us out the way. For it is rational to conclude, that our proper employment lies in those inquiries, and in that sort of knowledge which is most suited to our natural capacities, and carries in it our greatest interest, i.e. the condition of our eternal estate. Hence I think I may conclude, that *morality* is *the proper science and business of mankind in general* (who are both concerned and fitted to search out their *summum bonum*); as several arts, conversant about several parts of nature, are the lot and private talent of particular men, for the common use of human life, and their own particular subsistence in this world. Of what consequence the discovery of one natural body and its properties may be to human life, the whole great continent of America is a convincing instance: whose ignorance in useful arts, and want of the greatest part of the conveniences of life, in a country that abounded with all sorts of natural plenty, I think may be attributed to their ignorance of what was to be found in a very ordinary, despicable stone, I mean the mineral of *iron.* And whatever we think of our parts or improvements in this part of the world, where knowledge and plenty seem to vie with each other; yet to anyone that will seriously reflect on it, I suppose it will appear past doubt, that, were the use of iron lost among us, we should in a few ages be unavoidably reduced to the wants and ignorance of the ancient savage Americans, whose natural endowments and provisions come no way short of those of the most flourishing and polite nations. So that he who first made known the use of that contemptible mineral, may be truly styled the father of arts, and author of plenty.

I would not, therefore, be thought to disesteem or dissuade the study of *nature*. I readily agree the contemplation of His works gives us occasion to admire, revere, and glorify their Author: and, if rightly directed, may be of greater benefit to mankind than the monuments of exemplary charity that have at so great charge been raised by the founders of hospitals and almshouses. He that first invented printing, discovered the use of the compass, or made public the virtue and right use of *kin kina,* did more for the propagation of knowledge, for the supply and increase of useful commodities, and saved more from the grave than those who built colleges, workhouses, and hospitals. All that I would say is, that we should not be too forwardly possessed with the opinion or expectation of knowledge, where it is not to be had, or by ways that will not attain to it: that we should not take doubtful systems for complete sciences; nor unintelligible notions for scientifical demonstrations. In the knowledge of bodies, we must be content to glean what we can from particular experiments: since we cannot, from a discovery of their real essences, grasp at a time whole sheaves, and in bundles comprehend the nature and properties of whole species together. Where our inquiry is concerning co-existence, or repugnancy to co-exist, which by contemplation of our ideas we cannot discover; there experience, observation, and natural history, must give us, by our senses and by retail, an insight into corporeal substances. The knowledge of *bodies* we must get by our senses, warily employed in taking notice of their qualities and operations on one another: and what we hope to know of *separate spirits* in this world, we must, I think expect only from revelation. He that shall consider how little general maxims, precarious principles, and hypotheses laid down at pleasure, have promoted true knowledge, or helped to satisfy the inquiries of rational men after real improvements; how little, I say, the setting out at that end has, for many ages together, advanced men's progress, toward the knowledge of natural philosophy, will think we have reason to thank those who in this latter age have taken another course, and have trod out to us, though not an easier way to learned ignorance, yet a surer way to profitable knowledge.

Not that we may not, to explain any phenomena of nature, make use of any probable hypothesis whatsoever: hypotheses, if they are well made, are at least great helps to the memory, and often direct us to new discoveries. But my meaning is, that we should not take up any one too hastily (which the mind, that would always penetrate into the causes of things, and have principles to rest on, is very apt to do), till we have very well examined particulars, and made several experiments, in that thing which we would explain by our hypothesis, and see whether it will agree to them all; whether our principles will carry us quite through, and not be as inconsistent with one phenomenon of nature, as they seem to accommodate and explain another. And at least that we take care that the name of *principles* deceive us not, nor impose on us, by making us receive that for an unquestionable truth, which is really at best but a very doubtful conjecture; such as are most (I had almost said all) of the hypotheses in natural philosophy.

But whether natural philosophy be capable of certainty or no, the ways to enlarge our knowledge, as far as we are capable, seems to me, in short, to be these two:——

First, The first is to get and settle in our minds determined ideas of those things whereof we have general or specific names; at least, so many of them as we would consider and improve our knowledge in, or reason about. And if they be specific ideas of substances, we should endeavor also to make them as complete as we can, whereby I mean, that we should put together as many simple ideas as, being constantly observed to co-exist, may perfectly determine the species; and each of those simple ideas which are the ingredients of our complex ones, should be clear and distinct in our minds. For it being evident that our knowledge cannot exceed our ideas; as far as they are either imperfect, confused, or obscure, we cannot expect to have certain, perfect, or clear knowledge.

Secondly, The other is the art of finding out those intermediate ideas, which may show us the agreement or repugnancy of other ideas, which cannot be immediately compared.

XIII

Some Further Considerations Concerning Our Knowledge—Summary

[In Chapter XIII Locke points out that although the use of our faculties is voluntary, the will has no power to determine the knowledge which those faculties impart to the mind.]

X I V

Of Judgment

THE UNDERSTANDING FACULTIES being given to man, not barely for speculation, but also for the conduct of his life, man would be at a great loss if he had nothing to direct him but what has the certainty of true *knowledge*. For that being very short and scanty, as we have seen, he would be often utterly in the dark, and in most of the actions of his life, perfectly at a stand, had he nothing to guide him in the absence of clear and certain knowledge. He that will not eat till he has demonstration that it will nourish him; he that will not stir till he infallibly knows the business he goes about will succeed, will have little else to do but to sit still and perish.

Therefore, as God has set some things in broad daylight; as He has given us some certain knowledge, though limited to a few things in comparison, probably as a taste of what intellectual creatures are capable of to excite in us a desire and endeavor after a better state: so, in the greatest part of our concernments, He has afforded us only the twilight, as I may so say, of probability; suitable, I presume, to that state of mediocrity and probationership He has been pleased to place us in here; wherein, to check our overconfidence and presumption, we might, by every day's experience, be made sensible of our shortsightedness and liableness to error; the sense whereof might be a constant admonition to us, to spend the days of this our pilgrimage with industry and care, in the search and following of that way which might lead us to a state of greater perfection. It being highly rational to think, even were revelation silent in the case, that, as men employ those talents God has given them here, they shall accordingly receive their rewards at the close of the day, when their sun shall set, and night shall put an end to their labors.

The faculty which God has given man to supply the want of clear and certain knowledge, in cases where that cannot be had, is *judgment:* whereby the mind takes its ideas to agree or disagree; or, which is the same, any proposition to be true or false, without perceiving a demonstrative evidence in the proofs. The mind sometimes exercises this judgment out of necessity, where demonstrative proofs and certain knowledge are not to be had; and sometimes out of laziness, unskillfulness, or haste, even where demonstrative and certain proofs are to be had. Men often stay not warily to examine the agreement or disagreement of two ideas, which they are desirous or concerned to know; but, either incapable of such attention as is requisite in a long train of gradations, or impatient of delay, lightly cast their eyes on, or wholly pass by the proofs; and so, without making out the demonstration, determine of the agreement or disagreement of two ideas, as it were by a view of them as they are at a distance, and take it to be the one or the other, as seems mostly likely to them upon such a loose survey. This faculty of the mind, when it is exercised immediately about things, is called *judgment;* when about truths delivered in words, is most commonly called *assent* or *dissent:* which being the most usual way, wherein the mind has occasion to employ this faculty, I shall, under these terms, treat of it, as least liable in our language to equivocation.

Thus the mind has two faculties conversant about truth and falsehood:——

First, KNOWLEDGE, whereby it certainly *perceives,* and is undoubtedly satisfied of the agreement or disagreement of any ideas.

Secondly, JUDGMENT, which is the putting ideas together, or separating them from one another in the mind, when their certain agreement or disagreement is not perceived, but *presumed* to be so; which is, as the word imports, taken to be so before it certainly appears. And if it so unites or separates them as in reality things are, it is right judgment.

X V

Of Probability

AS DEMONSTRATION IS THE SHOWING the agreement or disagreement of two ideas, by the intervention of one or more proofs, which have a constant, immutable, and visible connection one with another; so *probability* is nothing but the appearance of such an agreement or disagreement, by the intervention of proofs, whose connection is not constant and immutable, or at least is not perceived to be so, but is, or appears for the most part to be so, and is enough to induce the mind to judge the proposition to be true or false, rather than the contrary. For example: in the demonstration of it a man perceives the certain, immutable connection there is of equality between the three angles of a triangle, and those intermediate ones which are made use of to show their equality to two right ones; and so, by an intuitive knowledge of the agreement or disagreement of the intermediate ideas in each step of the progress, the whole series is continued with an evidence, which clearly shows the agreement or disagreement of those three angles in equality to two right ones: and thus he has certain knowledge that it is so. But another man, who never took the pains to observe the demonstration, hearing a mathematician, a man of credit, affirm the three angles of a triangle to be equal to two right ones, assents to it, i.e. receives it for true: in which case the foundation of his assent is the probability of the thing; the proof being such as for the most part carries truth with it: the man on whose testimony he receives it, not being wont to affirm anything contrary to or besides his knowledge, especially in matters of this kind: so that that which causes his assent to this proposition, that the three angles of a triangle are equal to two right ones, that which makes him take these ideas to agree, without knowing them to do so, is the wonted veracity of the speaker in other cases, or his supposed veracity in this.

Our knowledge, as has been shown, being very narrow, and we not happy enough to find certain truth in everything which we have occasion to consider; most of the propositions we think, reason, discourse—nay, act upon, are such as we cannot have undoubted knowledge of their truth: yet some of them border so near upon certainty, that we make no doubt at all about them; but assent to them as firmly, and act, according to that assent, as resolutely as if they were infallibly demonstrated, and that our knowledge of them was perfect and certain. But there being degrees herein, from the very neighborhood of certainty and demonstration, quite down to improbability and unlikeness, even to the confines of impossibility; and also degrees of assent from full assurance and confidence, quite down to conjecture, doubt, and distrust: I shall come now (having, as I think, found out *the bounds of human knowledge and certainty*), in the next place, to consider *the several degrees and grounds of probability, and assent or faith.*

Probability is likeliness to be true, the very notation of the word signifying such a proposition, for which there be arguments or proofs to make it pass, or be received for true. The entertainment the mind gives this sort of propositions is called *belief, assent,* or *opinion,* which is the admitting or receiving any proposition for true, upon arguments or proofs that are found to persuade us to receive it as true, without certain knowledge that it is so. And herein lies the difference between *probability* and *certainty, faith,* and *knowledge,* that in all the parts of knowledge there is intuition; each immediate idea, each step has its visible and certain connection: in belief, not so. That which makes me believe, is something extraneous to the thing I believe; something not evidently joined on both sides to, and so not manifestly showing the agreement or disagreement of those ideas that are under consideration.

Probability then, being to supply the defect of our knowledge, and to guide us where that fails, is always conversant about propositions whereof we have no certainty, but only some inducements to receive them for true. The grounds of it are, in short, these two following:——

First, The conformity of anything with our own knowledge, observation, and experience.

Secondly, The testimony of others, vouching their observation and experience. In the testimony of others, is to be considered: 1. The number. 2. The integrity. 3. The skill of the witnesses. 4. The design of the author, where it is a testimony out of a book cited. 5. The consistency of the parts, and circumstances of the relation. 6. Contrary testimonies.

Probability wanting that intuitive evidence which infallibly determines the understanding and produces certain knowledge, the mind, if it *will proceed rationally,* ought to examine all the grounds of probability, and see how they make more or less for or against any proposition, before it assents to or dissents from it; and, upon a due balancing the whole, reject or receive it, with a more or less firm assent, proportionably to the preponderancy of the greater grounds of probability on one side or the other. For example:——

If I myself see a man walk on the ice, it is past probability; it is knowledge. But if another tells me he saw a man in England, in the midst of a sharp winter, walk upon water hardened with cold, this has so great conformity with what is usually observed to happen, that I am disposed by the nature of the thing itself to assent to it; unless some manifest suspicion attend the relation of that matter of fact. But if the same thing be told to one born between the tropics, who never saw nor heard of any such thing before, there the whole probability relies on testimony: and as the relators are more in number, and of more credit, and have no interest to speak contrary to the truth, so that matter of fact is like to find more or less belief. Though to a man whose experience has always been quite contrary, and who has never heard of anything like it, the most untainted credit of a witness will scarce be able to find belief. As it happened to a Dutch ambassador, who entertaining the king of Siam with the particularities of Holland, which he was inquisitive after, amongst other things told him, that the water in his country would sometimes, in cold weather, be so hard, that men walked upon it, and that it would bear an elephant, if he were there. To which the king replied, *Hitherto I have believed the strange things you have told me, because I look upon you as a sober fair man, but now I am sure you lie.*

Upon these grounds depends the probability of any proposition: and as the conformity of our knowledge, as the certainty of observations, as the frequency and constancy of experience, and the number and credibility of testimonies do more or less agree or disagree with it, so is any proposition in itself more or less probable.

XVI

Of the Degrees of Assent

THE GROUNDS OF PROBABILITY we have laid down in the foregoing chapter: as they are the foundations on which our *assent* is built, so are they also the measure whereby its several degrees are, or ought to be regulated: only we are to take notice, that, whatever grounds of probability there may be, they yet operate no further on the mind which searches after truth, and endeavors to judge right, than they appear; at least, in the first judgment or search that the mind makes. I confess, in the opinions men have, and firmly stick to in the world, their assent is not always from an actual view of the reasons that at first prevailed with them: it being in many cases almost impossible, and in most, very hard, even for those who have very admirable memories, to retain all the proofs which, upon a due examination, made them embrace that side of the question. It suffices that they have once with care and fairness sifted the matter as far as they could; and that they have searched into all the particulars, that they could imagine to give any light to the question; and, with the best of their skill, cast up the account upon the whole evidence: and thus, having once found on which side the probability appeared to *them,* after as full and exact an inquiry as they can make, they lay up the conclusion in their memories, as a truth they have discovered; and for the future they remain satisfied with the testimony of their memories, that this is the opinion that, by the proofs they have once seen of it, deserves such a degree of their assent as they afford it.

This is all that the greatest part of men are capable of doing, in regulating their opinions and judgments; unless a man will exact of them, either to retain distinctly in their memories all the proofs concerning any probable truth, and that too, in the same order, and regular deduction of consequences in which they have formerly placed or seen them; which sometimes is enough to fill a large volume on one single question: or else they must require a man, for every opinion that he embraces, every day to examine the proofs: both which are impossible. It is unavoidable, therefore, that the *memory* be relied on in the case, and that men be persuaded of several opinions, whereof the proofs are not actually in their thoughts; nay, which perhaps they are not able actually to recall. Without this, the greatest part of men must be either very sceptics; or change every moment, and yield themselves up to whoever, having lately studied the question, offers them arguments, which, for want of memory, they are not able presently to answer.

I cannot but own, that men's sticking to their past judgment, and adhering firmly to conclusions formerly made, is often the cause of great obstinacy in error and mistake. But the fault is not that they rely on their memories for what they have before well judged, but because they judged before they had well examined. May we not find a great number (not to say the greatest part) of men that think they have formed right judgments of several matters; and that for no other reason, but because they never thought otherwise? that imagine themselves to have judged right, only because they never questioned, never examined, their own opinions? Which is indeed to think they judged right, because they never judged at all. And yet these, of all men, hold their opinions with the greatest stiffness; those being generally the most fierce and firm in their tenets, who have least examined them. What we once *know,* we are certain is so: and we may be secure, that there are no latent proofs undiscovered, which may overturn our knowledge, or bring it in doubt. But, in matters of *probability,* it is not in every case we can be sure that we have all the particulars before us, that any way concern the question; and that there is no evidence behind, and yet unseen, which may cast the probability on the other side, and outweigh all that at present seems to preponderate with us. Who almost is there that hath the leisure, patience, and means to collect together all the proofs concerning most of the opinions he has, so as safely to conclude that he hath a clear and full view; and that there is no more to be alleged for his better information? And yet we are forced to determine ourselves on the one side or other. The conduct of our lives, and the management of our great concerns, will not bear delay: for those depend, for the most part, on the determination of our judgment in points wherein we are not capable of certain and demonstrative knowledge, and wherein it is necessary for us to embrace the one side or the other.

Since, therefore, it is unavoidable to the greatest part of

men, if not all, to have several *opinions*, without certain and indubitable proofs of their truth; and it carries too great an imputation of ignorance, lightness, or folly for men to quit and renounce their former tenets presently upon the offer of an argument which they cannot immediately answer, and show the insufficiency of: it would, methinks, become all men to maintain peace, and the common offices of humanity, and friendship, in the diversity of opinions; since we cannot reasonably expect that anyone should readily and obsequiously quit his own opinion, and embrace ours, with a blind resignation to an authority which the understanding of man acknowledges not. For however it may often mistake, it can own no other guide but reason, nor blindly submit to the will and dictates of another. If he you would bring over to your sentiments be one that examines before he assents, you must give him leave at his leisure to go over the account again, and, recalling what is out of his mind, examine all the particulars, to see on which side the advantage lies: and if he will not think our arguments of weight enough to engage him anew in so much pains, it is but what we often do ourselves in the like case; and we should take it amiss if others should prescribe to us what points we should study. And if he be one who takes his opinions upon trust, how can we imagine that he should renounce those tenets which time and custom have so settled in his mind, that he thinks them self-evident, and of an unquestionable certainty; or which he takes to be impressions he has received from God himself, or from men sent by him? How can we expect, I say, that opinions thus settled should be given up to the arguments or authority of a stranger or adversary, especially if there be any suspicion of interest or design, as there never fails to be, where men find themselves ill treated? We should do well to commiserate our mutual ignorance, and endeavor to remove it in all the gentle and fair ways of information; and not instantly treat others ill, as obstinate and perverse, because they will not renounce their own, and receive our opinions, or at least those we would force upon them, when it is more than probable that we are no less obstinate in not embracing some of theirs. For where is the man that has incontestable evidence of the truth of all that he holds, or of the falsehood of all he condemns; or can say that he has examined to the bottom all his own, or other men's opinions? The necessity of believing without knowledge, nay often upon very slight grounds, in this fleeting state of action and blindness we are in, should make us more busy and careful to inform ourselves than constrain others. At least, those who have not thoroughly examined to the bottom all their own tenets, must confess they are unfit to prescribe to others; and are unreasonable in imposing that as truth on other men's belief, which they themselves have not searched into, nor weighed the arguments of probability, on which they should receive or reject it. Those who have fairly and truly examined, and are thereby got past doubt in all the doctrines they profess and govern themselves by, would have a juster pretense to require others to follow them: but these are so few in number, and find so little reason to be magisterial in their opinions, that nothing insolent and imperious is to be expected from them: and there is reason to think, that, if men were better instructed themselves, they would be less imposing on others.

But to return to the grounds of assent, and the several degrees of it, we are to take notice, that the propositions we receive upon inducements of *probability* are of *two sorts:* either concerning some particular existence, or, as it is usually termed, matter of fact, which, falling under observation, is capable of human testimony; or else concerning things, which, being beyond the discovery of our senses, are not capable of any such testimony.

Concerning the *first* of these, viz. *particular matter of fact.*

1. Where any particular thing, consonant to the constant observation of ourselves and others in the like case, comes attested by the concurrent reports of all that mention it, we receive it as easily, and build as firmly upon it, as if it were certain knowledge; and we reason and act thereupon with as little doubt as if it were perfect demonstration. Thus, if all Englishmen, who have occasion to mention it, should affirm that it froze in England the last winter, or that there were swallows seen there in the summer, I think a man could almost as little doubt of it as that seven and four are eleven. The first, therefore, and *highest degree of probability,* is, when the general consent of all men, in all ages, as far as it can be known, concurs with a man's constant and never-failing experience in like cases, to confirm the truth of any particular matter of fact attested by fair witnesses: such are all the stated constitutions and properties of bodies, and the regular proceedings of causes and effects in the ordinary

course of nature. This we call an argument from the nature of things themselves. For what our own and other men's *constant observation* has found always to be after the same manner, that we with reason conclude to be the effect of steady and regular causes; though they come not within the reach of our knowledge. Thus, That fire warmed a man, made lead fluid, and changed the color or consistency in wood or charcoal; that iron sank in water, and swam in quicksilver: these and the like propositions about particular facts, being agreeable to our constant experience, as often as we have to do with these matters; and being generally spoke of (when mentioned by others) as things found constantly to be so, and therefore not so much as controverted by anybody—we are put past doubt that a relation affirming any such thing to have been, or any predication that it will happen again in the same manner, is very true. These *probabilities* rise so near to *certainty,* that they govern our thoughts as absolutely, and influence all our actions as fully, as the most evident demonstration; and in what concerns us we make little or no difference between them and certain knowledge. Our belief, thus grounded, rises to *assurance*.

II. The *next degree of probability* is, when I find by my own experience, and the agreement of all others that mention it, a thing to be for the most part so, and that the particular instance of it is attested by many and undoubted witnesses: v.g. history giving us such an account of men in all ages, and my own experience, as far as I had an opportunity to observe, confirming it, that most men prefer their private advantage to the public: if all historians that write of Tiberius, say that Tiberius did so, it is extremely probable. And in this case, our assent has a sufficient foundation to raise itself to a degree which we may call *confidence*.

III. In things that happen indifferently, as that a bird should fly this or that way; that it should thunder on a man's right or left hand, etc., when any particular matter of fact is vouched by the concurrent testimony of unsuspected witnesses, there our assent is also *unavoidable*. Thus: that there is such a city in Italy as Rome: that about one thousand seven hundred years ago, there lived in it a man, called Julius Caesar; that he was a general, and that he won a battle against another, called Pompey. This, though in the nature of the thing there be nothing for nor against it, yet being related by historians of credit, and contradicted by no one writer, a man cannot avoid believing it, and can as little doubt of it as he does of the being and actions of his own acquaintances, whereof he himself is a witness.

Thus far the matter goes easy enough. Probability upon such grounds carries so much evidence with it, that it naturally determines the judgment, and leaves us as little liberty to believe or disbelieve, as a demonstration does, whether we will know, or be ignorant. The difficulty is, when testimonies contradict common experience, and the reports of history and witnesses clash with the ordinary course of nature, or with one another; there it is, where diligence, attention, and exactness are required, to form a right judgment, and to proportion the assent to the different evidence and probability of the thing: which rises and falls, according as those two foundations of credibility, viz. *common observation in like cases,* and *particular testimonies in that particular instance,* favor or contradict it. These are liable to so great variety of contrary observations, circumstances, reports, different qualifications, tempers, designs, oversights, etc., of the reporters, that it is impossible to reduce to precise rules the various degrees wherein men give their assent. This only may be said in general, That as the arguments and proofs *pro* and *con,* upon due examination, nicely weighing every particular circumstance, shall to anyone appear, upon the whole matter, in a greater or less degree to preponderate on either side; so they are fitted to produce in the mind such different entertainments, as we call *belief, conjecture, guess, doubt, wavering, distrust, disbelief, etc.*

This is what concerns assent in matters wherein testimony is made use of: concerning which, I think, it may not be amiss to take notice of a rule observed in the law of England; which is, That though the attested copy of a record be good proof, yet the copy of a copy, ever so well attested, and by ever so credible witnesses, will not be admitted as a proof in judicature. This is so generally approved as reasonable, and suited to the wisdom and caution to be used in our inquiry after material truths, that I never yet heard of anyone that blamed it. This practice, if it be allowable in the decisions of right and wrong, carries this observation along with it, viz. *That any testimony, the further off it is from the original truth, the less force and proof it has.* The being and existence of the thing itself, is what I call the original truth. A credible man vouching his knowledge of it is a good proof; but if another equally credible do witness it from his report, the testimony is weaker: and a third that attests the hearsay of an hearsay is yet less considerable. So that in traditional truths, each remove weakens the force of the proof: and the more hands the tradition has successively passed through, the less strength and evidence does it receive from them. This I thought necessary to be taken notice of: because I find amongst some men the quite contrary commonly practiced, who look on opinions to gain force by growing older; and what a thousand years since would not, to a rational man contemporary with the first voucher, have appeared at all probable, is now urged as certain beyond all question, only because several have since, from him, said it one after another. Upon this ground propositions, evidently false or doubtful enough in their first beginning, come, by an inverted rule of probability, to pass for authentic truths; and those which found or deserved little credit from the mouths of their first authors, are thought to grow venerable by age, are urged as undeniable.

I would not be thought here to lessen the credit and use of *history:* it is all the light we have in many cases, and we receive from it a great part of the useful truths we have, with a convincing evidence. I think nothing more valuable than the records of antiquity: I wish we had more of them, and more uncorrupted. But this truth itself forces me to say, That no probability can rise higher than its first original. What has no other evidence than the single testimony of one only witness must stand or fall by his only testimony, whether good, bad, or indifferent; and though cited afterward by hundreds of others, one after another, is so far from receiving any strength thereby, that it is only the weaker. Passion, interest, inadvertency, mistake of his meaning, and a thousand odd reasons, or capricios, men's minds are acted by (impossible to be discovered), may make one man quote another man's words or meaning wrong. He that has but ever so little examined the citations of writers, cannot doubt how little credit the quotations deserve, where the originals are wanting; and consequently how much less quotations of quotations can be relied on. This is certain, that what in one age was affirmed upon slight grounds, can never after come to be more valid in future ages by being often repeated. But the further still it is from the original, the less valid it is, and has always less force in the mouth or writing of him that last made use of it than in his from whom he received it.

XVII

Of Reason

THE WORD REASON IN THE ENGLISH LANGUAGE has different significations: sometimes it is taken for true and clear principles: sometimes for clear and fair deductions from those principles: and sometimes for the cause, and particularly the final cause. But the consideration I shall have of it here is in a signification different from all these; and that is, as it stands for a faculty in man, that faculty whereby man is supposed to be distinguished from beasts, and wherein it is evident he much surpasses them.

If general knowledge, as has been shown, consists in a perception of the agreement or disagreement of our own ideas, and the knowledge of the existence of all things without us (except only of a God, whose existence every man may certainly know and demonstrate to himself from his own existence), be had only by our senses, what room is there for the exercise of any other faculty, but *outward sense* and *inward perception?* What need is there of *reason?* Very much: both for the enlargement of our knowledge, and regulating our assent. For it hath to do both in knowledge and opinion, and is necessary and assisting to all our other intellectual faculties, and indeed contains two of them, viz. *sagacity* and *illation.* By the one, it finds out; and by the other, it so orders the intermediate ideas as to discover what connection there is in each link of the chain, whereby the extremes are held together; and thereby, as it were, to draw into view the truth sought for, which is that which we call *illation* or *inference,* and consists in nothing but the perception of the connection there is between the ideas, in each step of the deduction; whereby the mind comes to see, either the certain agreement or disagreement of any two ideas, as in demonstration, in which it arrives at *knowledge;* or their probable connection, on which it gives or withholds its assent, as in *opinion.* Sense and intuition reach but a very little way. The greatest part of our knowledge depends upon deductions and intermediate ideas: and in those cases where we are fain to substitute assent instead of knowledge, and take propositions for true, without being certain they are so, we have need to find out, examine, and compare the grounds of their probability. In both these cases, the faculty which finds out the means, and rightly applies them, to discover certainty in the one, and probability in the other, is that which we call *reason*. For, as reason perceives the necessary and indubitable connection of all the ideas or proofs one to another, in each step of any demonstration that produces knowledge; so it likewise perceives the probable connection of all the ideas or proofs one to another, in every step of a discourse, to which it will think assent due. This is the lowest degree of that which can be truly called reason. For where the mind does not perceive this probable connection, where it does not discern whether there be any such connection or no; there men's opinions are not the product of judgment, or the consequence of reason, but the effects of chance and hazard, of a mind floating at all adventures, without choice and without direction.

So that we may in *reason* consider these *four degrees:* the first and highest is the discovering and finding out of truths; the second, the regular and methodical disposition of them, and laying them in a clear and fit order, to make their connection and force be plainly and easily perceived; the third is the perceiving their connection; and the fourth, a making a right conclusion. These several degrees may be observed in any mathematical demonstration; it being one thing to perceive the connection of each part, as the demonstration is made by another; another to perceive the dependence of the conclusion on all the parts; a third, to make out a demonstration clearly and neatly one's self; and something different from all these, to have first found out these intermediate ideas or proofs by which it is made.

[In the following paragraphs, Locke attacks the traditional Aristotelian notion that the syllogism is a great instrument of reason. He writes "God has not been so sparing of men as to make them barely two-legged creatures, and left it to Aristotle to make them rational." The syllogism neither discovers ideas nor the connection between ideas. It does not increase our knowledge, but only teaches us, at best, "the art of fencing with the little knowledge we have, without making any addition to it."]

Reason, though it penetrates into the depths of the sea and earth, elevates our thoughts as high as the stars, and leads us through the vast spaces and large rooms of this mighty fabric, yet it comes far short of the real extent of even corporeal being. And there are many instances wherein it fails us: as,

I. It perfectly fails us, where our ideas fail. It neither does nor can extend itself further than they do. And therefore, wherever we have no ideas, our reasoning stops, and we are at an end of our reckoning: and if at any time we reason about words which do not stand for any ideas, it is only about those sounds, and nothing else.

II. Our reason is often puzzled, and at a loss, because of the obscurity, confusion, or imperfection of the ideas it is employed about; and there we are involved in difficulties and contradictions. Thus, not having any perfect idea of the *least extension of matter,* nor of *infinity,* we are at a loss about the divisibility of matter; but having perfect, clear, and distinct ideas of *number,* our reason meets with none of those inextricable difficulties in numbers, nor finds itself involved in any contradictions about them. Thus, we having but imperfect ideas of the operations of our minds, and of the beginning of motion, or thought how the mind produces either of them in us, and much imperfecter yet of the operation of God, run into great difficulties about *free created agents,* which reason cannot well extricate itself out of.

III. Our reason is often at a stand, because it perceives not those ideas, which could serve to show the certain or probable agreement or disagreement of any other two ideas: and in this some men's faculties far outgo others. Till algebra, that great instrument and instance of human sagacity, was discovered, men with amazement looked on several of the demonstrations of ancient mathematicians, and could scarce forbear to think the finding several of those proofs to be something more than human.

IV. The mind, by proceeding upon false principles, is often engaged in absurdities and difficulties, brought into straits and contradictions, without knowing how to free itself: and in that case it is in vain to implore the help of reason, unless it be to discover the falsehood and reject the influence of those wrong principles. Reason is so far from clearing the difficulties which the building upon false foundations brings a man into, that if he will pursue it, it entangles him the more, and engages him deeper in perplexities.

V. As obscure and imperfect ideas often involve our reason, so, upon the same ground, do dubious words and uncertain signs, often, in discourses and arguings, when not warily attended to, puzzle men's reason, and bring them to a nonplus. But these two latter are our fault, and not the fault of reason. But yet the consequences of them are nevertheless obvious; and the perplexities or errors they fill men's minds with are everywhere observable.

Some of the ideas that are in the mind, are so there, that they can be by themselves immediately compared one with another: and in these the mind is able to perceive that they agree or disagree as clearly as that it has them. Thus the mind perceives, that an arch of a circle is less than the whole circle, as clearly as it does the idea of a circle: and this, therefore, as has been said, I call *intuitive knowledge;* which is certain, beyond all doubt, and needs no probation, nor can have any; this being the highest of all human certainty. In this consists the evidence of all those *maxims* which nobody has any doubt about, but every man (does not, as is said, only assent to, but) *knows* to be true, as soon as ever they are proposed to his understanding. In the discovery of and assent to these truths, there is no use of the discursive faculty, *no need of reasoning,* but they are known by a superior and higher degree of evidence. And such, if I may guess at things unknown, I am apt to think that angels have now, and the spirits of just men made perfect shall have, in a future state, of thousands of things which now either wholly escape our apprehensions, or which our shortsighted reason having got some faint glimpse of, we, in the dark, grope after.

But though we have, here and there, a little of this clear light, some sparks of bright knowledge, yet the greatest part of our ideas are such, that we cannot discern their agreement or disagreement by an immediate comparing them. And in all these we have *need of reasoning,* and must, by discourse and inference, make our discoveries. Now of these there are two sorts, which I shall take the liberty to mention here again:——

First, Those whose agreement or disagreement, though it cannot be seen by an immediate putting them together, yet may be examined by the intervention of other ideas which can be compared with them. In this case, when the agreement or disagreement of the intermediate idea, on both sides, with those which we would compare, is *plainly discerned:* there it amounts to *demonstration* whereby knowledge is produced, which, though it be certain, yet it is not so easy, nor altogether so clear as intuitive knowledge. Because in that there is barely one simple intuition, wherein there is no room for any the least mistake or doubt: the truth is seen all perfectly at once. In demonstration, it is true, there is intuition too, but not altogether at once; for there must be a remembrance of the intuition of the agreement of the medium, or intermediate idea, with that we compared it with before, when we compare it with the other: and where there be many mediums, there the danger of the mistake is the greater. For each agreement or disagreement of the ideas must be observed and seen in each step of the whole train, and retained in the memory, just as it is; and the mind must be sure that no part of what is necessary to make up the demonstration is omitted or overlooked. This makes some demonstrations long and perplexed, and too hard for those who have not strength of parts distinctly to perceive, and exactly carry so many particulars orderly in their heads. And even those who are able to master such intricate speculations, are fain sometimes to go over them again, and there is need of more than one review before they can arrive at certainty. But yet where the mind clearly retains the intuition it had of the agreement of any idea with another, and that with a third, and that with a fourth, etc., there the agreement of the first and the fourth is a demonstration, and produces certain knowledge; which may be called *rational knowledge,* as the other is intuitive.

Secondly, There are other ideas, whose agreement or disagreement can no otherwise be judged of but by the intervention of others which have not a certain agreement with the extremes, but an *usual* or *likely* one: and in these it is that the *judgment* is properly exercised; which is the acquiescing of the mind, that any ideas do agree, by comparing them with such probable mediums. This, though it never amounts to knowledge, no, not to that which is the lowest degree of it; yet sometimes the intermediate ideas tie the extremes so firmly together, and the probability is so clear and strong, that *assent* as necessarily follows it, as *knowledge* does demonstration. The great excellency and use of the judgment is to observe right, and take a true estimate of the force and weight of each probability; and then casting them up all right together, choose that side which has the overbalance.

Intuitive knowledge is the perception of the *certain* agreement or disagreement of two ideas immediately compared together.

Rational knowledge is the perception of the *certain* agreement or disagreement of any two ideas, by the intervention of one or more other ideas.

Judgment is the thinking or taking two ideas to agree or disagree, by the intervention of one or more ideas, whose certain agreement or disagreement with them it does not perceive, but hath observed to be *frequent* and *usual.*

Though the deducing one proposition from another, or making inferences in *words,* be a great part of reason, and that which it is usually employed about; yet the principal act of ratiocination is *the finding the agreement or disagreement of two ideas one with another, by the intervention of a third.* As a man, by a yard, finds two houses to be of the same length, which could not be brought together to measure their equality by juxtaposition. Words have their consequences, as the signs of such ideas: and things agree or disagree, as really they are; but we observe it only by our ideas.

Before we quit this subject, it may be worth our while a little to reflect on *four sorts of arguments,* that men, in their reasonings with others, do ordinarily make use of to prevail on their assent; or at least so to awe them as to silence their opposition.

I. The first is, to allege the opinions of men, whose parts, learning, eminency, power, or some other cause has gained a name, and settled their reputation in the common esteem with some kind of authority. When men are established in any kind of dignity, it is thought a breach of modesty for others to derogate any way from it, and question the authority of men who are in possession of it. This is apt to be censured, as carrying with it too much pride, when a man does not readily yield to the determination of approved authors, which is wont to be received with respect and submission by others: and it is looked upon as insolence, for a man to set up and adhere to his own opinion against the current stream of antiquity; or to put it in the balance against that of some learned doctor, or otherwise approved writer. Whoever backs his tenets with such authorities, thinks he ought thereby to carry the cause, and is ready to style it impudence in anyone who shall stand out against them. This I think may be called *argumentum ad verecundiam.*

II. Secondly, Another way that men ordinarily use to drive others, and force them to submit their judgments, and receive the opinion in debate, is to require the adversary to admit what they allege as a proof, or to assign a better. And this I call *argumentum ad ignorantiam.*

III. Thirdly, A third way is to press a man with consequences drawn from his own principles or concessions. This is already known under the name of *argumentum ad hominem.*

IV. The fourth is the using of proofs drawn from any of the foundations of knowledge or probability. This I call *argumentum ad judicium.* This alone, of all the four, brings true instruction with it, and advances us in our way to knowledge. For, 1. It argues not another man's opinion to be right, because I, out of respect, or any other consideration but that of conviction, will not contradict him. 2. It proves not another man to be in the right way, nor that I ought to take the same with him, because I know not a better. 3. Nor does it follow that another man is in the right way, because he has shown me that I am in the wrong. I may be modest, and therefore not oppose another man's persuasion: I may be ignorant, and not be able to produce a better: I may be in an error, and another may show me that I am so. This may dispose me, perhaps, for the reception of truth, but helps me not to it: that must come from proofs and arguments, and light arising from the nature of things themselves, and not from my shamefacedness, ignorance, or error.

By what has been before said of reason, we may be able to make some guess at the distinction of things, into those that are according to, above, and contrary to reason. 1. *According to reason* are such propositions whose truth we can discover by examining and tracing those ideas we have from sensation and reflection; and by natural deduction find to be true or probable. 2. *Above reason* are such propositions whose truth or probability we cannot by reason derive from those principles. 3. *Contrary to reason* are such propositions as are inconsistent with or irreconcilable to our clear and distinct ideas. Thus the existence of one God is according to reason; the existence of more than one God, contrary to reason; the resurrection of the dead, above reason. *Above reason* also may be taken in a double sense, viz. either as signifying above probability, or above certainty: and in that large sense also, *contrary to reason,* is, I suppose, sometimes taken.

There is another use of the word *reason,* wherein it is *opposed to faith:* which, though it be in itself a very improper way of speaking, yet common use has so authorized it, that it would be folly either to oppose or hope to remedy it. Only I think it may not be amiss to take notice, that, however faith be opposed to reason, faith is nothing but a firm assent of the mind: which, if it be regulated, as is our duty, cannot be afforded to anything but upon good reason; and so cannot be opposite to it. He that believes without having any reason for believing, may be in love with his own fancies; but neither seeks truth as he ought, nor pays the obedience due to his Maker, who would have him use those discerning faculties He has given him, to keep him out of mistake and error. He that does not this to the best of his power, however he sometimes lights on truth, is in the right but by chance; and I know not whether the luckiness of the accident will excuse the irregularity of his proceeding. This at least is certain, that he must be accountable for whatever mistakes he runs into: whereas he that makes use of the light and faculties God has given him, and seeks sincerely to discover truth by those helps and abilities he has, may have this satisfaction in doing his duty as a rational creature, that, though he should miss truth, he will not miss the reward of it. For he governs his assent right, and places it as he should, who, in any case or matter whatsoever, believes or disbelieves according as reason directs him. He that doth otherwise, transgresses against his own light, and misuses those faculties which were given him to no other end, but to search and follow the clearer evidence and greater probability. But since reason and faith are by some men opposed, we will so consider them in the following chapter.

XVIII

Of Faith and Reason, and Their Distinct Provinces

It has been above shown, 1. That we are of necessity ignorant, and want knowledge of all sorts, where we want ideas. 2. That we are ignorant, and want rational knowledge, where we want proofs. 3. That we want certain knowledge and certainty, as far as we want clear and determined specific ideas. 4. That we want probability to direct our assent in matters where we have neither knowledge of our own nor testimony of other men to bottom our reason upon.

From these things thus premised, I think we may come to lay down *the measures and boundaries between faith and reason:* the want whereof may possibly have been the cause, if not of great disorders, yet at least of great disputes, and perhaps mistakes in the world. For till it be resolved how far we are to be guided by reason, and how far by faith, we shall in vain dispute, and endeavor to convince one another in matters of religion.

I find every sect, as far as reason will help them, make use of it gladly: and where it fails them, they cry out, It is a matter of faith, and above reason. And I do not see how they can argue with anyone, or ever convince a gainsayer who makes use of the same plea, without setting down strict boundaries between faith and reason; which ought to be the first point established in all questions where faith has anything to do.

Reason, therefore, here, as contradistinguished to *faith,* I take to be the discovery of the certainty or probability of such propositions or truths, which the mind arrives at by deduction made from such ideas, which it has got by the use of its natural faculties; viz. by sensation or reflection.

Faith, on the other side, is the assent to any proposition, not thus made out by the deductions of reason, but upon the credit of the proposer, as coming from God, in some extraordinary way of communication. This way of discovering truths to men, we call *revelation.*

First, Then I say, that *no man inspired by God can by any revelation communicate to others any new simple ideas which they had not before from sensation or reflection.* For, whatsoever impressions he himself may have from the immediate hand of God, this revelation, if it be of new simple ideas, cannot be conveyed to another, either by words or any other signs. Because words, by their immediate operation on us, cause no other ideas but of their natural sounds: and it is by the custom of using them for signs, that they excite and revive in our minds latent ideas; but yet only such ideas as were there before. For words, seen or heard, recall to our thoughts those ideas only which to us they have been wont to be signs of, but cannot introduce any perfectly new, and formerly unknown simple ideas. The same holds in all other signs; which cannot signify to us things of which we have before never had any idea at all.

Thus whatever things were discovered to St. Paul, when he was rapt up into the third heaven; whatever new ideas his mind there received, all the description he can make to others of that place, is only this, That there are such things, "as eye hath not seen, nor ear heard, nor hath it entered into the heart of man to conceive." And supposing God should discover to anyone, supernaturally, a species of creatures inhabiting, for example, Jupiter or Saturn (for that it is possible there may be such, nobody can deny), which had six senses; and imprint on his mind the ideas conveyed to theirs by that sixth sense: he could no more, by words, produce in the minds of other men those ideas imprinted by that sixth sense, than one of us could convey the idea of any color, by the sound of words, into a man who, having the other four senses perfect, had always totally wanted the fifth, of seeing. For our simple ideas, then, which are the foundation, and sole matter of all our notions and knowledge, we must depend wholly on our reason, I mean our natural faculties; and can by no means receive them, or any of them, from traditional revelation. I say, *traditional revelation,* in distinction to *original revelation.* By the one, I mean that first impression which is made immediately by God on the mind of any man, to which we cannot set any bounds; and by the other, those impressions delivered over to others in words, and the ordinary ways of conveying our conceptions one to another.

Secondly, I say that *the same truths may be discovered, and conveyed down from revelation, which are discoverable to us by reason, and by those ideas we naturally may have.* So God might, by revelation, discover the truth of any proposition in Euclid; as well as men, by the natural use of their faculties, come to make the discovery themselves. In all things of this kind there is little need or use of revelation, God having furnished us with natural and surer means to arrive at the knowledge of them. For whatsoever truth we come to the clear discovery of, from the knowledge and contemplation of our own ideas, will always be certainer to us than those which are conveyed to us by *traditional revelation.* For the knowledge we have that this revelation came at first from God, can never be so sure as the knowledge we have from the clear and distinct perception of the agreement or disagreement of our own ideas: v.g. if it were revealed some ages since, that the three angles of a triangle were equal to two right ones, I might assent to the truth of that proposition, upon the credit of the tradition, that it was revealed: but that would never amount to so great a certainty as the knowledge of it, upon the comparing and measuring my own ideas of two right angles, and the three angles of a triangle. The like holds in matter of fact knowable by our senses; v.g. the history of the deluge is conveyed to us by writings which had their original from revelation: and yet nobody, I think, will say he has as certain and clear a knowledge of the flood as Noah, that saw it; or that he himself would have had, had he then been alive and seen it. For he has no greater an assurance than that of his senses, that it is writ in the book supposed writ by Moses inspired: but he has not so great an assurance that Moses wrote that book as if he had seen Moses write it. So that the assurance of its being a revelation is less still than the assurance of his senses.

In propositions, then, whose certainty is built upon the clear perception of the agreement or disagreement of our ideas, attained either by immediate intuition, as in self-evident propositions, or by evident deductions of reason in demonstrations we need not the assistance of revelation, as necessary to gain our assent, and introduce them into our minds. Because the natural ways of knowledge could settle them there, or had done it already; which is the greatest assurance we can possibly have of anything, unless where God immediately reveals it to us: and there too our assurance can be no greater than our knowledge is, that it *is* a revelation from God. But yet nothing, I think, can, under that title, shake or overrule plain knowledge; or rationally prevail with any man to admit it for true, in a direct contradiction to the clear evidence of his own understanding. For, since no evidence of our faculties, by which we receive such revelations, can exceed, if equal, the certainty of our intuitive knowledge, we can never receive for a truth anything that is directly contrary to our clear and distinct knowledge; v.g. the ideas of one body and one place do so clearly agree, and the mind has so evident a perception of their agreement, that we can never assent to a proposition that affirms the same body to be in two distant places at once, however it should pretend to the authority of a divine revelation: since the evidence, first, that we deceive not ourselves, in ascribing it to God; secondly, that we understand it right; can never be so great as the evidence of our own intuitive knowledge, whereby we discern it impossible for the same body to be in two places at once. And therefore *no proposition can be received for divine revelation, or obtain the assent due to all such, if it be contradictory to our clear intuitive knowledge*. Because this would be to subvert the principles and foundations of all knowledge, evidence, and assent whatsoever: and there would be left no difference between truth and falsehood, no measures of credible and incredible in the world, if doubtful propositions shall take place before self-evident; and what we certainly know give way to what we may possibly be mistaken in. In propositions therefore contrary to the clear perception of the agreement or disagreement of any of our ideas, it will be in vain to urge them as matters of faith. They cannot move our assent under that or any other title whatsoever. For faith can never convince us of anything that contradicts our knowledge. Because, though faith be founded on the testimony of God (who cannot lie) revealing any proposition to us: yet we cannot have an assurance of the truth of its being a divine revelation greater than our own knowledge. Since the whole strength of the certainty depends upon our knowledge that God revealed it; which, in this case, where the proposition supposed revealed contradicts our knowledge or reason, will always have this objection hanging to it, viz. that we cannot tell how to conceive that to come from God, the bountiful Author of our being, which, if received for true, must overturn all the principles and foundations of knowledge He has given us; render all our faculties useless; wholly destroy the most excellent part of His workmanship, our understandings; and put a man in a condition wherein he will have less light, less conduct than the beast that perisheth. For if the mind of man can never have a clearer (and perhaps not so clear) evidence of anything to be a divine revelation, as it has of the principles of its own reason, it can never have a ground to quit the clear evidence of its reason, to give a place to a proposition, whose revelation has not a greater evidence than those principles have.

Thus far a man has use of reason, and ought to hearken to it, even in immediate and original revelation, where it is supposed to be made to himself. But to all those who pretend not to immediate revelation, but are required to pay obedience, and to receive the truths revealed to others, which, by the tradition of writings, or word of mouth, are conveyed down to them, reason has a great deal more to do, and is that only which can induce us to receive them. For matter of faith being only divine revelation, and nothing else, faith, as we use the word (called commonly *divine faith*), has to do with no propositions, but those which are supposed to be divinely revealed. So that I do not see how those who make revelation alone the sole object of faith can say, That it is a matter of faith, and not of reason, to believe that such or such a proposition, to be found in such or such a book, is of divine inspiration; unless it be revealed that that proposition, or all in that book, was communicated by divine inspiration. Without such a revelation, the believing, or not believing, that proposition, or book, to be of divine authority, can never be matter of faith, but matter of reason; and such as I must come to an assent to only by the use of my reason, which can never require or enable me to believe that which is contrary to itself: it being impossible for reason ever to procure any assent to that which to itself appears unreasonable.

In all things, therefore, where we have clear evidence from our ideas, and those principles of knowledge I have above mentioned, reason is the proper judge; and revelation, though it may, in consenting with it, confirm its dictates, yet cannot in such cases invalidate its decrees: nor can we be obliged, where we have the clear and evident sentence of reason, to quit it for the contrary opinion, under a pretense that it is matter of faith: which can have no authority against the plain and clear dictates of reason.

But, *Thirdly*, There being many things wherein we have

very imperfect notions, or none at all; and other things, of whose past, present, or future existence, by the natural use of our faculties, we can have no knowledge at all; these, as being beyond the discovery of our natural faculties, and *above reason,* are, when revealed, *the proper matter of faith.* Thus, that part of the angels rebelled against God, and thereby lost their first happy state: and that the dead shall rise, and live again: these and the like, being beyond the discovery of reason, are purely matters of faith, with which reason has directly nothing to do.

But since God, in giving us the light of reason, has not thereby tied up his own hands from affording us, when he thinks fit, the light of revelation in any of those matters wherein our natural faculties are able to give a probable determination; *revelation,* where God has been pleased to give it, *must carry it against the probable conjectures of reason.* Because the mind not being certain of the truth of that it does not evidently know, but only yielding to the probability that appears in it, is bound to give up its assent to such a testimony which, it is satisfied, comes from one who cannot err, and will not deceive. But yet, it still belongs to reason to judge of the truth of its being a revelation, and of the signification of the words wherein it is delivered. Indeed, if anything shall be thought revelation which is contrary to the plain principles of reason, and the evident knowledge the mind has of its own clear and distinct ideas; there reason must be hearkened to, as to a matter within its province. Since a man can never have so certain a knowledge, that a proposition which contradicts the clear principles and evidence of his own knowledge was divinely revealed, or that he understands the words rightly wherein it is delivered, as he has that the contrary is true, and so is bound to consider and judge of it as a matter of reason, and not swallow it, without examination, as a matter of faith.

First, Whatever proposition is revealed, of whose truth our mind, by its natural faculties and notions, cannot judge, that is purely matter of faith, and above reason.

Secondly, All propositions whereof the mind, by the use of its natural faculties, can come to determine and judge, from naturally acquired ideas, are matter of reason; with this difference still, that, in those concerning which it has but an uncertain evidence, and so is persuaded of their truth only upon probable grounds, which still admit a possibility of the contrary to be true, without doing violence to the certain evidence of its own knowledge, and overturning the principles of all reason; in such probable propositions, I say, an evident revelation ought to determine our assent, even against probability. For where the principles of reason have not evidenced a proposition to be certainly true or false, there clear revelation, as another principle of truth and ground of assent, may determine; and so it may be matter of faith, and be also above reason. Because reason, in that particular matter, being able to reach no higher than probability, faith gave the determination where reason came short; and revelation discovered on which side the truth lay.

Thus far the dominion of faith reaches, and that without any violence or hindrance to reason; which is not injured or disturbed, but assisted and improved by new discoveries of truth, coming from the eternal fountain of all knowledge. Whatever God hath revealed is certainly true: no doubt can be made of it. This is the proper object of faith: but whether it be a *divine* revelation or no, reason must judge; which can never permit the mind to reject a greater evidence to embrace what is less evident, nor allow it to entertain probability in opposition to knowledge and certainty. There can be no evidence that any traditional revelation is of divine original, in the words we receive it, and in the sense we understand it, so clear and so certain as that of the principles of reason: and therefore *Nothing that is contrary to, and inconsistent with, the clear and self-evident dictates of reason, has a right to be urged or assented to as a matter of faith, wherein reason hath nothing to do*. Whatsoever is divine revelation, ought to overrule all our opinions, prejudices, and interest, and hath a right to be received with full assent. Such a submission as this, of our reason to faith, takes not away the landmarks of knowledge: this shakes not the foundations of reason, but leaves us that use of our faculties for which they were given us.

If the provinces of faith and reason are not kept distinct by these boundaries, there will, in matters of religion, be no room for reason at all; and those extravagant opinions and ceremonies that are to be found in the several religions of the world will not deserve to be blamed. For, to this crying up of faith in *opposition* to reason, we may, I think, in good measure ascribe those absurdities that fill almost all the religions which possess and divide mankind. For men having been principled with an opinion, that they must not consult reason in the things of religion, however apparently contradictory to common sense and the very principles of all their knowledge, have let loose their fancies and natural superstition; and have been by them led into so strange opinions, and extravagant practices in religion, that a considerate man cannot but stand amazed at their follies, and judge them so far from being acceptable to the great and wise God, that he cannot avoid thinking them ridiculous and offensive to a sober good man. So that, in effect, religion, which should most distinguish us from beasts, and ought most peculiarly to elevate us, as rational creatures, above brutes, is that wherein men often appear most irrational, and more senseless than beasts themselves. *Credo, quia impossible est:* I believe, because it is impossible, might, in a good man, pass for a sally of zeal; but would prove a very ill rule for men to choose their opinions or religion by.

XIX

Of Wrong Assent, or Error

KNOWLEDGE BEING TO BE HAD ONLY of visible and certain truth, *error* is not a fault of our knowledge, but a mistake of our judgment giving assent to that which is not true.

But if assent be grounded on likelihood, if the proper object and motive of our assent be probability, and that probability consists in what is laid down in the foregoing chapters, it will be demanded *how men come to give their assents contrary to probability*. For there is nothing more common than contrariety of opinions; nothing more obvious than that one man wholly disbelieves what another only doubts of, and a third steadfastly believes and firmly adheres to.

The reasons whereof, though they may be very various, yet, I suppose may all be reduced to these four:

I. *Want of proofs.*
II. *Want of ability to use them.*
III. *Want of will to see them.*
IV. *Wrong measures of probability.*

First, By *want of proofs*, I do not mean only the want of those proofs which are nowhere extant, and so are nowhere to be had; but the want even of those proofs which are in being, or might be procured. And thus men want proofs, who have not the convenience or opportunity to make experiments and observations themselves, tending to the proof of any proposition; nor likewise the convenience to inquire into and collect the testimonies of others: and in this state are the greatest part of mankind, who are given up to labor, and enslaved to the necessity of their mean condition, whose lives are worn out only in the provisions for living. These men's opportunities of knowledge and inquiry are commonly as narrow as their fortunes; and their understandings are but little instructed, when all their whole time and pains is laid out to still the croaking of their own bellies, or the cries of their children. It is not to be expected that a man who drudges on all his life in a laborious trade, should be more knowing in the variety of things done in the world than a packhorse, who is driven constantly forwards and backwards in a narrow lane and dirty road, only to market, should be skilled in the geography of the country. Nor is it at all more possible, that he who wants leisure, books, and languages, and the opportunity of conversing with variety of men, should be in a condition to collect those testimonies and observations which are in being, and are necessary to make out many, nay most, of the propositions that, in the societies of men, are judged of the greatest moment; or to find out grounds of assurance so great as the belief of the points he would build on them is thought necessary. So that a great part of mankind are, by the natural and unalterable state of things in this world, and the constitution of human affairs, unavoidably given over to invincible ignorance of those proofs on which others build, and which are necessary to establish those opinions: the greatest part of men, having much to do to get the means of living, are not in a condition to look after those of learned and laborious inquiries.

What shall we say, then? Are the greatest part of mankind, by the necessity of their condition, subjected to unavoidable ignorance, in those things which are of greatest importance to them? (for of those it is obvious to inquire). Have the bulk of mankind no other guide but accident and blind chance to conduct them to their happiness or misery? Are the current opinions, and licensed guides of every country sufficient evidence and security to every man to venture his great concernments on; nay, his everlasting happiness or misery? Or can those be the certain and infallible oracles and standards of truth, which teach one thing in Christendom and another in Turkey? Or shall a poor countryman be eternally happy, for having the chance to be born in Italy; or a day laborer be unavoidably lost, because he had the ill luck to be born in England? How ready some men may be to say some of these things, I will not here examine: but this I am sure, that men must allow one or other of these to be true (let them choose which they please), or else grant that God has furnished men with faculties sufficient to direct them in the way they should take, if they will but seriously employ them that way, when their ordinary vocations allow them the leisure. No man is so wholly taken up with the attendance on the means of living, as to have no spare time at all to think of his soul, and inform himself in matters of religion. Were men as intent upon this as they are on things of lower concernment, there are none so enslaved to the necessities of life who might not find many vacancies that might be husbanded to this advantage of their knowledge.

Besides those whose improvements and informations are straitened by the narrowness of their fortunes, there are others whose largeness of fortune would plentifully enough supply books, and other requisites for clearing of doubts, and discovering of truth: but they are cooped in close, by the laws of their countries, and the strict guards of those whose interest it is to keep them ignorant, lest, knowing more, they should believe the less in them. These are as far, nay further, from the liberty and opportunities of a fair inquiry, than these poor and wretched laborers we before spoke of: and however they may seem high and great, are confined to narrowness of thought, and enslaved in that which should be the freest part of man, their understandings. This is generally the case of all those who live in places where care is taken to propagate truth without knowledge; where men are forced, at a venture, to be of the religion of the country; and must therefore swallow down opinions, as silly people do empiric's pills, without knowing what they are made of, or how they will work, and having nothing to do but believe that they will do the cure: but in this are much more miserable than they, in that they are not at liberty to refuse swallowing what perhaps they had rather let alone; or to choose the physician, to whose conduct they would trust themselves.

Secondly, Those who *want skill to use those evidences they have of probabilities;* who cannot carry a train of consequences in their heads; nor weigh exactly the preponderancy of contrary proofs and testimonies, making every circumstance its due allowance; may be easily misled to assent to positions that are not probable. There are some men of one, some but of two syllogisms, and no more; and others that can but advance one step further. These cannot always discern that side on which the strongest proofs lie; cannot constantly follow that which in itself is the more probable opinion. Now that there is such a difference between men, in respect of their understandings, I think nobody, who has had any conversation with his neighbors, will question: though he never was at Westminster Hall or the Exchange on the one hand, nor at Alms houses or Bedlam on the other. Which great difference in men's intellectuals, whether it rises from any defect in the organs of the body, particularly adapted to thinking; or in the dullness or intractableness of those faculties for want of use; or, as some think, in the natural differences of men's souls themselves; or some, or all of these together; it matters not here to examine: only this is evident, that there is a difference of degrees in men's understandings, apprehensions, and reasonings, to so great a latitude, that one may, without doing injury to mankind, affirm, that there is a greater distance between some men and others in this respect, than between some men and some beasts. But how this comes about is a speculation, though of great consequence, yet not necessary to our present purpose.

Thirdly, There are another sort of people that want proofs, not because they are out of their reach, but *because they will not use them:* who, though they have riches and leisure enough, and want neither parts nor other helps, are yet never the better for them. Their hot pursuit of pleasure, or constant drudgery in business, engages some men's thoughts elsewhere: laziness and oscitancy in general, or a particular aversion for books, study, and meditation, keep others from any serious thoughts at all; and some out of fear that an impartial inquiry would not favor those opinions which best suit their prejudices, lives, and designs, content themselves, without examination, to take upon trust what they find convenient and in fashion. Thus, most men, even of those that might do otherwise, pass their lives without an acquaintance with, much less a rational assent to, probabilities they are concerned to know, though they lie so much within their view, that, to be convinced of them, they need but turn their eyes that way. We know some men will not read a letter which is supposed to bring ill news; and many men forbear to cast up their accounts, or so much as think upon their estates, who have reason to fear their affairs are in no very good posture. How men, whose plentiful fortunes allow them leisure to improve their understandings, can satisfy themselves with a lazy ignorance, I cannot tell: but methinks they have a low opinion of their souls, who lay out all their incomes in provisions for the body, and employ none of it to procure the means and helps of knowledge; who take great care to appear always in a neat and splendid outside, and would think themselves miserable in coarse clothes, or a patched coat, and yet contentedly suffer their minds to appear abroad in a piebald livery of coarse patches and borrowed shreds, such as it has pleased chance, or their country tailor (I mean the common opinion of those they have conversed with) to clothe them in. I will not here mention how unreasonable this is for men that ever think of a future state, and their concernment in it, which no rational man can avoid to do sometimes: nor shall I take notice what a shame and confusion it is to the greatest contemners of knowledge, to be found ignorant in things they are concerned to know. But this at least is worth the consideration of those who call themselves gentlemen, That, however they may think credit, respect, power, and authority the concomitants of their birth and fortune, yet they will find all these still carried away from them by men of lower condition, who surpass them in knowledge. They who are blind will always be led by those that see, or else fall into the ditch: and he is certainly the most subjected, the most enslaved, who is so in his understanding.

In the foregoing instances some of the causes have been shown of wrong assent, and how it comes to pass, that probable doctrines are not always received with an assent proportionable to the reasons which are to be had for their probability: but hitherto we have considered only such probabilities whose proofs do exist, but do not appear to him who embraces the error.

Fourthly, There remains yet the last sort, who, even where the real probabilities appear, and are plainly laid before them, do not admit of the conviction, nor yield unto manifest reasons, but do either suspend their assent, or give it to the less probable opinion. And to this danger are those exposed who have taken up *wrong measures of probability*, which are:

I. *Propositions that are not in themselves certain and evident, but doubtful and false, taken up for principles.*

II. *Received hypotheses.*

III. *Predominant passions or inclinations.*

IV. *Authority.*

I. The first and firmest ground of probability is the conformity anything has to our own knowledge; especially that part of our knowledge which we have embraced, and continue to look on as *principles*. These have so great an influence upon our opinions, that it is usually by them we judge of truth, and measure probability; to that degree, that what is inconsistent with our principles, is so far from passing for probable with us, that it will not be allowed possible. The reverence borne to these principles is so great, and their authority so paramount to all other, that the testimony, not only of other men, but the evidence of our own senses are often rejected, when they offer to vouch anything contrary to these established rules. How much the doctrine of *innate principles*, and that principles are not to be proved or questioned, has contributed to this, I will not here examine. This I readily grant, that one truth cannot contradict another: but withal I take leave also to say, that everyone ought very carefully to beware what he admits for a principle, to examine it strictly, and see whether he certainly knows it to be true of itself, by its own evidence, or whether he does only with assurance believe it to be so, upon the authority of others. For he hath a strong bias put into his understanding, which will unavoidably misguide his assent, who hath imbibed *wrong principles*, and has blindly given himself up to the authority of any opinion in itself not evidently true.

There is nothing more ordinary than children's receiving into their minds propositions (especially about matters of religion) from their parents, nurses, or those about them: which being insinuated into their unwary as well as unbiased understandings, and fastened by degrees, are at last (equally whether true or false) riveted there by long custom and education, beyond all possibility of being pulled out again. For men, when they are grown up, reflecting upon their opinions, and finding those of this sort to be as ancient in their minds as their very memories, not having observed their early insinuation, nor by what means they got them, they are apt to reverence them as sacred things, and not to suffer them to be profaned, touched, or questioned: they look on them as the Urim and Thummim set up in their minds immediately by God himself, to be the great and unerring deciders of truth and falsehood, and the judges to which they are to appeal in all manner of controversies.

This opinion of his principles (let them be what they will) being once established in anyone's mind, it is easy to be imagined what reception any proposition shall find, how clearly soever proved, that shall invalidate their authority, or at all thwart with these internal oracles; whereas the grossest absurdities and improbabilities, being but agreeable to such principles, go down glibly, and are easily digested. The great obstinacy that is to be found in men firmly believing quite contrary opinions, though many times equally absurd, in the various religions of mankind, are as evident a proof as they are an unavoidable consequence of this way of reasoning from received traditional principles. So that men will disbelieve their own eyes, renounce the evidence of their senses, and give their own experience the lie, rather than admit of anything disagreeing with these sacred tenets. Take an intelligent Romanist that, from the first dawning of any notions in his understanding, hath had this principle constantly inculcated, viz. that he must believe as the church (i.e. those of his communion) believes, or that the Pope is infallible, and this he never so much as heard questioned, till at forty or fifty years old he met with one of other principles: how is he prepared easily to swallow, not only against all probability, but even the clear evidence of his senses, the doctrine of *transubstantiation?* This principle has such an influence on his mind, that he will believe that to be flesh which he sees to be bread. And what way will you take to convince a man of any improbable opinion he holds, who, with some philosophers, hath laid down this as a foundation of reasoning, That he must believe his reason (for so men improperly call arguments drawn from their principles) against his senses? Let an enthusiast be principled that he or his teacher is inspired, and acted by an immediate communication of the Divine Spirit, and you in vain bring the evidence of clear reasons against his doctrine. Whoever, therefore, have imbibed wrong principles, are not, in things inconsistent with these principles, to be moved by the most apparent and convincing probabilities, till they are so candid and ingenuous to themselves, as to be persuaded to examine even those very principles, which many never suffer themselves to do.

II. Next to these are men whose understandings are cast into a mold, and fashioned just to the size of a received *hypothesis*. The difference between these and the former, is, that they will admit of matter of fact, and agree with dissenters in that; but differ only in assigning of reasons and explaining the manner of operation. These are not at that open defiance with their senses, with the former: they can endure to hearken to their information a little more patiently; but will by no means admit of their reports in the explanation of things; nor be prevailed on by probabilities, which would convince them that things are not brought about just after the same manner that they have decreed within themselves that they are. Would it not be an insufferable thing for a learned professor, and that which his scarlet would blush at, to have his authority of forty years standing, wrought out of hard rock, Greek and Latin, with no small expense of time and candle, and confirmed by general tradition and a reverend beard, in an instant overturned by an upstart novelist? Can anyone expect that he should be made to confess, that what he taught his scholars thirty years ago was all error and mistake; and that he sold them hard words and ignorance at a very dear rate? What probabilities, I say, are sufficient to prevail in such a case? And who ever, by the most cogent arguments, will be prevailed with to disrobe himself at once of all his old opinions, and pretenses to knowledge and learning, which with hard study he hath all this time been laboring for; and turn himself out stark naked, in quest afresh of new notions? All the arguments that can be used will be as little able to prevail, as the wind did with the traveler to part with his cloak, which he held only the faster. To this of wrong hypothesis may be reduced the errors that may be occasioned by a true hypothesis, or right principles, but not rightly understood. There is nothing more familiar than this. The instances of men contending for different opinions, which they all derive from the infallible truth of the Scripture, are an undeniable proof of it. All that call themselves Christians, allow the text that says, METANOEITE, to carry in it the obligation to a very weighty duty. But yet how very erroneous will one of their practices be, who, understanding nothing but the French, take this rule with one translation to be, *Repentez-vous,* repent; or with the other, *Fatiez pénitence,* do penance.

III. Probabilities which cross men's appetites and prevailing passions run the same fate. Let ever so much probability hang on one side of a covetous man's reasoning, and money on the other; it is easy to foresee which will outweigh. Earthly minds, like mud walls, resist the strongest batteries: and though, perhaps, sometimes the force of a clear argument may make some impression, yet they nevertheless stand firm, and keep out the enemy, truth, that would captivate or disturb them. Tell a man passionately in love, that he is jilted; bring a score of witnesses of the falsehood of his mistress, it is ten to one but three kind words of hers shall invalidate all their testimonies. *Quod volumus, facile credimus;* what suits our wishes, is forwardly believed, is, I suppose, what everyone hath more than once experimented: and though men cannot always openly gainsay or resist the force of manifest probabilities that make against them, yet yield they not to the argument. Not but that it is the nature of the understanding constantly to close with the more probable side; but yet a man hath a power to suspend and restrain its inquiries, and not permit a full and satisfactory examination, as far as the matter in question is capable, and will bear it to be made. Until that be done, there will be always these two ways left of evading the most apparent probabilities:

First, That the arguments being (as for the most part they are) brought in words, *there may be a fallacy latent in them:* and the consequences being, perhaps, many in train, they may be some of them incoherent. There are very few discourses so short, clear, and consistent, to which most men may not, with satisfaction enough to themselves, raise this doubt; and from whose conviction they may not, without reproach of disingenuity or unreasonableness, set themselves free with the old reply, *Non persuadebis, etiamsi persuaseris;* though I cannot answer, I will not yield.

Secondly, Manifest probabilities may be evaded, and the assent withheld, upon this suggestion, That *I know not yet all that may be said on the contrary side*. And therefore, though I be beaten, it is not necessary I should yield, not knowing what forces there are in reserve behind. This is a refuge against conviction so open and so wide, that it is hard to determine when a man is quite out of the verge of it.

But yet there is some end of it; and a man having carefully inquired into all the grounds of probability and unlikeliness; done his utmost to inform himself in all particulars fairly, and cast up the sum total on both sides; may, in most cases, come to acknowledge, upon the whole matter, on which side the probability rests: wherein some proofs in matter of reason, being suppositions upon universal experience, are so cogent and clear, and some testimonies in matter of fact so universal that he cannot refuse his assent. So that I think we may conclude, that, in propositions, where though the proofs in view are of most moment, yet there are sufficient grounds to suspect that there is either fallacy in words, or certain proofs as considerable to be produced on the contrary side; there assent, suspense, or dissent, are often voluntary actions. But where the proofs are such as make it highly probable, and there is not sufficient ground to suspect that there is either fallacy of words (which sober and serious consideration may discover) nor equally valid proofs yet undiscovered, latent on the other side (which also the nature of the thing may, in some cases, make plain to a considerate man); there, I think, a man who has weighed them can scarce refuse his assent to the side on which the greater probability appears. Whether it be probable that a promiscuous jumble of printing letters should often fall into a method and order, which should stamp on paper a coherent discourse; or that a blind fortuitous concourse of atoms, not guided by an understanding agent, should frequently constitute the bodies of any species of animals: in these and the like cases, I think, nobody that considers them can be one jot at a stand which side to take, nor at all waver in his assent. Lastly, when there can be no supposition (the thing in its own nature indifferent, and wholly depending upon the testimony of witnesses) that there is as fair testimony against, as for the matter of fact attested; which by inquiry is to be learned, v.g. whether there was one thousand seven hundred years ago such a man at Rome as Julius Caesar: in all such cases, I say, I think it is not in any rational man's power to refuse his assent; but that it necessarily follows, and closes with such probabilities. In other less clear cases, I think it is in man's power to suspend his assent; and perhaps content himself with the proofs he has, if they favor the opinion that suits with his inclination or interest, and so stop from further search. But that a man should afford his assent to that side on which the less probability appears to him, seems to me utterly impracticable, and as impossible as it is to believe the same thing probable and improbable at the same time.

As knowledge is no more arbitrary than perception; so, I think, assent is no more in our power than knowledge. When the agreement of any two ideas appears to our minds, whether immediately or by the assistance of reason, I can no more refuse to perceive, no more avoid knowing it, than I can avoid seeing those objects which I turn my eyes to, and look on in daylight; and what upon full examination I find the most probable, I cannot deny my assent to. But, though we cannot hinder our knowledge, where the agreement is once perceived;

nor our assent, where the probability manifestly appears upon due consideration of all the measures of it: yet we can hinder both *knowledge* and *assent, by stopping our inquiry,* and not employing our faculties in the search of any truth. If it were not so, ignorance, error, or infidelity, could not in any case be a fault. Thus, in some cases we can prevent or suspend our assent: but can a man versed in modern or ancient history doubt whether there is such a place as Rome, or whether there was such a man as Julius Caesar? Indeed, there are millions of truths that a man is not, or may not think himself concerned to know; as whether our King Richard the Third was crooked or no; or whether Roger Bacon was a mathematician or a magician. In these and such like cases, where the assent one way or other is of no importance to the interest of anyone; no action, no concernment of his following or depending thereon, there it is not strange that the mind should give itself up to the common opinion, or render itself to the first comer. These and the like opinions are of so little weight and moment, that, like motes in the sun, their tendencies are very rarely taken notice of. They are there, as it were, by chance, and the mind lets them float at liberty. But where the mind judges that the proposition has concernment in it: where the assent or not assenting is thought to draw consequences of moment after it, and good and evil to depend on choosing or refusing the right side, and the mind sets itself seriously to inquire and examine the probability: there I think it is not in our choice to take which side we please, if manifest odds appear on either. The greater probability, I think, in that case will determine the assent: and a man can no more avoid assenting, or taking it to be true, where he perceives the greater probability, than he can avoid knowing it to be true, where he perceives the agreement or disagreement of any two ideas.

If this be so, the foundation of error will lie in wrong measures of probability; as the foundation of vice in wrong measures of good.

IV. The fourth and last wrong measure of probability I shall take notice of, and which keeps in ignorance or error more people than all the other together, is that which I have mentioned in the foregoing chapter: I mean the giving up our assent to the common received opinions, either of our friends or party, neighborhood or country. How many men have no other ground for their tenets, than the supposed honesty, or learning, or number of those of the same profession? As if honest or bookish men could not err; or truth were to be established by the vote of the multitude: yet this with most men serves the turn. The tenet has had the attestation of reverend antiquity; it comes to me with the passport of former ages, and therefore I am secure in the reception I give it: other men have been and are of the same opinion (for that is all is said), and therefore it is reasonable for me to embrace it. A man may more justifiably throw up cross and pile for his opinions, than take them up by such measures. All men are liable to error, and most men are in many points, by passion or interest, under temptation to it. If we could but see the secret motives that influenced the men of name and learning in the world, and the leaders of parties, we should not always find that it was the embracing of truth for its own sake, that made them espouse the doctrines they owned and maintained. This at least is certain, there is not an opinion so absurd, which a man may not receive upon this ground. There is no error to be named, which has not had its professors: and a man shall never want crooked paths to walk in, if he thinks that he is in the right way, wherever he has the footsteps of others to follow.

But, notwithstanding the great noise is made in the world about errors and opinions, I must do mankind that right as to say, *There are not so many men in errors and wrong opinions as is commonly supposed*. Not that I think they embrace the truth; but indeed, because concerning those doctrines they keep such a stir about, they have no thought, no opinion at all. For if anyone should a little catechize the greatest part of the partisans of most of the sects in the world, he would not find, concerning those matters they are so zealous for, that they have any opinions of their own: much less would he have reason to think that they took them upon the examination of arguments and appearance of probability. They are resolved to stick to a party that education or interest has engaged them in; and there, like the common soldiers of an army, show their courage and warmth as their leaders direct, without ever examining, or so much as knowing, the cause they contend for. If a man's life shows that he has no serious regard for religion; for what reason should we think that he beats his head about the opinions of his church, and troubles himself to examine the grounds of this or that doctrine? It is enough for him to obey his leaders, to have his hand and his tongue ready for the support of the common cause, and thereby approve himself to those who can give him credit, preferment, or protection in that society. Thus men become professors of, and combatants, for, those opinions they were never convinced of nor proselytes to; no, nor ever had so much as floating in their heads: and though one cannot say there are fewer improbable or erroneous opinions in the world than there are, yet this is certain; there are fewer that actually assent to them, and mistake them for truths, than is imagined.

XX

Of the Division of the Sciences

ALL THAT CAN FALL within the compass of human understanding, being either, *First,* the nature of things, as they are in themselves, their relations, and their manner of operation: or, *Secondly,* that which man himself ought to do, as a rational and voluntary agent, for the attainment of any end, especially happiness: or, *Thirdly,* the ways and means whereby the knowledge of both the one and the other of these is attained and communicated; I think science may be divided properly into these three sorts:——

First, The knowledge of things, as they are in their own proper beings, their constitution, properties, and operations; whereby I mean not only matter and body, but spirits also, which have their proper natures, constitutions, and operations, as well as bodies. This, in a little more enlarged sense of the word, I call *Physica,* or *natural philosophy.* The end of this is bare speculative truth: and whatsoever can afford the mind of man any such, falls under this branch, whether it be God himself, angels, spirits, bodies; or any of their affections, as number, and figure, etc.

Secondly, Practica, The skill of right applying our own powers and actions, for the attainment of things good and useful. The most considerable under this head is *ethics,* which is the seeking out those rules and measures of human actions, which lead to happiness, and the means to practice them. The end of this is not bare speculation and the knowledge of truth; but right, and a conduct suitable to it.

Thirdly, the third branch may be called *Semeoitica,* or *the doctrine of signs;* the most usual whereof being words, it is aptly enough termed also *logic:* the business whereof is to consider the nature of signs, the mind makes use of for the understanding of things, or conveying its knowledge to others. For, since the things the mind contemplates are none of them, besides itself, present to the understanding, it is necessary that something else, as a sign or representation of the thing it considers, should be present to it: and these are *ideas.* And because the scene of ideas that makes one man's thoughts cannot be laid open to the immediate view of another, nor laid up anywhere but in the memory, a not very sure repository: therefore to communicate our thoughts to one another, as well as record them for our own use, signs of our ideas are also necessary: those which men have found most convenient, and therefore generally make use of, are *articulate sounds*. The consideration, then, of *ideas* and *words* as the great instruments of knowledge, makes no despicable part of their contemplation who would take a view of human knowledge in the whole extent of it. And perhaps if they were distinctly weighed, and duly considered, they would afford us another sort of logic and critic, than what we have been hitherto acquainted with.

This seems to me the first and most general, as well as natural division of the objects of our understanding. For a man can employ his thoughts about nothing, but either, the contemplation of *things* themselves, for the discovery of truth; or about the things in his own power, which are his own *actions*, for the attainment of his own ends; or the *signs* the mind makes use of both in the one and the other, and the right ordering of them, for its clearer information. All which three, viz. *things*, as they are in themselves knowable; *actions* as they depend on us, in order to happiness; and the right use of *signs* in order to knowledge, being *toto coelo* different, they seemed to me to be the three great provinces of the intellectual world, wholly separate and distinct one from another.

Bibliography

Works by Locke:

A Letter for Toleration (1689)
Two Treatises of Government (1690)
An Early Draft of Locke's Essay (R. I. Aaron and W. Gibb, eds.), (1936)
An Essay Concerning Human Understanding (1690)
A Second Letter Concerning Toleration (1690)
Some Considerations of the Consequences of Lowering of Interest and Raising the Value of Money (1692)
A Third Letter for Toleration (1693)
Some Thoughts Concerning Education (1693)
Further Considerations Concerning Raising the Value of Money (1695)
The Reasonableness of Christianity (1695)
A Vindication of the Reasonableness of Christianity (1695)
A Second Vindication of the Reasonableness of Christianity (1697)
A Letter to the Right Reverend Lord Bishop of Worcester (1697)
Posthumous Works (1706)
Remains (1714)
Essays on the Law of Nature (W. von Leyden, ed.), (1954)

Correspondence:

Some Familiar Letters between Mr. Locke and Several of his Friends (1708)
Original Letters of John Locke (T. Forster, ed.), (1830)
Lettres Inédites de John Locke (H. Ollion, ed.), (1912)
The Correspondence of John Locke and Edward Clarke (B. Rand, ed.), (1927)

Bibliography:

A Bibliographical Introduction to the Study of John Locke, by H. O. Christopherson (1930)

Biographical Studies:

Lord King, The Life of John Locke, Two vols., 1829.
H. R. F. Bourne, The Life of John Locke, Two vols., 1876.
W. Lough, Locke's Travels in France, 1953.
M. Cranston, John Locke: A Biography, 1957.

Critical Studies:

V. Cousin, La Philosophie de Locke, 1819.

C. Bastide, John Locke: Ses Théories Politiques, 1907.
J. Gibson, Locke's Theory of Knowledge, 1917.
S. Lamprecht, The Moral and Political Philosophy of John Locke, 1918.
G. de Paolis, Il Problema della conoscenza nell'empirisma del Locke, 1919.
B. Smyrniadis, Les Doctrines de Hobbes, Locke et Kant, 1921.
A. Bertolino, Locke Economista, 1928.
P. Larkin, Property in the Eighteenth Century, 1930.
C. Morris, Locke, Berkeley and Hume, 1931.
A. Hofstaedter, Locke and Scepticism, 1935.
K. Maclean, John Locke and the English Literature of the Eighteenth Century, 1935.
R. I. Aaron, John Locke, 1937.
Willmoore Kendall, John Locke and the Doctrine of Majority Rule, 1941.
D. J. O'Connor, John Locke, 1952.
J. W. Yolton, John Locke and the Way of Ideas, 1956.
P. Laslett, Locke's Two Treatises of Government, 1960.
Massimo Salvadori, Locke and Liberty, 1960.
R. H. Cox, Locke on War and Peace, 1961.